A Treasury of Humor in Large Print

**Edited by
Pinky Chin and
Daphne Abeel**

G.K. HALL & CO.
Boston, Massachusetts
1985

G. K. Hall Large Print Book Series.

Set in 16 pt Plantin.

Library of Congress Cataloguing in Publication Data

Main entry under title:

A Treasury of humor in large print.

   (G. K. Hall large print book series)
   Includes index
   1. American wit and humor.   2. Large type books.
I. Chin, Pinky.   II. Abeel, Daphne.
[PN6157.T7   1985]   817′.008   85–17603
ISBN 0–8161–3937–7 (lg. print)

Acknowledgments

The editors gratefully acknowledge permission to reproduce the copyright material included in this volume. In the event of any error or omission, they will be pleased to make the necessary correction in future editions of this book.

"The 'Tonight Show' Is Born," Steve Allen, from *Bigger Than a Breadbox*, by Steve Allen, copyright © 1967, Doubleday & Company, Inc. Reprinted by permission of the author.

"The Kuglemass Episode," Woody Allen, from *Side Effects* by Woody Allen. Copyright © 1977 by Woody Allen. Reprinted by permission of Random House, Inc.

"On Conning Ed," Russell Baker, copyright © 1975 by The New York Times Company. Reprinted by permission of The New York Times Company.

"The Ballet Visits the Splendide's Magician," Ludwig Bemelmans, copyright 1940 by F-R Publishing Corporation. Originally appeared in *The New Yorker*, July 6, 1940. Copyright renewed 1968 by Madeleine Bemelmans and Barbara Bemelmans Marciano. Reprinted by permission of Madeleine Bemelmans.

"Christmas Afternoon," Robert Benchley, from *Of All Things* by Robert Benchley. Copyright 1921 by Harper & Row, Publishers, Inc. Copyright renewed 1949 by Gertrude Benchley. Reprinted by permission of Harper & Row, Publishers, Inc.

"Ladies Wild," Robert Benchley, from *The Benchley Roundup* selected by Nathaniel Benchley. Copyright 1938 by Robert C. Benchley. Copyright renewed 1966 by Gertrude Benchley. Reprinted by permission of Harper & Row, Publishers, Inc.

"The Socks Problem," Roy Blount, Jr., from *One Fell Soup Or I'm Just a Bug on the Windshield of Life* by Roy Blount, Jr. Copyright © 1977. Originally appeared in *OUI*. Reprinted by permission of Little, Brown and Company in association with the Atlantic Monthly Press.

"The New Airlines," Art Buchwald, from *While Reagan Slept* by Art Buchwald. Copyright © 1983 by Art Buchwald. Reprinted by permission of the Putnam Publishing Group.

"Saving Paper," Art Buchwald, from *Laid Back in Washington* by Art Buchwald. Copyright © 1978–81 by Art Buchwald. Reprinted by permission of the Putnam Publishing Group.

Table of Contents

Editors' Note

Every civilization throughout history has valued the faculty in man that is his sense of humor. Animals do not laugh, and it is our ability to laugh that, in part, makes us human. It is no surprise that the writers and comedians who capture and immortalize the comic side of life are often the most beloved and best known folk heroes of their age.

It is the intention of this collection to bring you the funniest, most hilarious writers, past and present, in a compilation that will entertain, stimulate, and amuse. If the dialects of an Artemus Ward tickle your ear, if you savor the homespun, political humor of a Will Rogers, if you double up at S. J. Perelman's view of the absurd, or long for the mock-rural world of Garrison Keillor, you will be certain to find here a story, an anecdote, a joke that suits your taste.

We hope this anthology of humor in Large Print will offer its readers many happy hours and the gift of laughter.

Boston, Massachusetts
Pinky Chin
Daphne Abeel

Good, Old-fashioned
Humor

The Deacon's Masterpiece,
or, The Wonderful "One-Hoss Shay,"
A Logical Story

Oliver Wendell Holmes

Have you heard of the wonderful one-hoss
    shay,
That was built in such a logical way
It ran a hundred years to a day,
And then, of a sudden, it — ah, but stay,
I'll tell you what happened without delay,
Scaring the parson into fits,
Frightening people out of their wits, —
Have you ever heard of that, I say?

Seventeen hundred and fifty-five.
Georgius Secundus was then alive, —
Snuffy old drone from the German hive.
That was the year when Lisbon-town
Saw the earth open and gulp her down,
And Braddock's army was done so brown,
Left without a scalp to its crown.
It was on the terrible Earthquake-day
That the Deacon finished the one-hoss
    shay.

3

Now in building of chaises, I tell you what,
There is always *somewhere* a weakest
spot, —
In hub, tire, felloe, in spring or thill,
In panel, or crossbar, or floor, or sill,
In screw, bolt, thoroughbrace, — lurking
still,
Find it somewhere you must and will, —
Above or below, or within or without, —
And that's the reason, beyond a doubt,
That a chaise *breaks down*, but doesn't *wear
out.*

But the Deacon swore, (as Deacons do,
With an "I dew vum," or an "I tell *yeou,*")
He would build one shay to beat the taown
'N' the keounty 'n' all the kentry raoun';
It should be so built that it *couldn'* break
daown:
— "Fur," said the Deacon, " 't's mighty
plain
Thut the weakes' place mus' stan' the
strain;
'N' the way t' fix it, uz I maintain,
Is only jest
T' make that place uz strong uz the rest."

So the Deacon inquired of the village folk
Where he could find the strongest oak,
That couldn't be split nor bent nor
broke, —
That was for spokes and floor and sills;

He sent for lancewood to make the thills;
The crossbars were ash, from the straightest
   trees,
The panels of whitewood, that cuts like
   cheese,
But lasts like iron for things like these;
The hubs of logs from the "Settler's
   ellum," —
Last of its timber, — they couldn't sell 'em,
Never an axe had seen their chips,
And the wedges flew from between their
   lips,
Their blunt ends frizzled like celery-tips;
Step and prop-iron, bolt and screw,
Springs, tire, axle, and linchpin too,
Steel of the finest, bright and blue;
Thoroughbrace bison-skin, thick and wide;
Boot, top, dasher, from tough old hide
Found in the pit when the tanner died.
That was the way he "put her through." —
"There!" said the Deacon, "naow she'll
   dew!"

Do! I tell you, I rather guess
She was a wonder, and nothing less!
Colts grew horses, beards turned gray.
Deacon and deaconess dropped away,
Children and grandchildren — where were
   they?
But there stood the stout one-hoss shay
As fresh as on Lisbon-earthquake-day!

EIGHTEEN HUNDRED; — It came and found
The Deacon's masterpiece strong and
    sound.
Eighteen hundred increased by ten; —
"Hahnsum kerridge" they called it then.
Eighteen hundred and twenty came; —
Running as usual; much the same.
Thirty and forty at last arrive,
And then come fifty, and FIFTY-FIVE.
Little of all we value here
Wakes on the morn of its hundredth year
Without both feeling and looking queer.
In fact, there's nothing that keeps its youth,
So far as I know, but a tree and truth.
(This is a moral that runs at large;
Take it. — You're welcome. — No extra
    charge.)

FIRST OF NOVEMBER, — The Earthquake-
    day —
There are traces of age in the one-hoss
    shay,
A general flavor of mild decay,
But nothing local, as one may say.
There couldn't be, — for the Deacon's art
Had made it so like in every part
That there wasn't a chance for one to start.
For the wheels were just as strong as the
    thills,
And the floor was just as strong as the
    sills,
And the panels just as strong as the floor,

6

And the whipple-tree neither less nor more,
And the back-crossbar as strong as the fore,
And the spring and axle and hub *encore.*
And yet, as a *whole,* it is past a doubt
In another hour it will be *worn out!*

First of November, 'Fifty-five!
This morning the parson takes a drive.
Now, small boys, get out of the way!
Here comes the wonderful one-hoss shay,
Drawn by a rat-tailed, ewe-necked bay.
"Huddup!" said the parson. — Off went
   they.
The parson was working his Sunday's
   text, —
Had got to *fifthly,* and stopped perplexed
At what the — Moses — was coming next.
All at once the horse stood still,
Close by the meet'n'-house on the hill.
— First a shiver, and then a thrill,
Then something decidedly like a spill, —
And the parson was sitting upon a rock,
At half past nine by the meet'n'-house
   clock, —
Just the hour of the Earthquake shock!
— What do you think the parson found,
When he got up and stared around?
The poor old chaise in a heap or mound,
As if it had been to the mill and ground!
You see, of course, if you're not a dunce,
How it went to pieces all at once, —
All at once, and nothing first, —

Just as bubbles do when they burst.

End of the wonderful one-hoss shay.
Logic is logic. That's all I say.

The Mule

Josh Billings

The mule is haf hoss, and haf Jackass, and then kums tu a full stop, natur diskovering her mistake. Tha weigh more, akordin tu their heft, than enny other kreetur, except a crowbar. Tha kant hear enny quicker, nor further than the hoss, yet their ears are big enuff for snow shoes. You kan trust them with enny one whose life aint worth enny more than the mules. The only wa tu keep them into a paster, is tu turn them into a medder jineing, and let them jump out. Tha are reddy for use, just as soon as they will du tu abuse. Tha haint got enny friends, and will live on huckel berry brush, with an ockasional chanse at Kanada thissels. Tha are a modern invenshun, i dont think the Bible deludes tu them at tall. Tha sel for more money than enny other domestik animile. Yu kant tell their age by looking into their mouth, enny more than you kould a Mexican cannons. Tha never hav no dissease that a good club wont heal. If tha ever die tha must kum rite tu life

9

agin, for i never herd nobody sa "ded mule." Tha are like sum men, very korrupt at harte; ive known them tu be good mules for 6 months, just tu git a good chanse to kick sumbody. I never owned one, nor never mean to, unless there is a United Staits law passed, requiring it. The only reason why tha are pashunt, is bekause tha are ashamed ov themselfs. I have seen eddikated mules in a sirkus. Tha kould kick, and bite, tremenjis. I would not sa what I am forced tu sa again the mule, if his birth want an outrage, and man want tu blame for it. Enny man who is willing tu drive a mule ought to be exempt by law from running for the legislatur. Tha are the strongest creeturs on earth, and heaviest, ackording tu their sise; I herd tell ov one who fell oph from the tow path, on the Eri kanawl, and sunk as soon as he touched bottom, but he kept rite on towing the boat tu the nex stashun, breathing thru his ears, which stuck out ov the water about 2 feet 6 inches; i didn't see this did, but an auctioneer told me ov it, and i never knew an auctioneer tu lie unless it was absolutely convenient.

The Casting Away of Mrs. Lecks and Mrs. Aleshine*

Frank R. Stockton

I was on my way from San Francisco to Yokohama, when in a very desultory and gradual manner I became acquainted with Mrs. Lecks and Mrs. Aleshine. The steamer, on which I was making a moderately rapid passage toward the land of the legended fan and the lacquered box, carried a fair complement of passengers, most of whom were Americans; and, among these, my attention was attracted from the very first day of the voyage to two middle-aged women who appeared to me very unlike the ordinary traveler or tourist. At first sight they might have been taken for farmers' wives who,

*This is Part I of the Stockton novel "The Casting Away of Mrs. Lecks and Mrs. Aleshine." A few cuts have been made, and a few sentences from Part II have been added — this last for the purpose of getting the ladies into smooth water and within reach of land. It seemed the decent thing to do.

11

for some unusual reason, had determined to make a voyage across the Pacific; but, on closer observation, one would have been more apt to suppose that they belonged to the families of prosperous tradesmen in some little country town, where, besides the arts of rural house-wifery, there would be opportunities of becoming acquainted in some degree with the ways and manners of the outside world. They were not of that order of persons who generally take first-class passages on steamships, but the stateroom occupied by Mrs. Lecks and Mrs. Aleshine was one of the best in the vessel.

Mrs. Lecks was a rather tall woman, large-boned and muscular, and her well-browned countenance gave indications of that conviction of superiority which gradually grows up in the minds of those who for a long time have had absolute control of the destinies of a state, or the multifarious affairs of a country household. Mrs. Aleshine was somewhat younger than her friend, somewhat shorter, and a great deal fatter. She had the same air of reliance upon her individual worth that characterized Mrs. Lecks, but there was a certain geniality about her which indicated that she would have a good deal of forbearance for those who never had had the opportunity or the ability of becoming the thoroughly good housewife which she was herself.

These two worthy dames spent the greater part of their time on deck, where they always sat together in a place at the stern of the vessel which was well sheltered from wind and weather. As they sat thus they were generally employed in knitting, although this occupation did not prevent them from keeping up what seemed to me, as I passed them in my walks about the deck, a continuous conversation. From a question which Mrs. Lecks once asked me about a distant sail, our acquaintance began. There was no one on board for whose society I particularly cared, and as there was something quaint and odd about these countrywomen on the ocean which interested me, I was glad to vary my solitary promenades by an occasional chat with them. They were not at all backward in giving me information about themselves. They were both widows, and Mrs. Aleshine was going out to Japan to visit a son who had a position there in a mercantile house. Mrs. Lecks had no children, and was accompanying her friend because, as she said, she would not allow Mrs. Aleshine to make such a voyage as that by herself, and because, being quite able to do so, she did not know why she should not see the world as well as other people.

These two friends were not educated women. They made frequent mistakes in their grammar, and a good deal of Middle States provincialism showed itself in their pronunciation and expressions. But although they brought many of their rural ideas to sea with them, they possessed a large share of that common sense which is available anywhere, and they frequently made use of it in a manner which was very amusing to me. I think, also, that they found in me a quarry of information concerning nautical matters, foreign countries, and my own affairs, the working of which helped to make us very good ship friends.

Our steamer touched at the Sandwich Islands; and it was a little more than two days after we left Honolulu that, about nine o'clock in the evening, we had the misfortune to come into collision with an eastern-bound vessel. This vessel, which appeared to be a small steamer, struck us with great force near our bows, and then, backing, disappeared into the fog, and we never saw or heard of her again.

It was soon discovered that our injuries were serious and, indeed, disastrous. The hull of our steamer had been badly shattered on the port bow, and the water came in at a most alarming rate. For nearly two hours the crew and many of the passengers worked at the pumps, and everything possible was done to stop the enormous leak; but all labor to save the vessel was found to be utterly unavailing, and a little before midnight the captain announced that it was impossible to keep the steamer afloat, and that we must all take to the boats. The night was now clear, the stars were bright, and, as there was little wind, the sea was comparatively smooth. With all these advantages, the captain assured us that there was no reason to apprehend danger, and he thought that by noon of the following day we could easily make a small inhabited island, where we could be sheltered and cared for until we should be taken off by some passing vessel.

There was plenty of time for all necessary preparations, and these were made with much order and subordination. Everybody obeyed the captain's orders, and all prepared themselves for the transfer to the boats. The first officer came among us, and told each of us what boats we were to take, and where we were to place ourselves on deck. I was assigned to a large boat which was to be principally occupied by steerage passengers; and as I came up from my stateroom, where I had gone to secure my money and some portable valuables, I met on the companionway Mrs. Lecks and Mrs. Aleshine, who expressed considerable dissatisfaction when they found that I was not going in the boat with them. They, however, hurried below, and I went on deck, where in about ten minutes I was joined by Mrs. Lecks, who apparently had been looking for me. She told me she had something very particular to say to me, and conducted me toward the stern of the vessel, where, behind one of the deck-houses, we found Mrs. Aleshine.

"Look here," said Mrs. Lecks, leading me to the rail, and pointing downward; "do you see that boat there? It has been let down, and there is nobody in it. The boat on the other side has just gone off, full to the brim. I never saw so many people crowded into a boat. The other ones will be just as packed, I expect. I don't see why we shouldn't take this empty boat, now we've got a chance, instead of squeezin' ourselves into those crowded ones. If any of the other people come afterward, why, we shall have our choice of seats, and that's considerable of a p'int, I should say, in a time like this."

"That's so," said Mrs. Aleshine; "and me and Mrs. Lecks would 'a' got right in when we saw the boat was empty, if we hadn't been afraid to be there without any man, for it might have floated off, and neither of us don't know nothin' about rowin'. And then Mrs. Lecks she thought of you, supposin' a young man who knew so much about the sea would know how to row."

"Oh, yes," said I; "but I cannot imagine why this boat should have been left empty. I see a keg of water in it, and the oars, and some tin cans, and so I suppose it has been made ready for somebody. Will you wait here a minute until I run forward and see how things are going on there?"

Amidships and forward I saw that there was some confusion among the people who were not yet in their boats, and I found that there was to be rather more crowding than at first was expected. People who had supposed that they were to go in a certain boat found there

16

no place, and were hurrying to other boats. It now became plain to me that no time should be lost in getting into the small boat which Mrs. Lecks had pointed out, so I slipped quietly aft, and joined Mrs. Lecks and Mrs. Aleshine.

"We must get in as soon as we can," said I, in a low voice, "for this boat may be discovered, and then there will be a rush for it. I suspect it may have been reserved for the captain and some of the officers, but we have as much right in it as they."

"And more too," replied Mrs. Lecks; "for we had nothin' to do with the steerin' and smashin'."

"But how are we goin' to get down there?" said Mrs. Aleshine. "There's no steps."

"That is true," said I. "I shouldn't wonder if this boat is to be taken forward when the others are filled. We must scramble down as well as we can by the tackle at the bow and stern. I'll get in first and keep her close to the ship's side."

"That's goin' to be a scratchy business," said Mrs. Lecks, "and I'm of the opinion we ought to wait till the ship has sunk a little more, so we'll be nearer to the boat."

"It won't do to wait," said I, "or we shall not get in it at all."

"And goodness gracious!" exclaimed Mrs. Aleshine, "I can't stand here and feel the ship sinkin' cold-blooded under me, till we've got where we can make an easy jump!"

"Very well, then," said Mrs. Lecks, "we won't wait. But the first thing to be done is for each one of us to put on one of these life-preservers. Two of them I brought from Mrs. Aleshine's and my cabin, and the other one I got next door, where the people had gone off and left it on the floor. I thought if anythin' happened on the way to the island, these would give us a chance to look about us; but it seems to me we'll need 'em more gettin' down them ropes than anywhere else. I did intend puttin' on two myself to make up for Mrs. Aleshine's fat; but you must wear one of 'em, sir, now that you are goin' to join the party."

As I knew that two life-preservers would not be needed by Mrs. Lecks, and would greatly inconvenience her, I accepted the one offered me, but declined to put it on until it should be necessary, as it would interfere with my movements.

"Very well," said Mrs. Lecks, "if you think you are safe in gettin' down without it. But Mrs. Aleshine and me will put ours on before we begin sailor-scramblin'. We know how to do it, for we tried 'em on soon after we started from San Francisco. And now, Barb'ry Aleshine, are you sure you've got everythin' you want? for it'll be no use thinkin' about anythin' you've forgot after the ship has sunk out of sight."

"There's nothin' else I can think of," said Mrs. Aleshine; "at least, nothin' I can carry;

18

and so I suppose we may as well begin, for your talk of the ship sinkin' under our feet gives me a sort o' feelin' like an oyster creepin' up and down my back."

Mrs. Lecks looked over the side at the boat, into which I had already descended. "I'll go first, Barb'ry Aleshine," said she, "and show you how."

The sea was quiet, and the steamer had already sunk so much that Mrs. Lecks's voice sounded frightfully near me, although she spoke in a low tone.

"Watch me," said she to her companion. "I'm goin' to do just as he did, and you must follow in the same way."

So saying, she stepped on a bench by the rail; then, with one foot on the rail itself, she seized the ropes which hung from one of the davits to the bow of the boat. She look down for a moment, and then she drew back.

"It's no use," she said. "We must wait until she sinks more, and I can get in easier."

This remark made me feel nervous. I did not know at what moment there might be a rush for this boat, nor when, indeed, the steamer might go down. The boat amidships on our side had rowed away some minutes before, and through the darkness I could distinguish another boat, near the bow, pushing off. It would be too late now for us to try to get into any other boat, and I did not feel that there was time enough for me to take this one to a place where the two women could more easily descend to her. Standing upright, I urged them not to delay.

"You see," said I, "I can reach you as soon as you swing yourself off the ropes, and I'll help you down."

"If you're sure you can keep us from comin' down too sudden, we'll try it," said Mrs. Lecks; "but I'd as soon be drowned as to get to an island with a broken leg. And as to Mrs. Aleshine, if she was to slip she'd go slam through that boat to the bottom of the sea. Now, then, be ready! I'm comin' down."

So saying, she swung herself off, and she was then so near me that I was able to seize her and make the rest of her descent comparatively easy. Mrs. Aleshine proved to be a more difficult subject. Even after I had a firm grasp of her capacious waist she refused to let go the ropes, for fear that she might drop into the ocean instead of the boat. But the reproaches of Mrs. Lecks and the downward weight of myself made her loosen her nervous grip; and, although we came very near going overboard together, I safely placed her on one of the thwarts.

I now unhooked the tackle from the stern; but before casting off at the bow I hesitated, for I did not wish to desert any of those who might be expecting to embark in this boat. But I could hear no approaching footsteps, and from my position, close to the side of the steamer, I could see nothing. Therefore I cast off, and, taking the oars, I pushed away and rowed to a little distance, where I could get whatever view was possible of the deck of the steamer. Seeing no forms moving about, I called out, and, receiving no answer, I shouted again at the top of my voice. I waited for nearly a minute, and, hearing nothing and seeing nothing, I became convinced that no one was left on the vessel.

"They are all gone," said I, "and we will pull after them as fast as we can."

And I began to row toward the bow of the steamer, in the direction which the other boats had taken.

"It's a good thing you can row," said Mrs. Lecks, settling herself comfortably in the stern-sheets, "for what Mrs. Aleshine and me would ha' done with them oars I am sure I don't know."

"I'd never have got into this boat," said Mrs. Aleshine, "if Mr. Craig hadn't been here."

"No, indeed," replied her friend. "You'd ha' gone to the bottom, hangin' for dear life to them ropes."

When I had rounded the bow of the steamer, which appeared to me to be rapidly settling in the water, I perceived at no great distance several lights, which of course belonged to the other boats, and I rowed as hard as I could, hoping to catch up with them, or at least to keep sufficiently near. It might be my duty to

21

take off some of the people who had crowded into the other boats, probably supposing that this one had been loaded and gone. How such a mistake could have taken place I could not divine, and it was not my business to do so. Quite certain that no one was left on the sinking steamer, all I had to do was to row after the other boats, and to overtake them as soon as possible. I thought it would not take me very long to do this, but after rowing for half an hour, Mrs. Aleshine remarked that the lights seemed as far off, if not farther, than when we first started after them. Turning, I saw that this was the case, and was greatly surprised. With only two passengers I ought soon to have come up with those heavily laden boats. But after I had thought over it a little, I considered that as each of them was probably pulled by half a dozen stout sailors, it was not so very strange that they should make as good or better headway than I did.

It was not very long after this that Mrs. Lecks said that she thought that the lights on the other boats must be going out, and that this, most probably, was due to the fact that the sailors had forgotten to fill their lanterns before they started. "That sort of thing often happens," she said, "when people leave a place in a hurry."

But when I turned around, and peered over the dark waters, it was quite plain to me that it was not want of oil, but increased distance, which made those lights so dim. I could now perceive but three of them. We were being left behind, that was certain, and all I could do was to row on as long and as well as I could in the direction which the other boats had taken.

"I don't believe this boat has been emptied out since the last rain," said Mrs. Aleshine, "for my feet are wet, though I didn't notice it before."

At this I shipped my oars, and began to examine the boat. The bottom was covered with a movable floor of slats, and as I put my hand down I could feel the water welling up between the slats. The flooring was in sections, and lifting the one beneath me, I felt under it, and put my hand into six or eight inches of water.

The exact state of the case was now as plain to me as if it had been posted up on a bulletin-board. This boat had been found to be unseaworthy, and its use had been forbidden, all the people having been crowded into the others. This had caused confusion at the last moment, and, of course, we were supposed to be on some one of the other boats.

And now here was I, in the middle of the Pacific Ocean, in a leaky boat, with two middle-aged women!

"Anythin' the matter with the floor?" asked Mrs. Lecks.

I let the section fall back into its place, and looked aft. By the starlight I could see that my two companions had each fixed upon me a

23

steadfast gaze. They evidently felt that something was the matter, and wanted to know what it was. I did not hesitate for a moment to inform them. They appeared to me to be women whom it would be neither advisable nor possible to deceive in a case like this.

"This boat has a leak in it," I said. "There is a lot of water in her already, and that is the reason we have got along so slowly."

"And that is why," said Mrs. Aleshine, "it was left empty. We ought to have known better than to expect to have a whole boat just for three of us. It would have been much more sensible, I think, if we had tried to squeeze into one of the others."

"Now, Barb'ry Aleshine," said Mrs. Lecks, "don't you begin findin' fault with good fortune, when it comes to you. Here we've got a comfortable boat, with room enough to set easy and stretch out if we want to. If the water is comin' in, what we've got to do is to get it out again just as fast as we can. What's the best way to do that, Mr. Craig?"

"We must bail her out, and lose no time about it," said I. "If I can find the leak I may be able to stop it."

I now looked about for something to bail with, and the two women aided actively in the search. I found one leather scoop in the bow; but as it was well that we should all go to work, I took two tin cans that had been put in by some one who had begun to provision the boat, and proceeded to cut the tops from them with my jack-knife.

"Don't lose what's in 'em," said Mrs. Lecks; "that is, if it's anythin' we'd be likely to want to eat. If it's tomatoes, pour it into the sea, for nobody ought to eat tomatoes put up in tins."

I hastily passed the cans to Mrs. Lecks, and I saw her empty the contents of one into the sea, and those of the other on a newspaper which she took from her pocket and placed in the stern.

I pulled up the movable floor and threw it overboard, and then began to bail.

"I thought," said Mrs. Aleshine, "that they always had pumps for leaks."

"Now, Barb'ry Aleshine," said Mrs. Lecks, "just gether yourself up on one of them seats, and go to work. The less talkin' we do, and the more scoopin', the better it'll be for us."

I soon perceived that it would have been difficult to find two more valuable assistants in the bailing of a boat than Mrs. Lecks and Mrs. Aleshine. They were evidently used to work, and were able to accommodate themselves to the unusual circumstances in which they were placed. We threw out the water very rapidly, and every little while I stopped bailing and felt about to see if I could discover where it came in. As these attempts met with no success, I gave them up after a time, and set about bailing with new vigor, believing that if we could get the boat nearly dry I should surely be able to find the leak.

But, after working half an hour more, I found that the job would be a long one; and if we all worked at once we would all be tired out at once, and that might be disastrous. Therefore I proposed that we should take turns in resting, and Mrs. Aleshine was ordered to stop work for a time. After this Mrs. Lecks took a rest, and when she went to work I stopped bailing and began again to search for the leak.

For about two hours we worked in this way, and then I concluded it was useless to continue any longer this vain exertion. With three of us bailing we were able to keep the water at the level we first found it; but with only two at work, it slightly gained upon us, so that now there was more water in the boat than when we first discovered it. The boat was an iron one, the leak in it I could neither find nor remedy, and it was quite plain that the water was now coming in more rapidly than it did at first. We were very tired, and even Mrs. Lecks, who had all along counseled us to keep at work, and not to waste one breath in talking, now admitted that it was of no use to try to get water out of that boat.

It had been some hours since I had used the oars, but whether we had drifted, or remained where we were when I stopped rowing, of course I could not know; but this mattered very little; our boat was slowly sinking beneath us, and it could make no difference whether we went down in one spot or another. I sat and racked my brain to think what could be done in this fearful emergency. To bail any longer was useless labor, and what else was there that we could do?

"When will it be time," asked Mrs. Lecks, "for us to put on the life-preservers? When the water gets nearly to the seats?"

I answered that we should not wait any longer than that, but in my own mind I could not see any advantage in putting them on at all. Why should we wish to lengthen our lives by a few hours of helpless floating upon the ocean?

"Very good," said Mrs. Lecks; "I'll keep a watch on the water. One of them cans was filled with lobster, which would be more than likely to disagree with us, and I've throwed it out; but the other had baked beans in it, and the best thing we can do is to eat some of these right away. They are mighty nourishin', and will keep up strength as well as anythin', and then, as you said there's a keg of water in the boat, we can all take a drink of that, and it'll make us feel like new cre'tur's. You'll have to take the beans in your hands, for we've got no spoons nor forks."

Mrs. Lecks and Mrs. Aleshine were each curled up out of reach of the water, the first in the stern, and the other on the aft thwart. The day was now beginning to break, and we could see about us very distinctly. Before reaching out her hands to receive her beans, Mrs.

27

Aleshine washed them in the water in the boat, remarking at the same time that she might as well make use of it since it was there. Having wiped her hands on some part of her apparel, they were filled with beans from the newspaper held by Mrs. Lecks, and these were passed over to me. I was very hungry, and when I had finished my beans I agreed with my companions that although they would have been a great deal better if heated up with butter, pepper, and salt, they were very comforting as they were. One of the empty cans was now passed to me, and after having been asked by Mrs. Lecks to rinse it out very carefully, we all satisfied our thirst from the water in the keg.

"Cold baked beans and lukewarm water ain't exactly company vittles," said Mrs. Aleshine, "but there's many a poor wretch would be glad to get 'em."

I could not imagine any poor wretch who would be glad of the food together with the attending circumstances; but I did not say so.

"The water is just one finger from the bottom of the seat," said Mrs. Lecks, who had been stooping over to measure, "and it's time to put on the life-preservers."

"Very good," said Mrs. Aleshine; "hand me mine."

Each of us now buckled on a life-preserver, and as I did so I stood up upon a thwart and looked about me. It was quite light now, and I could see for a long distance over the surface of the ocean, which was gently rolling in wide, smooth swells. As we rose upon the summit of one of these I saw a dark spot upon the water, just on the edge of our near horizon. "Is that the steamer?" I thought; "and has she not yet sunk?"

At this there came to me a glimmering of courageous hope. If the steamer had remained afloat so long, it was probable that on account of water-tight compartments, or for some other reason, her sinking had reached its limit, and that if we could get back to her we might be saved. But, alas, how were we to get back to her? This boat would sink long, long before I could row that distance.

However, I soon proclaimed the news to my companions, whereupon Mrs. Aleshine prepared to stand upon a thwart and see for herself. But Mrs. Lecks restrained her.

"Don't make things worse, Barb'ry Aleshine," said she, "by tumblin' overboard. If we've got to go into the water, let us do it decently and in order. If that's the ship, Mr. Craig, don't you suppose we can float ourselves to it in some way?"

I replied that by the help of a life-preserver a person who could swim might reach the ship.

"But neither of us can swim," said Mrs. Lecks, "for we've lived where the water was never more'n a foot deep, except in time of freshets, when there's no swimmin' for man or beast. But if we see you swim, perhaps we can

29

follow, after a fashion. At any rate, we must do the best we can, and that's all there is to be done."

"The water now," remarked Mrs. Aleshine, "is so near to the bottom of my seat that I've got to stand up, tumble overboard or no."

"All right," remarked Mrs. Lecks; "we'd better all stand up, and let the boat sink under us. That will save our jumpin' overboard, or rollin' out any which way, which might be awkward."

"Goodness gracious me!" exclaimed Mrs. Aleshine. "You set the oysters creepin' over me again! First you talk of the ship sinkin' under us, and now it's the boat goin' to the bottom under our feet. Before any sinkin' 's to be done I'd ruther get out."

"Now, Barb'ry Aleshine," said Mrs. Lecks, "stand up straight, and don't talk so much. It'll be a great deal better to be let down gradual than to flop into the water all of a bunch."

"Very well," said Mrs. Aleshine; "it may be best to get used to it by degrees; but I must say I wish I was home."

As for me, I would have much preferred to jump overboard at once, instead of waiting in this cold-blooded manner; but as my companions had so far preserved their presence of mind, I did not wish to do anything which might throw them into a panic. I believed there would be no danger from the suction caused by the sinking of a small boat like this, and if we took care not to entangle ourselves with it in any way, we might as well follow Mrs. Lecks's advice as not. So we all stood up, Mrs. Lecks in the stern, I in the bow, and Mrs. Aleshine on a thwart between us. The last did not appear to have quite room enough for a steady footing, but, as she remarked, it did not matter very much, as the footing, broad or narrow, would not be there very long.

I am used to swimming, and have never hesitated to take a plunge into river or ocean, but I must admit that it was very trying to my nerves to stand up this way and wait for a boat to sink beneath me. How the two women were affected I do not know. They said nothing, but their faces indicated that something disagreeable was about to happen, and that the less that was said about it the better.

The boat had now sunk so much that the water was around Mrs. Aleshine's feet, her standing-place being rather lower than ours. I made myself certain that there were no ropes nor any other means of entanglement near my companions or myself, and then I waited. There seemed to be a good deal of buoyancy in the bow and stern of the boat, and it was a frightfully long time in sinking. The suspense became so utterly unendurable that I was tempted to put one foot on the edge of the boat, and, by tipping it, put an end to this nerve-rack; but I refrained, for I probably would throw the women off their balance, when they might fall against some part of the boat, and do themselves a hurt. I had just relinquished this intention, when two little waves seemed to rise one on each side of Mrs. Aleshine, and gently flowing over the side of the boat, they flooded her feet with water.

"Hold your breaths!" I shouted. And now I experienced a sensation which must have been very like that which comes to a condemned criminal at the first indication of the pulling of the drop. Then there was a horrible sinking, a gurgle, and a swash, and the ocean over which I had been gazing appeared to rise up and envelop me.

In a moment, however, my head was out of the water, and, looking hastily about me, I saw, close by, the heads and shoulders of Mrs. Lecks and Mrs. Aleshine. The latter was vigorously winking her eyes and blowing from her mouth some sea-water that had got into it; but as soon as her eyes fell upon me she exclaimed: "That was ever so much more suddint than I thought it was goin' to be!"

"Are you both all right?"

"I suppose I am," said Mrs. Aleshine, "but I never thought that a person with a life-preserver on would go clean under the water."

"But since you've come up again, you ought to be satisfied," said Mrs. Lecks. "And now," she added, turning her face toward me, "which way ought we to try to swim and have we got everythin' we want to take with us?"

"What we haven't got we can't get," remarked Mrs. Aleshine; "and as for swimmin', I expect I'm goin' to make a poor hand at it."

I had a hope, which was not quite strong enough to be a belief, that, supported by their life-preservers, the two women might paddle themselves along; and that, by giving them in turn a helping hand, I might eventually get them to the steamer. There was a strong probability that I would not succeed, but I did not care to think of that.

I now swam in front of my companions, and endeavored to instruct them in the best method of propelling themselves with their arms and their hands. If they succeeded in this, I thought I would give them some further lessons in striking out with their feet. After watching me attentively, Mrs. Lecks did manage to move herself slowly through the smooth water, but poor Mrs. Aleshine could do nothing but splash.

"If there was anythin' to take hold of," she said to me, "I might get along; but I can't get any grip on the water, though you seem to do it well enough. Look there!" she added in a higher voice. "Isn't that an oar floatin' over there? If you can get that for me, I believe I can row myself much better than I can swim."

This seemed an odd idea, but I swam over to the floating oar, and brought it her. I was about to show her how she could best use it, but she declined my advice.

33

"If I do it at all," she said, "I must do it in my own way." And taking the oar in her strong hands, she began to ply it on the water very much in the way in which she would handle a broom. At first she dipped the blade too deeply, but, correcting this error, she soon began to paddle herself along at a slow but steady rate.

"Capital!" I cried. "You do that admirably!"

"Anybody who's swept as many rooms as I have," she said, "ought to be able to handle anythin' that can be used like a broom."

"Isn't there another oar?" cried Mrs. Lecks, who had now been left a little distance behind us. "If there is, I want one."

Looking about me, I soon discovered another floating oar, and brought it to Mrs. Lecks, who, after holding it in various positions, so as to get "the hang of it," as she said, soon began to use it with as much skill as that shown by her friend. If either of them had been obliged to use an oar in the ordinary way, I fear they would have had a bad time of it; but, considering the implement in the light of a broom, its use immediately became familiar to them, and they got on remarkably well.

I now took a position a little in advance of my companions, and as I swam slowly they were easily able to keep up with me. Mrs. Aleshine, being so stout, floated much higher out of the water than either Mrs. Lecks or I, and this permitted her to use her oar with a great deal of freedom. Sometimes she would give such a vigorous brush to the water that she would turn herself almost entirely around, but after a little practice she learned to avoid undue efforts of this kind.

I was not positively sure that we were going in the right direction, for my position did not allow me to see very far over the water; but I remembered that when I was standing up in the boat, and made my discovery, the sun was just about to rise in front of me, while the dark spot on the ocean lay to my left. Judging, therefore, from the present position of the sun, which was not very high, I concluded that we were moving toward the north, and therefore in the right direction. How far off the steamer might be I had no idea, for I was not accustomed to judging distances at sea; but I believed that if we were careful of our strength, and if the ocean continued as smooth as it now was, we might eventually reach the vessel, provided she were yet afloat.

"After you are fairly in the water," said Mrs. Aleshine, as she swept along, although without the velocity which that phrase usually implies, "it isn't half so bad as I thought it would be. For one thing, it don't feel a bit salt, although I must say it tasted horribly that way when I first went into it."

"You didn't expect to find pickle-brine, did you?" said Mrs. Lecks. "Though, if it was, I suppose we could float on it settin'."

"And as to bein' cold," said Mrs. Aleshine,

"the part of me that's in is actually more comfortable than that which is out."

"There's one thing I would have been afraid of," said Mrs. Lecks, "if we hadn't made preparations for it, and that's sharks."

"Preparations!" I exclaimed. "How in the world did you prepare for sharks?"

"Easy enough," said Mrs. Lecks. "When we went down into our room to get ready to go away in the boats we both put on black stockin's. I've read that sharks never bite colored people, although if they see a white man in the water they'll snap him up as quick as lightnin'; and black stockin's was the nearest we could come to it. You see, I thought as like as not we'd have some sort of an upset before we got through."

"It's a great comfort," remarked Mrs. Aleshine, "and I'm very glad you thought of it, Mrs. Lecks. After this I shall make it a rule: Black stockin's for sharks."

"I suppose in your case," said Mrs. Lecks, addressing me, "dark trousers will do as well."

To which I answered that I sincerely hoped they would.

"Another thing I'm thankful for," said Mrs. Aleshine, "is that I thought to put on a flannel skeert."

"And what's the good of it," said Mrs. Lecks, "when it's soppin' wet?"

"Flannel's flannel," replied her friend, "whether it's wet or dry; and if you'd had the rheumatism as much as I have, you'd know it."

To this Mrs. Lecks replied with a sniff, and asked me how soon I thought we would get sight of the ship; for if we were going the wrong way, and had to turn round and go back, it would certainly be very provoking.

I should have been happy indeed to be able to give a satisfactory answer to this question. Every time that we rose upon a swell I threw a rapid glance around the whole circle of the horizon; and at last, not a quarter of an hour after Mrs. Lecks's question, I was rejoiced to see, almost in the direction in which I supposed it ought to be, the dark spot which I had before discovered. I shouted the glad news, and as we rose again my companions strained their eyes in the direction to which I pointed. They both saw it, and were greatly satisfied.

"Now, then," said Mrs. Aleshine, "it seems as if there was somethin' to work for"; and she began to sweep her oar with great vigor.

"If you want to tire yourself out before you get there, Barb'ry Aleshine," said Mrs. Lecks, "you'd better go on in that way. Now what I advise is that we stop rowin' altogether, and have somethin' to eat; for I'm sure we need it to keep up our strength."

"Eat!" I cried. "What are you going to eat? Do you expect to catch fish?"

"And eat 'em raw?" said Mrs. Lecks. "I should think not. But do you suppose, Mr. Craig, that Mrs. Aleshine and me would go off and leave that ship without somethin' to eat by the way? Let's all gether here in a bunch, and see what sort of a meal we can make. And now, Barb'ry Aleshine, if you lay your oar down there on the water, I recommend you to tie it to one of your bonnet-strings, or it'll be floatin' away, and you won't get it again."

As she said this, Mrs. Lecks put her right hand down into the water, and fumbled about, apparently in search of a pocket. I could not but smile as I thought of the condition of food when, for an hour or more, it had been a couple of feet under the surface of the ocean; but my ideas on the subject were entirely changed when I saw Mrs. Lecks hold up in the air two German sausages, and shake the briny drops from their smooth and glittering surfaces.

"There's nothin'," she said, "like sausages for shipwreck and that kind o' thing. They're very sustainin', and bein' covered with a tight skin, water can't get at 'em, no matter how you carry 'em. I wouldn't bring these out in the boat, because, havin' the beans, we might as well eat them. Have you a knife about you, Mr. Craig?"

I produced a dripping jack-knife, and after the open blade had been waved in the air to dry it a little, Mrs. Lecks proceeded to divide one of the sausages, handing the other to me to hold meanwhile.

"Now don't go eatin' sausages without bread, if you don't want 'em to give you dyspepsy," said Mrs. Aleshine, who was tugging at a submarine pocket.

"I'm very much afraid your bread is all soaked," said Mrs. Lecks.

To which her friend replied that that remained to be seen, and forthwith produced, with a splash, a glass preserve-jar with a metal top.

"I saw this nearly empty, as I looked into the ship's pantry, and I stuffed into it all the soft biscuits it would hold. There was some sort of jam left at the bottom, so the one who gets the last biscuit will have somethin' of a little spread on it. And now, Mrs. Lecks," she continued triumphantly, as she unscrewed the top, "that rubber ring has kept 'em as dry as chips. I'm mighty glad of it, for I had trouble enough gettin' this jar into my pocket, and gettin' it out, too, for that matter."

Floating thus, with our hands and shoulders above the water, we made a very good meal from the sausages and soft biscuit.

"Barb'ry Aleshine," said Mrs. Lecks, as her friend proceeded to cut the second sausage, "don't you lay that knife down, when you've done with it, as if't was an oar; for if you do it'll sink, as like as not, about six miles. I've read that the ocean is as deep as that in some places."

"Goodness gracious me!" exclaimed Mrs. Aleshine, "I hope we are not over one of them deep spots."

"There's no knowin'," said Mrs. Lecks, "but

if it's more comfortin' to think it's shallerer, we'll make up our minds that way. Now, then," she continued, "we'll finish off this meal with a little somethin' to drink. I'm not given to takin' spirits, but I never travel without a little whisky, ready mixed with water, to take if it should be needed."

So saying, she produced from one of her pockets a whisky-flask tightly corked, and of its contents we each took a sip, Mrs. Aleshine remarking that, leaving out being chilled or colicky, we were never likely to need it more than now.

Thus refreshed and strengthened, Mrs. Lecks and Mrs. Aleshine took up their oars, while I swam slightly in advance, as before. When, with occasional intermissions of rest, and a good deal of desultory conversation, we had swept and swum for about an hour, Mrs. Lecks suddenly exclaimed: "I can see that thing ever so much plainer now, and I don't believe it's a ship at all. To me it looks like bushes."

"You're mighty long-sighted without your specs," said Mrs. Aleshine, "and I'm not sure but what you're right."

For ten minutes or more I had been puzzling over the shape of the dark spot, which was now nearly all the time in sight. Its peculiar form had filled me with a dreadful fear that it was the steamer, bottom upward, although I knew enough about nautical matters to have no good reason to suppose that this could be the case. I am not far-sighted, but when Mrs. Lecks suggested bushes, I gazed at the distant object with totally different ideas, and soon began to believe that it was not a ship, either right side up or wrong side up, but that it might be an island. This belief I proclaimed to my companions, and for some time we all worked with increased energy in the desire to get near enough to make ourselves certain in regard to this point.

"As true as I'm standin' here," said Mrs. Lecks, who, although she could not read without spectacles, had remarkably good sight at long range, "them is trees and bushes that I see before me, though they do seem to be growin' right out of the water."

"There's an island under them; you may be sure of that!" I cried. "Isn't this ever so much better than a sinking ship?"

"I'm not so sure about that," said Mrs. Aleshine. "I'm used to the ship, and as long as it didn't sink I'd prefer it. There's plenty to eat on board of it, and good beds to sleep on, which is more than can be expected on a little bushy place like that ahead of us. But then, the ship might sink all of a suddint, beds, vittles, and all."

"Do you suppose that is the island the other boats went to?" asked Mrs. Lecks.

This question I had already asked of myself. I had been told that the island to which the captain intended to take his boats lay about thirty miles south of the point where we left the steamer. Now I knew very well that we had not come thirty miles, and had reason to believe, moreover, that the greater part of the progress we had made had been toward the north. It was not at all probable that the position of this island was unknown to our captain; and it must, therefore, have been considered by him as an unsuitable place for the landing of his passengers. There might be many reasons for this unsuitableness: the island might be totally barren and desolate; it might be the abode of unpleasant natives; and, more important than anything else, it was, in all probability, a spot where steamers never touched.

But, whatever its disadvantages, I was most wildly desirous to reach it.

"I do not believe," I said, in answer to Mrs. Lecks, "that that is the island to which the captain would have taken us; but, whatever it is, it is dry land, and we must get there as soon as we can."

"That's true," said Mrs. Aleshine, "for I'd like to have ground nearer to my feet than six miles; and if we don't find anything to eat and any place to sleep when we get there, it's no more than can be said of the place where we are now."

"You're too particular, Barb'ry Aleshine," said Mrs. Lecks, "about your comforts. If you find the ground too hard to sleep on, when you

42

get there, you can put on your life-preserver, and go to bed in the water."

"Very good," said Mrs. Aleshine; "and if these islands are made of coral, as I've heard they are, and if they're as full of small p'ints as some coral I've got at home, you'll be glad to take a berth by me, Mrs. Lecks."

I counseled my companions to follow me as rapidly as possible, and we all pushed vigorously forward. When we had approached near enough to the island to see what sort of place it really was, we perceived that is was a low-lying spot, apparently covered with verdure, and surrounded, as far as we could see as we rose on the swells, by a rocky reef, against which a tolerably high surf was running.

Before us we could see a continuous line of white-capped breakers, and so I led my little party to the right, hoping that we would soon see signs of an opening in the reef.

We swam and paddled, however, for a long time and still the surf rolled menacingly on the rocks before us. At last we perceived, at no great distance, a spot where there seemed to be no breakers; and when we reached it we found, to our unutterable delight, that here was smooth water flowing through a wide opening in the reef.

I swam through into an open lagoon followed closely by Mrs. Lecks and Mrs. Aleshine.

The first thing that arrested our attention was a little wharf or landing-stage, erected upon

43

the narrow beach of the island, almost opposite to us.

"As sure as I stand here," exclaimed Mrs. Lecks, who never seemed to forget her upright position, "somebody lives in this place!"

"And it isn't a stickery coral island, either," cried Mrs. Aleshine, "for that sand's as smooth as any I ever saw."

"Whoever does live here," resumed Mrs. Lecks, "has got to take us in, whether they like it or not, and the sooner we get over there the better."

The Showman's Courtship

Artemus Ward

Thare was many affectin ties which made me hanker arter Betsy Jane. Her father's farm jined our'n; their cows and our'n squencht their thurst at the same spring; our old mares both had stars in their forrerds; the measles broke out in both famerlies at nearly the same period; our parients (Betsy's and mine) slept regularly every Sunday in the same meetin house, and the nabers used to obsarve, "How thick the Wards and Peasleys air!" It was a surblime site, in the Spring of the year, to see our sevral mothers (Betsy's and mine) with their gowns pin'd up so thay couldn't sile 'em, affecshunitly Bilin sope together & aboozin the nabers.

Altho I hankered intensly arter the objeck of my affecshuns, I darsunt tell her of the fires which was rajin in my manly Buzzum. I'd try to do it, but my tung would kerwollup up agin the roof of my mouth & stick thar, like deth to a deseast Afrikan or a country postmaster to his offiss, while my hart whanged agin my ribs like a old fashioned wheat Flale agin a barn door.

'Twas a carm still nite in Joon. All nater was husht and nary zeffer disturbed the sereen silens. I sot with Betsy Jane on the fense of her farther's pastur. We'd been rompin threw the woods, kullin flours & drivin the woodchuck from his Nativ Lair (so to speak) with long sticks. Wall we sot thar on the fense, a swingin our feet two and fro, blushin as red as the Baldinsville skool house when it was fust painted, and lookin very simple, I make no doubt. My left arm was ockepied in ballunsin myself on the fense, while my rite was woundid luvinly round her waste.

I cleared my throat and tremblinly sed, "Betsy, you're a Gazelle."

I though that air was putty fine. I waited to see what effeck it would hav upon her. It evidently didn't fetch her, for she up and sed:

"You're a sheep!"

Sez I, "Betsy, I think very muchly of you."

"I don't b'leeve a word you say — so there now, cum!" with which obsarvashun she hitched away from me.

"I wish thar was winders to my Sole," sed I, "so that you could see some of my feelins. There's fire enuff in here," sed I, strikin my buzzum with my fist, "to bile all the corn beef and turnips in the naberhood. Versoovius and the Critter ain't a circumstans!"

46

She bowd her hed down and commenst chawin the strings to her sunbonnet.

"Ar could you know the sleeplis nites I worry threw with on your account, how vittles has seized to be attractiv to me, & how my lims has shrunk up, you wouldn't dowt me. Gase on this wastin form and these 'ere sunken cheeks —"

I should have continnered on in this strane probly for sum time, but unfortnitly I lost my ballunse and fell over into the pastur kersmash, tearin my close and seveerly damagin myself ginerally.

Betsy Jane sprung to my assistance in dubble quick time and dragged me 4th. Then drawin herself up to her full hite she sed:

"I won't listen to your noncents no longer. Jes say rite strate out what you're drivin at. If you mean getting hitched, I'M IN!"

I considered that air enuff for all practical purpusses, and we proceeded immejitly to the parson's & was made 1 that very nite.

I've parst threw many tryin ordeels sins then, but Betsy Jane has bin troo as steel. By attendin strickly to bizniss I've amarsed a handsum Pittance. No man on this foot-stool can rise & git up & say I ever knowinly injered no man or wimmin folks, while all agree that my Show is ekalled by few and exceld by none, embracin as it does a wonderful colleckshun of livin wild

Beests of Pray, snaix in grate profushun, a endliss variety of life-size wax figgers, & the only traned kangaroo in Amerika — the most amoozin little cus ever introjuced to a discriminatin public.

Extracts from Adam's Diary
Translated from the Original MS.

Mark Twain

Monday. — This new creature with the long hair is a good deal in the way. It is always hanging around and following me about. I don't like this; I am not used to company. I wish it would stay with the other animals. . . . Cloudy today, wind in the east; think we shall have rain. . . . *We?* Where did I get that word? . . . I remember now — the new creature uses it.

Tuesday. — Been examining the great waterfall. It is the finest thing on the estate, I think. The new creature calls it Niagara Falls — why, I am sure I do not know. Says it *looks* like Niagara Falls. That is not a reason; it is mere waywardness and imbecility. I get no chance to name anything myself. The new creature names everything that comes along, before I can get in a protest. And always that same pretext is offered — it *looks* like the thing. There is the dodo, for instance. Says the moment one looks at it one sees at a glance that it "looks like a dodo." It will have to keep that name, no doubt. It wearies me to fret about it, and it does no good, anyway. Dodo! It looks no more like a dodo than I do.

Wednesday. — Built me a shelter against the rain, but could not have it to myself in peace. The new creature intruded. When I tried to put it out it shed water out of the holes it looks with, and wiped it away with the back of its paws, and made a noise such as some of the other animals make when they are in distress. I wish it would not talk; it is always talking. That sounds like a cheap fling at the poor creature, a slur; but I do not mean it so. I have never heard the human voice before, and any new and strange sound intruding itself here upon the solemn hush of these dreaming solitudes offends my ear and seems a false note. And this new sound is so close to me; it is right at my shoulder, right at my ear, first on one side and then on the other, and I am used only to sounds that are more or less distant from me.

Friday. — The naming goes recklessly on, in spite of anything I can do. I had a very good name for the estate, and it was musical and pretty — GARDEN-OF-EDEN. Privately, I continue to call it that, but not any longer publicly. The new creature says it is all woods and rocks and scenery, and therefore has no resemblance to a garden. Says it *looks* like a park, and does not look like anything *but* a park. Consequently, without consulting me, it has been new-named

— NIAGARA FALLS PARK. This is sufficiently high-handed, it seems to me. And already there is a sign up:

KEEP OFF
THE GRASS

My life is not as happy as it was.

Saturday. — The new creature eats too much fruit. We are going to run short, most likely. "We" again — that is *its* word; mine too, now, from hearing it so much. Good deal of fog this morning. I do not go out in the fog myself. The new creature does. It goes out in all weathers, and stumps right in with its muddy feet. And talks. It used to be so pleasant and quiet here.

Sunday. — Pulled through. This day is getting to be more and more trying. It was selected and set apart last November as a day of rest. I already had six of them per week, before. This morning found the new creature trying to clod apples out of that forbidden tree.

Monday. — The new creature says its name is Eve. That is all right, I have no objections. Says it is to call it by when I want it to come. I said it was superfluous, then. The word evidently raised me in its respect; and indeed it is a large, good word, and will bear repetition. It says it is not an It, it is a She. This is probably doubtful; yet it is all one to me; what she is were nothing to me if she would but go

51

by herself and not talk.

Tuesday. — She has littered the whole estate with execrable names and offensive signs:

☞ THIS WAY TO THE WHIRLPOOL.
☞ THIS WAY TO GOAT ISLAND.
☞ CAVE OF THE WINDS THIS WAY.

She says this park would make a tidy summer resort, if there was any custom for it. Summer resort — another invention of hers — just words, without any meaning. What is a summer resort? But it is best not to ask her, she has such a rage for explaining.

Friday. — She has taken to beseeching me to stop going over the Falls. What harm does it do? Says it makes her shudder. I wonder why. I have always done it — always liked the plunge, and the excitement, and the coolness. I supposed it was what the Falls were for. They have no other use that I can see, and they must have been made for something. She says they were only made for scenery — like the rhinoceros and the mastodon.

I went over the Falls in a barrel — not satisfactory to her. Went over in a tub — still not satisfactory. Swam the Whirlpool and the Rapids in a fig-leaf suit. It got much damaged. Hence, tedious complaints about my extravagance. I am too much hampered here. What I need is change of scene.

Saturday. — I escaped last Tuesday night,

and traveled two days, and built me another shelter, in a secluded place, and obliterated my tracks as well as I could, but she hunted me out by means of a beast which she has tamed and calls a wolf, and came making that pitiful noise again, and shedding that water out of the places she looks with. I was obliged to return with her, but will presently emigrate again, when occasion offers. She engages herself in many foolish things: among others, trying to study out why the animals called lions and tigers live on grass and flowers, when, as she says, the sort of teeth they wear would indicate that they were intended to eat each other. This is foolish, because to do that would be to kill each other, and that would introduce what, as I understand it, is called "death"; and death, as I have been told, has not yet entered the Park. Which is a pity, on some accounts.

Sunday. — Pulled through.

Monday. — I believe I see what the week is for: it is to give time to rest up from the weariness of Sunday. It seems a good idea. . . . She has been climbing that tree again. Clodded her out of it. She said nobody was looking. Seems to consider that a sufficient justification for chancing any dangerous thing. Told her that. The word justification moved her admiration — and envy too, I thought. It is a good word.

Thursday. — She told me she was made out of a rib taken from my body. This is at least doubtful, if not more than that. I have not missed any rib. . . . She is in much trouble about the buzzard; says grass does not agree with it; is afraid she can't raise it; thinks it was intended to live on decayed flesh. The buzzard must get along the best it can with what is provided. We cannot overturn the whole scheme to accommodate the buzzard.

Saturday. — She fell in the pond yesterday, when she was looking at herself in it, which she is always doing. She nearly strangled, and said it was most uncomfortable. This made her sorry for the creatures which live in there, which she calls fish, for she continues to fasten names onto things that don't need them and don't come when they are called by them, which is a matter of no consequence to her, as she is such a numskull anyway; so she got a lot of them out and brought them in last night and put them in my bed to keep warm, but I have noticed them now and then all day, and I don't see that they are any happier there than they were before, only quieter. When night comes I shall throw them outdoors. I will not sleep with them again, for I find them clammy and unpleasant to lie among when a person hasn't anything on.

Sunday. — Pulled through.

Tuesday. — She has taken up with a snake now. The other animals are glad, for she was always experimenting with them and bothering them; and I am glad, because the snake talks, and this enables me to get a rest.

Friday. — She says the snake advises her to try the fruit of that tree, and says the result will be a great and fine and noble education. I told her there would be another result, too — it would introduce death into the world. That was a mistake — it had been better to keep the remark to myself; it only gave her an idea — she could save the sick buzzard, and furnish fresh meat to the despondent lions and tigers. I advised her to keep away from the tree. She said she wouldn't. I foresee trouble. Will emigrate.

Wednesday. — I have had a variegated time. I escaped that night, and rode a horse all night as fast as he could go, hoping to get clear out of the Park and hide in some other country before the trouble should begin; but it was not to be. About an hour after sunup, as I was riding through a flowery plain where thousands of animals were grazing, slumbering, or playing with each other, according to their wont, all of a sudden they broke into a tempest of frightful noises, and in one moment the plain was in a frantic commotion and every beast was destroying its neighbor. I knew what it meant — Eve had eaten that fruit, and death was come into the world. . . . The tigers ate my horse, paying no attention when I ordered them to desist, and they would even have eaten me if I had staid — which I didn't, but went away in much haste. . . . I found this place, outside the

Park, and was fairly comfortable for a few days, but she has found me out. Found me out, and has named the place Tonawanda — says it *looks* like that. In fact I was not sorry she came, for there are but meagre pickings here, and she brought some of those apples. I was obliged to eat them, I was so hungry. It was against my principles, but I find that principles have no real force except when one is well fed. . . . She came curtained in boughs and bunches of leaves, and when I asked her what she meant by such nonsense, and snatched them away and threw them down, she tittered and blushed. I had never seen a person titter and blush before, and to me it seemed unbecoming and idiotic. She said I would soon know how it was myself. This was correct. Hungry as I was, I laid down the apple half eaten — certainly the best one I ever saw, considering the lateness of the season — and arrayed myself in the discarded boughs and branches, and then spoke to her with some severity and ordered her to go and get some more and not make such a spectacle of herself. She did it, and after this we crept down to where the wild-beast battle had been, and collected some skins, and I made her patch together a couple of suits proper for public occasions. They are uncomfortable, it is true, but stylish, and that is the main point about clothes. . . . I find she is a good deal of a companion. I see I should be lonesome and depressed without her, now that I have lost my property. Another thing, she says it is ordered that we work for our living hereafter. She will be useful. I will superintend.

Ten Days Later. — She accuses *me* of being the cause of our disaster! She says, with apparent sincerity and truth, that the Serpent assured her that the forbidden fruit was not apples, it was chestnuts. I said I was innocent, then, for I had not eaten any chestnuts. She said the Serpent informed her that "chestnut" was a figurative term meaning an aged and mouldy joke. I turned pale at that, for I have made many jokes to pass the weary time, and some of them could have been of that sort, though I had honestly supposed that they were new when I made them. She asked me if I had made one just at the time of the catastrophe. I was obliged to admit that I had made one to myself, though not aloud. It was this. I was thinking about the Falls, and I said to myself, "How wonderful it is to see that vast body of water tumble down there!" Then in an instant a bright thought flashed into my head, and I let it fly, saying, "It would be a deal more wonderful to see it tumble *up* there!" — and I was just about to kill myself with laughing at it when all nature broke loose in war and death, and I had to flee for my life. "There," she said, with triumph, "that is just it; the Serpent mentioned that very jest, and called it the First Chestnut, and said it was coeval with the creation." Alas, I am indeed to blame. Would that I were not witty;

oh, would that I had never had that radiant thought!

Next Year. — We have named it Cain. She caught it while I was up country trapping on the North Shore of the Erie; caught it in the timber a couple of miles from our dug-out — or it might have been four, she isn't certain which. It resembles us in some ways, and may be a relation. That is what she thinks, but this is an error, in my judgment. The difference in size warrants the conclusion that it is a different and new kind of animal — a fish, perhaps, though when I put it in the water to see, it sank, and she plunged in and snatched it out before there was opportunity for the experiment to determine the matter. I still think it is a fish, but she is indifferent about what it is, and will not let me have it to try. I do not understand this. The coming of the creature seems to have changed her whole nature and made her unreasonable about experiments. She thinks more of it than she does of any of the other animals, but is not able to explain why. Her mind is disordered — everything shows it. Sometimes she carries the fish in her arms half the night when it complains and wants to get to the water. At such times the water comes out of the places in her face that she looks out of, and she pats the fish on the back and makes soft sounds with her mouth to soothe it, and betrays sorrow and solicitude in a hundred ways. I have never seen her do like this with

58

any other fish, and it troubles me greatly. She used to carry the young tigers around so, and play with them, before we lost our property; but it was only play; she never took on about them like this when their dinner disagreed with them.

Sunday. — She doesn't work, Sundays, but lies around all tired out, and likes to have the fish wallow over her; and she makes fool noises to amuse it, and pretends to chew its paws, and that makes it laugh. I have not seen a fish before that could laugh. This makes me doubt. . . . I have come to like Sunday myself. Superintending all the week tires a body so. There ought to be more Sundays. In the old days they were tough, but now they come handy.

Wednesday. — It isn't a fish. I cannot quite make out what it is. It makes curious devilish noises when not satisfied, and says "goo-goo" when it is. It is not one of us, for it doesn't walk; it is not a bird, for it doesn't fly; it is not a frog, for it doesn't hop; it is not a snake, for it doesn't crawl; I feel sure it is not a fish, though I cannot get a chance to find out whether it can swim or not. It merely lies around, and mostly on its back, with its feet up. I have not seen any other animal do that before. I said I believed it was an enigma, but she only admired the word without understanding it. In my judgment it is either an enigma or some kind of a bug. If it dies, I will take it apart and see what its arrangements are. I never had a thing perplex me so.

Three Months Later. — The perplexity augments instead of diminishing. I sleep but little. It has ceased from lying around, and goes about on its four legs, now. Yet it differs from the other four-legged animals in that its front legs are unusually short, consequently this causes the main part of its person to stick up uncomfortably high in the air, and this is not attractive. It is built much as we are, but its method of traveling shows that it is not of our breed. The short front legs and long hind ones indicate that it is of the kangaroo family, but it is a marked variation of the species, since the true kangaroo hops, whereas this one never does. Still it is a curious and interesting variety, and has not been catalogued before. As I discovered it, I have felt justified in securing the credit of the discovery by attaching my name to it, and hence have called it *Kangaroorum Adamiensis.* . . . It must have been a young one when it came, for it has grown exceedingly since. It must be five times as big, now, as it was then, and when discontented is able to make from twenty-two to thirty-eight times the noise it made at first. Coercion does not modify this, but has the contrary effect. For this reason I discontinued the system. She reconciles it by persuasion, and by giving it things which she had previously told it she wouldn't give it. As already observed, I was not at home when it

60

first came, and she told me she found it in the woods. It seems odd that it should be the only one, yet it must be so, for I have worn myself out these many weeks trying to find another one to add to my collection, and for this one to play with; for surely then it would be quieter, and we could tame it more easily. But I find none, nor any vestige of any; and strangest of all, no tracks. It has to live on the ground, it cannot help itself; therefore, how does it get about without leaving a track? I have set a dozen traps, but they do no good. I catch all small animals except that one; animals that merely go into the trap out of curiosity, I think, to see what the milk is there for. They never drink it.

Three Months Later. — The kangaroo still continues to grow, which is very strange and perplexing. I never knew one to be so long getting its growth. It has fur on its head now; not like kangaroo fur, but exactly like our hair, except that it is much finer and softer, and instead of being black is red. I am like to lose my mind over the capricious and harassing developments of this unclassifiable zoological freak. If I could catch another one — but that is hopeless; it is a new variety, and the only sample; this is plain. But I caught a true kangaroo and brought it in, thinking that this one, being lonesome, would rather have that for company than have no kin at all, or any animal it could feel a nearness to or get sympathy from in its forlorn condition here among strangers who do not know its ways or habits, or what to do to make it feel that it is among friends; but it was a mistake — it went into such fits at the sight of the kangaroo that I was convinced it had never seen one before. I pity the poor noisy little animal, but there is nothing I can do to make it happy. If I could tame it — but that is out of the question; the more I try, the worse I seem to make it. It grieves me to the heart to see it in its little storms of sorrow and passion. I wanted to let it go, but she wouldn't hear of it. That seemed cruel and not like her; and yet she may be right. It might be lonelier than ever; for since I cannot find another one, how could *it?*

Five Months Later. — It is not a kangaroo. No, for it supports itself by holding to her finger, and thus goes a few steps on its hind legs, and then falls down. It is probably some kind of a bear; and yet it has no tail — as yet — and no fur, except on its head. It still keeps on growing — that is a curious circumstance, for bears get their growth earlier than this. Bears are dangerous — since our catastrophe — and I shall not be satisfied to have this one prowling about the place much longer without a muzzle on. I have offered to get her a kangaroo if she would let this one go, but it did no good — she is determined to run us into all sorts of foolish risks, I think. She was not like this before she lost her mind.

A Fortnight Later. — I examined its mouth. There is no danger yet; it has only one tooth. It has no tail yet. It makes more noise now than it ever did before — and mainly at night. I have moved out. But I shall go over, mornings, to breakfast, and to see if it has more teeth. If it gets a mouthful of teeth it will be time for it to go, tail or no tail, for a bear does not need a tail in order to be dangerous.

Four Months Later. — I have been off hunting, and fishing a month, up in the region that she calls Buffalo; I don't know why, unless it is because there are not any buffaloes there. Meantime the bear has learned to paddle around all by itself on its hind legs, and says "poppa" and "momma." It is certainly a new species. This resemblance to words may be purely accidental, of course, and may have no purpose or meaning; but even in that case it is still extraordinary, and is a thing which no other bear can do. This imitation of speech, taken together with general absence of fur and entire absence of tail, sufficiently indicates that this is a new kind of bear. The further study of it will be exceedingly interesting. Meantime I will go off on a far expedition among the forests of the North and make an exhaustive search. There must certainly be another one somewhere, and this one will be less dangerous when it has company of its own species. I will go straightway; but I will muzzle this one first.

Three Months Later. — It has been a weary,

weary hunt, yet I have had no success. In the meantime, without stirring from the home estate, she has caught another one! I never saw such luck. I might have hunted these woods a hundred years, I never should have run across that thing.

Next Day. — I have been comparing the new one with the old one, and it is perfectly plain that they are the same breed. I was going to stuff one of them for my collection, but she is prejudiced against it for some reason or other; so I have relinquished the idea, though I think it is a mistake. It would be an irreparable loss to science if they should get away. The old one is tamer than it was, and can laugh and talk like the parrot, having learned this, no doubt, from being with the parrot so much, and having the imitative faculty in a highly developed degree. I shall be astonished if it turns out to be a new kind of parrot; and yet I ought not to be astonished, for it has already been everything else it could think of, since those first days when it was a fish. The new one is as ugly now as the old one was at first; has the same sulphur-and-raw-meat complexion and the same singular head without any fur on it. She calls it Abel.

Ten Years Later. — They are boys; we found it out long ago. It was their coming in that small, immature shape that puzzled us; we were not used to it. There are some girls now. Abel is a good boy, but if Cain had staid a bear it would have improved him. After all these years,

I see that I was mistaken about Eve in the beginning; it is better to live outside the Garden with her than inside it without her. At first I thought she talked too much; but now I should be sorry to have that voice fall silent and pass out of my life. Blessed be the chestnut that brought us near together and taught me to know the goodness of her heart and the sweetness of her spirit!

A Night Of Terror

Mark Twain

When we got back to the hotel I wound and set the pedometer and put it in my pocket, for I was to carry it next day and keep record of the miles we made. The work which we had given the instrument to do during the day which had just closed, had not fatigued it perceptibly.

We were in bed by ten, for we wanted to be up and away on our tramp homeward with the dawn. I hung fire, but Harris went to sleep at once. I hate a man who goes to sleep at once; there is a sort of indefinable something about it which is not exactly an insult, and yet is an insolence; and one which is hard to bear, too. I lay there fretting over this injury, and trying to go to sleep; but the harder I tried, the wider awake I grew. I got to feeling very lonely in the dark, with no company but an undigested dinner. My mind got a start by and by, and began to consider the beginning of every subject which has ever been thought of; but it never went further than the beginning; it was touch and go; it fled from topic to topic with a frantic speed. At the end of an hour my head was in a perfect whirl and I was dead tired, fagged out.

The fatigue was so great that it presently began to make some head against the nervous excitement; while imagining my self wide awake, I would really doze into momentary unconsciousness, and come suddenly out of them with a physical jerk which nearly wrenched my joints apart, — the delusion of the instant being that I was tumbling backwards over a precipice. After I had fallen over eight or nine precipices and thus found out that one half of my brain had been asleep eight or nine times without the wide-awake, hard-working other half suspecting it, the periodical unconsciousnesses began to extend their spell gradually over more of my brain-territory, and at last I sank into a drowse which grew deeper and deeper and was doubtless just on the very point of becoming a solid, blessed, dreamless stupor, when, — what was that?

My dulled faculties dragged themselves partly back to life and took a receptive attitude. Now out of an immense, a limitless distance, came a something which grew and grew, and approached, and presently was recognizable as a sound, — it had rather seemed to be a feeling, before. This sound was a mile away, now — perhaps it was the murmur of a storm; and now it was nearer, — not a quarter of a mile away; was it the muffled rasping and grinding of distant machinery? No, it came still nearer; was it the measured tramp of a marching troop? But it came nearer still, and still nearer, — and at last it was right in the room: it was merely a mouse gnawing the wood-work. So I had held my breath all that time for such a trifle.

Well, what was done could not be helped; I would go to sleep at once and make up the lost time. That was a thoughtless thought. Without intending it, — hardly knowing it, — I fell to listening intently to that sound, and even unconsciously counting the strokes of the mouse's nutmeg-grater. Presently I was deriving exquisite suffering from this employment, yet maybe I could have endured it if the mouse had attended steadily to his work; but he did not do that; he stopped every now and then, and I suffered more while waiting and listening for him to begin again than I did while he was gnawing. Along at first I was mentally offering a reward of five, — six, — seven, — ten — dollars for that mouse; but toward the last I was offering rewards which were entirely beyond my means. I close-reefed my ears, — that is to say, I bent the flaps of them down and furled them into five or six folds, and pressed them against the hearing-orifice, — but it did no good: the faculty was so sharpened by nervous excitement that it was become a microphone and could hear through the overlays without trouble.

My anger grew to a frenzy. I finally did what all persons before me have done, clear back to Adam, — resolved to throw something. I reached down and got my walking shoes, then sat up in bed and listened, in order to exactly locate the noise. But I couldn't do it; it was as unlocatable as a cricket's noise; and where one thinks that that is, is always the very place where it isn't. So I presently hurled a shoe at random, and with a vicious vigor. It struck the wall over Harris's head and fell down on him; I had not imagined I could throw so far. It woke Harris, and I was glad of it until I found he was not angry; then I was sorry. He soon went to sleep again, which pleased me; but straightway the mouse began again, which roused my temper once more. I did not want to wake Harris a second time, but the gnawing continued until I was compelled to throw the other shoe. This time I broke a mirror, — there were two in the room, — I got the largest one, of course. Harris woke again, but did not complain, and I was sorrier than ever. I resolved that I would suffer all possible torture before I would disturb him a third time.

The mouse eventually retired, and by and by I was sinking to sleep, when a clock began to strike; I counted, till it was done, and was about to drowse again when another clock began; I counted; then the two great Rathhaus clock angels began to send forth soft, rich, melodious blasts from their long trumpets. I had never heard anything that was so lovely, or weird, or mysterious, — but when they got to blowing the quarter-hours, they seemed to me to be overdoing the thing. Every time I dropped off for a moment, a new noise woke me. Each time I woke I missed my coverlet, and had to reach down to the floor and get it again.

At last all sleepiness forsook me. I recognized the fact that I was hopelessly and permanently wide awake. Wide awake, and feverish and thirsty. When I had lain tossing there as long as I could endure it, it occurred to me that it would be a good idea to dress and go out in the great square and take a refreshing wash in the fountain, and smoke and reflect there until the remnant of the night was gone.

I believed I could dress in the dark without waking Harris. I had banished my shoes after the mouse, but my slippers would do for a summer night. So I rose softly, and gradually got on everything, — down to one sock. I couldn't seem to get on the track of that sock, any way I could fix it. But I had to have it; so I went down on my hands and knees, with one slipper on and the other in my hand, and began to paw gently around and rake the floor, but with no success. I enlarged my circle, and went on pawing and raking. With every pressure of my knee, how the floor creaked! and every time I chanced to rake against any article, it seemed to give out thirty-five or thirty-six times more noise than it would have done in the day time. In those cases I always stopped and held my breath till I was sure Harris had not awakened, — then I crept along again. I moved on and on, but I could not find the sock; I could not seem to find anything but furniture. I could not remember that there was much furniture in the room when I went to bed, but the place was alive with it now, — especially chairs, — chairs everywhere, — had a couple of families moved in, in the meantime? And I never could seem to *glance* on one of those chairs, but always struck it full and square with my head. My temper rose, by steady and sure degrees, and as I pawed on and on, I fell to making vicious comments under my breath.

Finally, with a venomous access of irritation, I said I would leave without the sock; so I rose up and made straight for the door, — as I supposed, — and suddenly confronted my dim spectral image in the unbroken mirror. It startled the breath out of me, for an instant; it also showed me that I was lost, and had no sort of idea where I was. When I realized this, I was so angry that I had to sit down on the floor and take hold of something to keep from lifting the roof off with an explosion of opinion. If there had been only one mirror, it might possibly have helped to locate me; but there were two, and two were as bad as a thousand; besides these were on opposite sides of the room. I could see the dim blur of the windows, but in my turned-around condition they were exactly where they ought not to be, and so they only confused me instead of helping me.

I started to get up, and knocked down an umbrella; it made a noise like a pistol-shot when it struck that hard, slick carpetless floor; I grated my teeth and held my breath, — Harris did not stir. I set the umbrella slowly and carefully on end against the wall, but as soon as I took my hand away, its heel slipped from under it, and down it came again with another bang. I shrunk together and listened a moment in silent fury, — no harm done, everything quiet. With the most painstaking care and nicety I stood the umbrella up once more, took my hand away, and down it came again.

I have been strictly reared, but if it had not been so dark and solemn and awful there in that lonely vast room, I do believe I should have said something then which could not be put into a Sunday School book without injuring the sale of it. If my reasoning powers had not been already sapped dry by my harassments, I would have known better than to try to set an umbrella on end on one of those glassy German floors in the dark; it can't be done in the daytime without four failures to one success. I had one comfort, though, — Harris was yet still and silent, — he had not stirred.

The umbrella could not locate me, — there were four standing around the room, and all alike. I thought I would feel along the wall and find the door in that way. I rose up and began this operation, but raked down a picture. It was not a large one, but it made noise enough for a panorama. Harris gave out no sound, but I felt that if I experimented any further with the pictures I should be sure to wake him. Better give up trying to get out. Yes, I would find King Arthur's Round Table once more, — I had already found it several times, — and use it for a base of departure on an exploring tour for my bed; if I could find my bed I could then find my water pitcher; I would quench my raging thirst and turn in. So I started on my hands and knees, because I could go faster that way, and with more confidence, too, and not knock down things. By and by I found the table, — with my head, — rubbed the bruise a little, then rose up and started, with hands abroad and fingers spread, to balance myself. I found a chair; then the wall; then another chair; then a sofa; then an alpenstock, then another sofa; this confounded me, for I had thought there was only one sofa. I hunted up the table again and took a fresh start; found some more chairs.

It occurred to me, now, as it ought to have done before, that as the table was round, it was therefore of no value as a base to aim from; so I moved off once more, and at random among the wilderness of chairs and sofas, — wandered off into unfamiliar regions, and presently knocked a candlestick off a mantel-piece;

grabbed at the candlestick and knocked off a lamp; grabbed at the lamp and knocked off a water-pitcher with a rattling crash, and thought to myself, "I've found you at last, — I judged I was close upon you." Harris shouted "murder," and "thieves," and finished with "I'm absolutely drowned."

The crash had roused the house. Mr. X. pranced in, in his long night garment, with a candle, young Z. after him with another candle; a procession swept in at another door, with candles and lanterns, — landlord and two German guests in their nightgowns, and a chambermaid in hers.

I looked around; I was at Harris's bed, a Sabbath day's journey from my own. There was only one sofa; it was against the wall; there was only one chair where a body could get at it, — I had been revolving around it like a planet, and colliding with it like a comet half the night.

I explained how I had been employing myself, and why. Then the landlord's party left, and the rest of us set about our preparations for breakfast, for the dawn was ready to break. I glanced furtively at my pedometer, and found I had made 47 miles. But I did not care, for I had come out for a pedestrian tour anyway.

The Laramie Postoffice

Bill Nye

ACCEPTING THE LARAMIE
POSTOFFICE

*Office of Daily Boomerang, Laramie City,
Wy.*
August 9, 1882

My dear General:
I have received by telegraph the news of
my nomination by the President and my
confirmation by the Senate, as postmaster at
Laramie, and wish to extend my thanks for
the same.

I have ordered an entirely new set of
boxes and post-office outfit, including new
corrugated cuspidors for the lady clerks.

I look upon the appointment as a great
triumph of eternal truth over error and
wrong. It is one of the epochs, I may say,
in the Nation's onward march toward political purity and perfection. I do not know

75

when I have noticed any stride in the affairs of state, which so thoroughly impressed me with its wisdom.

Now that we are co-workers in the same department, I trust that you will not feel shy or backward in consulting me at any time relative to matters concerning postoffice affairs. Be perfectly frank with me, and feel free to bring anything of that kind right to me. Do not feel reluctant because I may at times appear haughty and indifferent, cold or reserved. Perhaps you do not think I know the difference between a general delivery window and a three-em quad, but that is a mistake.

My general information is far beyond my years.

With profoundest regard, and a hearty endorsement of the policy of the President and the Senate, whatever it may be,

> *I remain, sincerely yours,*
> BILL NYE, P.M.

A RESIGN

Postoffice Divan, Laramie City, W.T.,
Ct. 1, 1883

To the President of the United States:
Sir: I beg leave at this time officially to tender my resignation as postmaster at this place, and in due form to deliver the great

seal and the key to the front door of the office. The safe combination is set on the numbers 33, 66 and 99, though I do not remember at this moment which comes first, or how many times you revolve the knob, or in which direction you should turn it first to make it operate.

There is some mining stock in my private drawer in the safe, which I have not yet removed. It is a luxury, but you may have it. I have decided to keep a horse instead of this mining stock. The horse may not be so pretty, but it will cost less to keep him.

You will find the postal cards that have not been used under the distributing table, and the coal down in the cellar. If the stove draws too hard, close the damper in the pipe and shut the general delivery window.

Looking over my stormy and eventful administration as postmaster here, I find abundant cause for thanksgiving. At the time I entered upon the duties of my office the department was not yet on a paying basis. It was not even self-sustaining. Since that time, with the active coöperation of the chief executive and the heads of the department, I have been able to make our postal system a paying one, and on top of that I am now able to reduce the tariff on average-sized letters from three cents to two. I might add that this is rather too too, but I will not say anything that might seem undignified in an official resignation which is to become a matter of history.

Acting under the advice of Gen. Hatton, a year ago, I removed the feather bed with which my predecessor, Deacon Hayford, had bolstered up his administration by stuffing the window, and substituted glass. Finding nothing in the book of instructions to postmasters which made the feather bed a part of my official duties, I filed it away in an obscure place and burned it in effigy, also in the gloaming.

It was not long after I had taken my official oath before an era of unexampled prosperity opened for the American people. The price of beef rose to a remarkable altitude, and other vegetables commanded a good figure and a ready market. We then began to make active preparations for the introduction of the strawberry-roan two-cent stamps and the black-and-tan postal note. One reform has crowded upon the heels of another, until the country is to-day upon the foam-crested wave of permanent prosperity.

Mr. President, I cannot close this letter without thanking yourself and the heads of departments at Washington for your active, cheery and prompt coöperation in these matters. You may do as you see fit, of course, about incorporating this idea into your Thanksgiving proclamation, but rest

78

assured it would not be ill-timed or inopportune. It is not alone a credit to myself. It reflects credit upon the administration also.

I need not say that I herewith transmit my resignation with great sorrow and genuine regret. We have toiled on together month after month, asking for no reward except the innate consciousness of rectitude and the salary as fixed by law. Now we are to separate. Here the roads seem to fork, as it were, and you and I, and the cabinet, must leave each other at this point.

You will find the key under the door-mat, and you had better turn the cat out at night when you close the office. If she does not go readily, you can make it clearer to her mind by throwing the cancelling stamp at her.

If Deacon Hayford does not pay up his box-rent, you might as well put his mail in the general delivery, and when Bob Head gets drunk and insists on a letter from one of his wives every day in the week, you can salute him through the box delivery with an old Queen Anne tomahawk, which you will find near the Etruscan water-pail. This will not in any manner surprise either of these parties.

Tears are unavailing! I once more become a private citizen, clothed only with the right to read such postal cards as may be addressed to me, and to curse the inefficiency of the postoffice department. I believe the voting class to be divided into two parties; viz., those who are in the postal service, and those who are mad because they cannot receive a registered letter every fifteen minutes of each day, including Sunday.

Mr. President, as an official of this Government I now retire. My term of office would not expire until 1886. I must, therefore, beg pardon for my eccentricity in resigning. It will be best, perhaps, to keep the heart-breaking news from the ears of European powers until the dangers of a financial panic are fully past. Then hurl it broadcast with a sickening thud.

The Waist-band that was Taut Up to the Moment it Gave Way

George Ade

Once there was a Family consisting of Mr. and Mrs. Stuffer and three little Stuffers.

Mrs. Stuffer had belonged to the Bolt Family back in Fodderville, where she put on Weight before being shipped up to the City.

Her Mother was a Gullep, and Lineal Descendant of a New England Pilgrim named Grubb.

Mr. Stuffer also was well connected, never fear.

His Mother had been one of the Gobbels and his Grandsire on the other Branch of the Tree was often referred to, for he was none other than Phillip Gormann-Deizer, with a Colonial Home near the Gorge at Eatonville.

Their Folks, as far back as Records carried, had regarded America as the Land of Plenty and Then Some.

Also one of the Traditions coming from the grand old Pioneer Stock seemed to be that the Main Tract of the Alimentary System is the

81

Home of the Soul.

The Stuffers could say truly that not one of their previous Relatives ever permitted a Guest to go away Hungry.

Sometimes he was taking Bi-Carb when he departed, but, Thank Edna, he never was craving Nourishment.

So the Family Honour stood safe and intact.

Back in the Country, where the Stuffers received their early Schooling as two-handed Scoopers, no Man could hold up his Head unless he was a bountiful Provider, and no Woman was respected unless she had Apple Butter and two kinds of Pie on the Table.

Those were the Blissful Days when the Deacon with the Throat-Warmers would close his Eyes and ask that this Food be Blessed and Sanctified to our Uses.

And take it from Hortense, when the Deacon made that reasonable Request, there was something piled in front of him waiting to be Sanctified.

No one ever heard of Luxuries during that oleaginous Period.

Anything that could be Et was a Necessity.

The family that wanted a Sunday Dinner away back Yonder did not have to hock the Morris Chairs.

The Barn Lot was swarming with Springers; the Garden had many rows of Sass; Berries could be had for the Picking.

Anything you might think of was Ten Cents.

For one measly Dime, the genial Grocer would let you have a Pound of Butter or a Dozen Eggs or a Peck of Murphys or a hunk of Bacon or an armful of Roasting Ears.

Beans were about as costly as Gravel.

Off in the Pantry, the solid loaves of Salt-Rising Bread were stacked, careless-like, the same as Cord-Wood.

The Humble Toiler who stowed away 14 to 16 Spare-Ribs smothered with Kraut, four or five helpings of Fresh Vegetables, a few light Biscuits inlaid with golden Butter, and possibly a quarter of a mile of Noodles, would trick out his Modest Snack with Spiced Peaches, frosty Doughnuts, and a little quart Bowl of preserved Cherries, to say nothing of Coffee curdled with heavy Cream, and never suspect that he was living somewhat Snooky.

He was simply getting regular every-day Chow of the Farm-Hand variety.

It was on Sunday, when the Minister and his Wife or Cousin Elam's Family came over, that Mother extended herself and showed Class.

The Family never had Flowers on the Table, because the Space was taken up with Jams and Jells.

At that time, Dinner did not open with *Canapé Scabouche* followed by *Potage à la Bohonque.*

It opened with a Breast and a Second Joint and a couple of Drumsticks and much Gravy, with here and there a Giblet, and enough

Mashed Potatoes to plaster a Small Room, and a Million Green Peas that never had been to Market, and an awful mix-up of String Beans, while the Odd Corners were chinked in with Cottage Cheese and Pickled Watermelon Rind and Sweet Peppers.

Butter was not rolled into Marbles during the Seventies.

Well, we should say Not!

It was lifted in half-pound Gobs, and those who smeared it never felt Improvident.

What is now called Service consisted of cleaning up the Trough and going back for another Load.

The Conversation was wholly made up of:

(1) Urgent appeals for every one to Pack in a little bit more;

(2) Weak Protests from the Packees;

(3) Contrite Apologies from the Cook as to the Quality and Amount of Eatables in sight;

(4) Stereotyped Assurances to perturbed Hostess that everything was Swell, Elegant, and Hunky.

If the Fig Cake was a Triumph and the Jelly Cake held its Shape but the Hickory-Nut Cake went Blah, that called for a lot of Explaining.

There was a Time when every Woman thought that a soggy Cake was a Reflection on her Character. Then, if the Visitors moved slowly from the Dining Room with their eyes protruding slightly, the Meal was voted a Success.

Not every Parlour sported an upright Piano,

and the Citizen who guided a team of Bays from the front Pad of a two-seated Carriage was some Rajah, but the humblest Family waded knee-deep in Vittles.

When Winter came on, each Cellar in the Township was loaded to the Guards with Turnips, Punkins, Bell-Flower Apples, Pop-Corn, Vinegar, Walnuts, Cabbage, Potatoes, Lye Hominy, Side-Meat, Canned Stuff, Hard Cider, Sorghum Molasses, Lard, Honey in the Comb, Rutabagas, Fruit-Jars in Platoons, Jelly-Glasses in Brigades, Sage, Carrots, Navy Beans, Corn Meal, Buckwheat Flour, Onions, and other Medicinal Herbs, with possibly a few chilled Geese and Rabbits for immediate Consumption.

A barbed-wire Entanglement could have been strung around any Domicile in the Autumn, and the imprisoned Family would have come out on May 1st wearing Double Chins.

After the Stuffers landed in Town and had to use pleading Language to get a couple of fibrous Chops, they would become sentimental over Memories of Hog-Killing.

Oh, Elmer!

The Steaming Kettles of Water and the sound of scraping Knives.

Pallid Carcasses suspended in the frosty Air and the gleeful Eviscerators singing "Molly Darling" as they Rummaged.

If a close-figuring Landlady, who tries to set a Table for Seven Per, could have seen the

Cans of Lard, the Platters of Tenderloin, the Hams Waiting to be Cured, and the Sausage Meat ready to glide into the Links, she would have declared it was all a Mirage.

It is hard for some People to realize, along in this Stretch of Tribulation, that not long ago, out where Things are Grown, everyone who sat down to a Repast was urged to make a Grand Drive and go as far as he liked.

The mere Thought of any one going light on new-laid Eggs, or laying off on Butter, or messing around with Bran, Excelsior, Sawdust, Husks, Chop-Feed, and other Substitutes for Something to Eat would have been too silly for Utterance.

The Practice of Economy was well-nigh Universal, but it did not involve playing a Joke on the Œsophagus.

The Woman of the House was Thrifty, for she fed her Cook-Stove a Splinter at a Time.

When Pa's red Unmentionables with the Glass Buttons became too Intimate and Itchy, they were chopped down for Ulysses or Grover.

Patches were made into Quilts and Rags worked over into Carpets.

A Peach-Basket, treated with a Nickel's Worth of Gold Paint and decked out with Bows of Ribbon, became a Hanging Basket for the Pet Geranium.

All the spare Coppers went into the little Tin Bank.

Only a favoured Few were permitted to walk

on the Brussels Carpet.

Any good Citizen of Jasper Township would have assured you that Frugality was his Middle Name.

But Frugality did not mean getting up from the Table unsatiated.

For any one to back away before he felt himself Distended would have been regarded as Evidence of a cowardly Nature.

As soon as a Member of the Family began to fly at the Menu with a lack of wolfish Enthusiasm, he was subject to treatment as an Invalid.

The real Local Gazimbat was the Lad who held the Flapjack Record and was ready to meet all Comers during the Sweet-Corn Season.

A never-failing Appetite for anything that could be carried in and planked on the Table was classed as one of the Christian Virtues.

The Owner was held in Regard as one who had acquired Moral Grandeur and lifted himself above the Weaklings.

He went around blowing that he could Eat Anything, and all the Light Feeders slunk into the Background when he lifted his Bazoo.

Now that you have a Steer on the Pre-Natal Influences and Environment of the Stuffer Family, can you see the Bunch dropped down in a Residence Thoroughfare of a congested Metropolis, three miles from a Cow and six miles from a Hen that could be relied upon to come across every Day?

Although badly separated from the Base of Supplies, they were still true to the honoured Customs of the Grubbs and the Gobbels and the Gulleps.

Mrs. Stuffer often said that she would rather cut off her Right Hand than have an Acquaintance drop in and find one Section of the Dining-Room Table unoccupied by tempting Viands.

She remarked time and again that, Come what Might, she never would Stint her Loved Ones or deny them such simple Essentials as Fresh Eggs, Sure-Enough Butter, Steak cut thick, Leg of Lamb, and submerged Short-Cake.

And there were a Hundred Thousand More like her.

If one is accustomed to the Best — and no real Daughter of a generous Mother ever compromised on Seconds or Culls — one must not Pike when telephoning the Orders.

This elaborate Overture will give you a Rough Idea of what Mr. Stuffer was up against.

He came to the City on a Guarantee.

His Salary looked like the Income of J. P. Morgan until he began to check up the Outgo.

Back in Fodderville, a neat frame Dwelling with a scroll-saw Veranda, a bed of Peonies, and Exposure on four Sides would set you back about $15 per Moon.

Up in the City, you couldn't get a Hat-Rack for any such Money.

It seemed to the Stuffers that everything in Town was sold by the Minute or the Ounce.

It was a grievous Shock to the Missus when they began to weigh the Vegetables on her.

She had got used to having them thrown at her with a Shovel.

The Neighbors no longer brought in Produce at Special inside Prices — Eggs figured by the wear and tear on the Fowl and no Overhead Charge on Honey except the Time put in by the Bees.

The Stuffers suddenly discovered that when you go out to spend a Dollar in the City, you don't have to take a Wheelbarrow along.

But Mr. Stuffer and Mrs. Stuffer and each of the miniature Stuffers had it firmly fixed in the Coke that the Minute you begin letting down on That to which you have been Accustomed you lose Self-Respect and indirectly confess to being in Straitened Circumstances.

It was all right for those living in Huts and Hovels to cheapen the Standards of Living, but the Stuffers could not endure the Thought of giving up any of the old Stand-by Dishes.

Some Persons of a Poetical Turn mark the changing Seasons by the Trailing Arbutus, which precedes the bold Iris; then old-fashioned Roses, followed by a riotous show of Dahlias; Autumn Leaves tinged Red and Yellow, harbingers of snowy Fields and icy Boughs.

Every Sign of the Zodiac meant a new Item in the Bill of Fare for the practical Stuffers.

With the first warm days of Spring, did they go looking for Wood-Violets?

Not one Look.

They began to sit up and demand Green Onions, Asparagus, Head Lettuce, and Strawberries.

June is the Month of Roses. Also of Fried Chicken and a pleasant gateway to Corn on the Cob.

Autumn Days need not be Melancholy if one is surrounded by Turkey and Mincemeat.

Even Winter has a Charm of its own, if Sausage and Buckwheat Cakes are ever smiling in the Background.

When Prices began to Sizz-Boom-Ah, the old Pay Envelope failed to stand up under the Strain, but can you expect one reared on the Fat of the Land to accept Macaroni as a Compromise?

The Producer would let out a Howl every time the Meat Bill came in, but he would have howled in a higher Key if the Good Woman had failed to throw him his Roast Beef and Mutton Chops.

He wielded a very consistent Knife and Fork and his daily Demand was for something that Sticks to the Ribs.

Of course, both of them saw the Article in the Paper, entitled "How to feed a Family of Five on 80 Cents a Day."

Once, just after the 1st of the Month, while Mr. Stuffer was still Bleeding, his Companion tried out a Sample Menu recommended by Hazel McGinnis Updyke, a famous Tipster weighing between 80 and 90 pounds.

He stirred the watery Soup as if moved by a dull Curiosity as to the grains of Barley hiding at the Bottom, and then he gave Friend Wife a Look — but, Ooey, such a Look!

It seemed to say, "And this is the Woman who promised to Love, Honour, and be of some Help!"

Then came Rice Croquettes, one of the most startling Specimens of Near-Food ever touted by a Lady writing Syndicate Come-Ons and boarding at an Italian Table d'Hôte.

You eat it, but after you get through you are not sure that anything has Happened.

After which, Bread Pudding, said to have broken up more Homes than High White Shoes.

As Mr. Stuffer left the House, his well-meaning Partner felt in her Heart of Hearts that he was going out to a Restaurant to get some Ham and Eggs.

She resolved that never again would she ask him to be Untrue to his Nobler Self.

So, at the next Meal, she jollied him up with Lamb Steak and Kidneys, Mushrooms in Cream, Succotash, Waffles and Maple Syrup, Endive Salad and Sharp Cheese, with a Finale of Blueberry Pie *à la Mode*.

Experts tell us that Blueberry Pie, showing its bold Colour between the slopes of Vanilla Ice Cream, is practically the Last Word with those who want something to hit the Spot.

It is the *Pièce de Résistance*, the *Dénouement*, the Dramatic Climax, the Grand Transformation, Little Eva ascending to Paradise.

Nothing comes after it except the Pepsin Tablet and the Hot-Water Bag.

Mrs. Stuffer watched her Husband as he lighted his Sublima.

He had a Sleepy Look, which is always a Good Sign.

Then he Groaned, and she knew that she had won back his Love.

Any time you get them to Groaning, you are a Jewel of a Housekeeper.

Having set out to defy the Increased Cost and indulge themselves within Reason, the little Family soon found itself riding a troublous Sea with the Breakers just ahead. Man's Chief Enemies, they had been told long ago, are Pride, Lust, Avarice, etc.

Now they learned Different. They came to know that the two principal Destroyers of Happiness are the Middleman and the Cold-Storage Warehouse.

Hemmed in by extortionate Retailers, Food Pirates, and Commission Sharks, they stood Resolute and vowed they would never Surrender.

As they were riding over the Hills to the Poor-House, Mr. Stuffer made the dismal Observation that it was a Blue Finish for a Life of

Honest Endeavour.

"That may be true," said Mrs. Stuffer, "but I have this Satisfaction," as she lifted her Head proudly: "I set a scrumptious Table to the very last."

Moral: Cling to your Ideals, such as they are.

My Financial Career

Stephen Leacock

When I go into a bank, I get rattled. The clerks rattle me; the wickets rattle me; the sight of money rattles me; everything rattles me.

The moment I cross the threshold of a bank and attempt to transact business there, I become an irresponsible idiot.

I knew this beforehand, but my salary had been raised to fifty dollars a month and I felt that the bank was the only place for it.

So I shambled in and looked timidly round at the clerks. I had an idea that a person about to open an account must needs consult the manager.

I went up to a wicket marked "Accountant." The accountant was a tall, cool devil. The very sight of him rattled me. My voice was sepulchral.

"Can I see the manager?" I said, and added solemnly, "alone." I don't know why I said "alone."

"Certainly," said the accountant, and fetched

94

him.

The manager was a grave, calm man. I held my fifty-six dollars clutched in a crumpled ball in my pocket.

"Are you the manager?" I said. God knows I didn't doubt it.

"Yes," he said.

"Can I see you," I asked, "alone?" I didn't want to say "alone" again, but without it the thing seemed self-evident.

The manager looked at me in some alarm. He felt that I had an awful secret to reveal.

"Come in here," he said, and led the way to a private room. He turned the key in the lock.

"We are safe from interruption here," he said; "sit down."

We both sat down and looked at each other. I found no voice to speak.

"You are one of Pinkerton's men, I presume," he said.

He had gathered from my mysterious manner that I was a detective. I knew what he was thinking, and it made me worse.

"No, not from Pinkerton's," I said, seeming to imply that I came from a rival agency.

"To tell the truth," I went on, as if I had been prompted to lie about it, "I am not a detective at all. I have come to open an account. I intend to keep all my money in this bank."

The manager looked relieved, but still serious; he concluded now that I was a son of Baron Rothschild or a young Gould.

"A large account, I suppose," he said.

"Fairly large," I whispered. "I propose to deposit fifty-six dollars now and fifty dollars a month regularly."

The manager got up and opened the door. He called to the accountant.

"Mr. Montgomery," he said unkindly loud, "this gentleman is opening an account, he will deposit fifty-six dollars. Good morning."

I rose.

A big iron door stood open at the side of the room.

"Good morning," I said, and stepped into the safe.

"Come out," said the manager coldly, and showed me the other way.

I went up to the accountant's wicket and poked the ball of money at him with a quick convulsive movement as if I were doing a conjuring trick.

My face was ghastly pale.

"Here," I said, "deposit it." The tone of the words seemed to mean, "Let us do this painful thing while the fit is on us."

He took the money and gave it to another clerk.

He made me write the sum on a slip and sign my name in a book. I no longer knew what I was doing. The bank swam before my eyes.

"Is it deposited?" I asked in a hollow, vibrating voice.

"It is," said the accountant.

"Then I want to draw a check."

My idea was to draw out six dollars of it for present use. Someone gave me a check-book through a wicket and someone else began telling me how to write it out. The people in the bank had the impression that I was an invalid millionaire. I wrote something on the check and thrust it in at the clerk. He looked at it.

"What! are you drawing it all out again?" he asked in surprise. Then I realized that I had written fifty-six instead of six. I was too far gone to reason now. I had a feeling that it was impossible to explain the thing. All the clerks had stopped writing to look at me.

Reckless with misery, I made a plunge.

"Yes, the whole thing."

"You withdraw your money from the bank?"

"Every cent of it."

"Are you not going to deposit any more?" said the clerk, astonished.

"Never."

An idiot hope struck me that they might think something had insulted me while I was writing the check and that I had changed my mind. I made a wretched attempt to look like a man with a fearfully quick temper.

The clerk prepared to pay the money.

"How will you have it?" he said.

"What?"

"How will you have it?"

"Oh" — I caught his meaning and answered without even trying to think — "in fifties."

He gave me a fifty-dollar bill.

"And the six?" he asked dryly.

"In sixes," I said.

He gave it me and I rushed out.

As the big door swung behind me, I caught the echo of a roar of laughter that went up to the ceiling of the bank. Since then I bank no more. I keep my money in cash in my trousers pocket and my savings in silver dollars in a sock.

Gertrude the Governess
or Simple Seventeen

Stephen Leacock

Synopsis of Previous Chapters:
There are no Previous Chapters.

It was a wild and stormy night on the West Coast of Scotland. This, however, is immaterial to the present story, as the scene is not laid in the West of Scotland. For the matter of that the weather was just as bad on the East Coast of Ireland.

But the scene of this narrative is laid in the South of England and takes place in and around Knotacentinum Towers (pronounced as if written Nosham Taws), the seat of Lord Knotacent (pronounced as if written Nosh).

But it is not necessary to pronounce either of these names in reading them.

Nosham Taws was a typical English home. The main part of the house was an Elizabethan structure of warm red brick, while the elder portion, of which the Earl was inordinately proud, still showed the outlines of a Norman

Keep, to which had been added a Lancastrian Jail and a Plantagenet Orphan Asylum. From the house in all directions stretched magnificent woodland and park with oaks and elms of immemorial antiquity, while nearer the house stood raspberry bushes and geranium plants which had been set out by the Crusaders.

About the grand old mansion the air was loud with the chirping of thrushes, the cawing of partridges and the clear sweet note of the rook, while deer, antelope, and other quadrupeds strutted about the lawn so tame as to eat off the sun-dial. In fact, the place was a regular menagerie.

From the house downwards through the park stretched a beautiful broad avenue laid out by Henry VII.

Lord Nosh stood upon the hearthrug of the library. Trained diplomat and statesman as he was, his stern aristocratic face was upside down with fury.

"Boy," he said, "you shall marry this girl or I disinherit you. You are no son of mine."

Young Lord Ronald, erect before him, flung back a glance as defiant as his own.

"I defy you," he said. "Henceforth you are no father of mine. I will get another. I will marry none but a woman I can love. This girl that we have never seen —"

"Fool," said the Earl, "would you throw aside our estate and name of a thousand years? The girl, I am told, is beautiful; her aunt is willing; they are French; pah! they understand such things in France."

"But your reason —"

"I give no reason," said the Earl. "Listen, Ronald, I give you one month. For that time you remain here. If at the end of it you refuse me, I cut you off with a shilling."

Lord Ronald said nothing; he flung himself from the room, flung himself upon his horse and rode madly off in all directions.

As the door of the library closed upon Ronald the Earl sank into a chair. His face changed. It was no longer that of the haughty nobleman, but of the hunted criminal. "He must marry the girl," he muttered. "Soon she will know all. Tutchemoff has escaped from Siberia. He knows and will tell. The whole of the mines pass to her, this property with it, and I — but enough." He rose, walked to the sideboard, drained a dipper full of gin and bitters, and became again a high-bred English gentleman.

It was at this moment that a high dogcart, driven by a groom in the livery of Earl Nosh, might have been seen entering the avenue of Nosham Taws. Beside him sat a young girl, scarce more than a child, in fact not nearly so big as the groom.

The apple-pie hat which she wore, surmounted with black willow plumes, concealed from view a face so face-like in its appearance as to be positively facial.

It was — need we say it — Gertrude the

Governess, who was this day to enter upon her duties at Nosham Taws.

At the same time that the dogcart entered the avenue at one end there might have been seen riding down it from the other a tall young man, whose long, aristocratic face proclaimed his birth and who was mounted upon a horse with a face even longer than his own.

And who is this tall young man who draws nearer to Gertrude with every revolution of the horse? Ah, who, indeed? Ah, who, who? I wonder if any of my readers could guess that this was none other than Lord Ronald.

The two were destined to meet. Nearer and nearer they came. And then still nearer. Then for one brief moment they met. As they passed, Gertrude raised her head and directed towards the young nobleman two eyes so eye-like in their expression as to be absolutely circular, while Lord Ronald directed towards the occupant of the dogcart a gaze so gaze-like that nothing but a gazelle, or a gas-pipe, could have emulated its intensity.

Was this the dawn of love? Wait and see. Do not spoil the story.

Let us speak of Gertrude. Gertrude De-Mongmorenci McFiggin had known neither father nor mother. They had both died years before she was born. Of her mother she knew nothing, save that she was French, was extremely beautiful, and that all her ancestors and even her business acquaintances had perished in the Revolution.

Yet Gertrude cherished the memory of her parents. On her breast the girl wore a locket in which was enshrined a miniature of her mother, while down her neck inside at the back hung a daguerreotype of her father. She carried a portrait of her grandmother up her sleeve and had pictures of her cousins tucked inside her boot, while beneath her — but enough, quite enough.

Of her father Gertrude knew even less. That he was a high-born English gentleman who had lived as a wanderer in many lands, this was all she knew. His only legacy to Gertrude had been a Russian grammar, a Roumanian phrase-book, a theodolite, and a work on mining engineering.

From her earliest infancy Gertrude had been brought up by her aunt. Her aunt had carefully instructed her in Christian principles. She had also taught her Mohammedanism to make sure.

When Gertrude was seventeen her aunt had died of hydrophobia.

The circumstances were mysterious. There had called upon her that day a strange bearded man in the costume of the Russians. After he had left, Gertrude had found her aunt in a syncope from which she passed into an apostrophe and never recovered.

To avoid scandal it was called hydrophobia. Gertrude was thus thrown upon the world. What to do? That was the problem that confronted her.

It was while musing one day upon her fate that Gertrude's eye was struck with an advertisement.

"Wanted a governess; must possess a knowledge of French, Italian, Russian, and Roumanian, Music, and Mining Engineering. Salary £1, 4 shillings and 4 pence halfpenny per annum. Apply between half-past eleven and twenty-five minutes to twelve at No. 41 A Decimal Six, Belgravia Terrace. The Countess of Nosh."

Gertrude was a girl of great natural quickness of apprehension, and she had not pondered over this announcement more than half an hour before she was struck with the extraordinary coincidence between the list of items desired and the things that she herself knew.

She duly presented herself at Belgravia Terrace before the Countess, who advanced to meet her with a charm which at once placed the girl at her ease.

"You are proficient in French?" she asked.

"Oh, oui," said Gertrude modestly.

"And Italian?" continued the Countess.

"Oh, si," said Gertrude.

"And German?" said the Countess in delight.

"Ah, ja," said Gertrude.

"And Russian?"

"Yaw."

"And Roumanian?"

"Jep."

Amazed at the girl's extraordinary proficiency in modern languages, the Countess looked at her narrowly. Where had she seen those lineaments before? She passed her hand over her brow in thought, and spit upon the floor, but no, the face baffled her.

"Enough," she said, "I engage you on the spot; tomorrow you go down to Nosham Taws and begin teaching the children. I must add that in addition you will be expected to aid the Earl with his Russian correspondence. He has large mining interests at Tschminsk."

Tschminsk! why did the simple word reverberate upon Gertrude's ears? Why? Because it was the name written in her father's hand on the title page of his book on mining. What mystery was here?

It was on the following day that Gertrude had driven up the avenue.

She descended from the dogcart, passed through a phalanx of liveried servants drawn up seven-deep, to each of whom she gave a sovereign as she passed and entered Nosham Taws.

"Welcome," said the Countess, as she aided Gertrude to carry her trunk upstairs.

The girl presently descended and was ushered into the library, where she was presented to the Earl. As soon as the Earl's eye fell upon the face of the new governess he started visibly. Where had he seen those lineaments? Where was it? At the races? or the theatre? on a bus?

No. Some subtler thread of memory was stirring in his mind. He strode hastily to the sideboard, drained a dipper and a half of brandy, and became again the perfect English gentleman.

While Gertrude has gone to the nursery to make the acquaintance of the two tiny golden-haired children who are to be her charges, let us say something here of the Earl and his son.

Lord Nosh was the perfect type of the English nobleman and statesman. The years that he had spent in the diplomatic service at Constantinople, St. Petersburg, and Salt Lake City had given to him a peculiar finesse and noblesse, while his long residence at St. Helena, Pitcairn Island, and Hamilton, Ontario, had rendered him impervious to external impressions. As deputy paymaster of the militia of the county he had seen something of the sterner side of military life, while his hereditary office of Groom of the Sunday Breeches had brought him into direct contact with Royalty itself.

His passion for outdoor sports endeared him to his tenants. A keen sportsman, he excelled in fox-hunting, dog-hunting, pig-killing, bat-catching and the pastimes of his class.

In this latter respect Lord Ronald took after his father. From the start the lad had shown the greatest promise. At Eton he had made a splendid showing at battledore and shuttlecock, and at Cambridge had been first in his class at needlework. Already his name was whispered in connection with the All England ping-pong championship, a triumph which would undoubtedly carry with it a seat in Parliament.

Thus was Gertrude the Governess installed at Nosham Taws.

The days and the weeks sped past.

The simple charm of the beautiful orphan girl attracted all hearts. Her two little pupils became her slaves. "Me loves oo," the little Rasehellfrida would say, leaning her golden head in Gertrude's lap. Even the servants loved her. The head gardener would bring a bouquet of beautiful roses to her room before she was up, the second gardener a bunch of early cauliflowers, the third a spray of late asparagus, and even the tenth and eleventh a sprig of mangel-wurzel or an armful of hay. Her room was full of gardeners all the time, while at evening the aged butler, touched at the friendless girl's loneliness, would tap softly at her door to bring her a rye whisky and seltzer or a box of Pittsburg Stogies. Even the dumb creatures seemed to admire her in their own dumb way. The dumb rooks settled on her shoulder and every dumb dog around the place followed her.

And Ronald! ah, Ronald! Yes, indeed! They had met. They had spoken.

"What a dull morning," Gertrude had said. *"Quel triste matin! Was für ein allerverdamnter Tag!"*

"Beastly!!" The word rang in Gertrude's ears all day.

After that they were constantly together. They played tennis and ping-pong in the day, and in the evening, in accordance with the stiff routine of the place, they sat down with the Earl and Countess to twenty-five-cent poker, and later still they sat together on the verandah and watched the moon sweeping in great circles around the horizon.

It was not long before Gertrude realized that Lord Ronald felt towards her a warmer feeling than that of mere ping-pong. At times in her presence he would fall, especially after dinner, into a fit of profound subtraction.

Once at night, when Gertrude withdrew to her chamber and before seeking her pillow, prepared to retire as a preliminary to disrobing — in other words, before going to bed, she flung wide the casement (opened the window) and perceived (saw) the face of Lord Ronald. He was sitting on a thorn bush beneath her, and his upturned face wore an expression of agonized pallor.

Meantime the days passed. Life at the Taws moved in the ordinary routine of a great English household. At 7 a gong sounded for rising, at 8 a horn blew for breakfast, at 8:30 a whistle sounded for prayers, at 1 a flag was run up at half-mast for lunch, at 4 a gun was fired for afternoon tea, at 9 a first bell sounded for dressing, at 9:15 a second bell for going on dressing, while at 9:30 a rocket was sent up to indicate that dinner was ready. At midnight dinner was over and at 1 a.m. the tolling of a bell summoned the domestics to evening prayers.

Meanwhile the month allotted by the Earl to Lord Ronald was passing away. It was already July 15, then within a day or two it was July 17, and, almost immediately afterwards, July 18.

At times the Earl, in passing Ronald in the hall, would say sternly, "Remember, boy, your consent, or I disinherit you."

And what were the Earl's thoughts of Gertrude? Here was the one drop of bitterness in the girl's cup of happiness. For some reason that she could not divine, the Earl showed signs of marked antipathy.

Once as she passed the door of the library he threw a bootjack at her. On another occasion at lunch alone with her he struck her savagely across the face with a sausage.

It was her duty to translate to the Earl his Russian correspondence. She sought in it in vain for the mystery. One day a Russian telegram was handed to the Earl. Gertrude translated it to him aloud.

"Tutchemoff went to the woman. She is dead."

On hearing this the Earl became livid with fury, in fact this was the day that he struck her with the sausage.

Then one day while the Earl was absent on a bat hunt, Gertrude, who was turning over his correspondence, with that sweet feminine instinct of interest that rose superior to ill-treatment, suddenly found the key to the mystery.

Lord Nosh was not the rightful owner of the Taws. His distant cousin of the older line, the true heir, had died in a Russian prison to which the machinations of the Earl, while Ambassador at Tschminsk, had consigned him. The daughter of this cousin was the true owner of Nosham Taws.

The family story, save only that the documents before her withheld the name of the rightful heir, lay bare to Gertrude's eye.

Strange is the heart of woman. Did Gertrude turn from the Earl with spurning? No. Her own sad fate had taught her sympathy.

Yet still the mystery remained! Why did the Earl start perceptibly each time that he looked into her face? Sometimes he started as much as four centimetres, so that one could distinctly see him do it. On such occasions he would hastily drain a dipper of rum and Vichy water and become again the correct English gentleman.

The denouement came swiftly. Gertrude never forgot it.

It was the night of the great ball at Nosham Taws. The whole neighbourhood was invited. How Gertrude's heart had beat with anticipation, and with what trepidation she had overhauled her scant wardrobe in order to appear not unworthy in Lord Ronald's eyes. Her resources were poor indeed, yet the inborn genius for dress that she inherited from her French mother stood her in good stead. She twined a single rose in her hair and contrived herself a dress out of a few old newspapers and the inside of an umbrella that would have graced a court. Round her waist she bound a single braid of bagstring, while a piece of old lace that had been her mother's was suspended to her ear by a thread.

Gertrude was the cynosure of all eyes. Floating to the strains of the music she presented a picture of bright girlish innocence that no one could see undisenraptured.

The ball was at its height. It was away up!

Ronald stood with Gertrude in the shrubbery. They looked into one another's eyes.

"Gertrude," he said, "I love you."

Simple words, and yet they thrilled every fibre in the girl's costume.

"Ronald!" she said, and cast herself about his neck.

At this moment the Earl appeared standing beside them in the moonlight. His stern face was distorted with indignation.

"So!" he said, turning to Ronald, "it appears that you have chosen!"

"I have," said Ronald with hauteur.

"You prefer to marry this penniless girl rather than the heiress I have selected for you."

Gertrude looked from father to son in amazement.

"Yes," said Ronald.

"Be it so," said the Earl, draining a dipper of gin which he carried, and resuming his calm. "Then I disinherit you. Leave this place, and never return to it."

"Come, Gertrude," said Ronald tenderly, "let us flee together."

Gertrude stood before them. The rose had fallen from her head. The lace had fallen from her ear and the bagstring had come undone from her waist. Her newspapers were crumpled beyond recognition. But dishevelled and illegible as she was, she was still mistress of herself.

"Never, " she said firmly. "Ronald, you shall never make this sacrifice for me." Then to the Earl, in tones of ice, "There is a pride, sir, as great even as yours. The daughter of Metschnikoff McFiggin need crave a boon from no one."

With that she hauled from her bosom the daguerreotype of her father and pressed it to her lips.

The Earl started as if shot. "That name!" he cried, "that face! that photograph! stop!"

There! There is no need to finish; my readers have long since divined it. Gertrude was the heiress.

The lovers fell into one another's arms. The Earl's proud face relaxed. "God bless you," he said. The Countess and the guests came pouring out upon the lawn. The breaking day illuminated a scene of gay congratulations.

Gertrude and Ronald were wed. Their happiness was complete. Need we say more? Yes, only this. The Earl was killed in the hunting-field a few days after. The Countess was struck by lightning. The two children fell down a well. Thus the happiness of Gertrude and Ronald was complete.

Whitey

Booth Tarkington

Penrod and Sam made a gloomy discovery one morning in mid-October. All the week had seen amiable breezes and fair skies until Saturday, when, about breakfast-time, the dome of heaven filled solidly with gray vapour and began to drip. The boys' discovery was that there is no justice about the weather.

They sat in the carriage-house of the Schofields' empty stable; the doors upon the alley were open, and Sam and Penrod stared torpidly at the thin but implacable drizzle which was the more irritating because there was barely enough of it to interfere with a number of things they had planned to do.

"Yes; this is *nice!*" Sam said, in a tone of plaintive sarcasm. "This is a *perty* way to do!" (He was alluding to the personal spitefulness of the elements.) "I'd like to know what's the sense of it — ole sun pourin' down every day in the week when nobody needs it, then cloud up and rain all Saturday! My father said it's goin' to be a three days' rain."

"Well, nobody with any sense cares if it rains Sunday and Monday," said Penrod. "I wouldn't care if it rained every Sunday as long as I lived; but I just like to know what's the reason it had to go and rain to-day. Got all the days o' the week to choose from and goes and picks on Saturday. That's a fine biz'nuss!"

"Well, in vacation — " Sam began, but at a sound from a source invisible to him he paused. "What's that?" he said, somewhat startled.

It was a curious sound, loud and hollow and unhuman, yet it seemed to be a cough. Both boys rose, and Penrod asked uneasily:

"Where'd that noise come from?"

"It's in the alley," said Sam.

Perhaps if the day had been bright, both of them would have stepped immediately to the alley doors to investigate; but their actual procedure was to move a little distance in the opposite direction. The strange cough sounded again.

"*Say!*" Penrod quavered. "What *is* that?"

Then both boys uttered smothered exclamations and jumped, for the long, gaunt head which appeared in the doorway was entirely unexpected. It was the cavernous and melancholy head of an incredibly thin, old, whitish horse. This head waggled slowly from side to side; the nostrils vibrated; the mouth opened, and the hollow cough sounded again.

Recovering themselves, Penrod and Sam

underwent the customary human reaction from alarm to indignation.

"What you want, you ole horse, you?" Penrod shouted. "Don't you come coughin' around *me!*"

And Sam, seizing a stick, hurled it at the intruder.

"Get out o' here!" he roared.

The aged horse nervously withdrew his head, turned tail, and made a rickety flight up the alley, while Sam and Penrod, perfectly obedient to inherited impulse, ran out into the drizzle and uproariously pursued. They were but automatons of instinct, meaning no evil. Certainly they did not know the singular and pathetic history of the old horse who had wandered into the alley and ventured to look through the open door.

This horse, about twice the age of either Penrod or Sam, had lived to find himself in a unique position. He was nude, possessing neither harness nor halter; all he had was a name, Whitey, and he would have answered to it by a slight change of expression if any one had thus properly addressed him. So forlorn was Whitey's case, he was actually an independent horse; he had not even an owner. For two days and a half he had been his own master.

Previous to that period he had been the property of one Abalene Morris, a person of colour, who would have explained himself as engaged in the hauling business. On the contrary, the hauling business was an insignificant side line with Mr. Morris, for he had long ago given himself, as utterly as fortune permitted, to that talent which, early in youth, he had recognized as the greatest of all those surging in his bosom. In his waking thoughts and in his dreams, in health and in sickness, Abalene was a crap-shooter. The hauling business was a disguise.

A concentration of events had brought it about that, at one and the same time, Abalene, after a dazzling run of the dice, found the hauling business an actual danger to the preservation of his liberty. He won seventeen dollars and sixty cents, and within the hour found himself in trouble with an officer of the Humane Society on account of an altercation with Whitey. Abalene had been offered four dollars for Whitey some ten days earlier; wherefore he at once drove to the shop of the junk-dealer who had made the offer and announced his acquiescence in the sacrifice.

"*No*, suh!" said the junk-dealer, with emphasis. "I awready done got me a good mule fer my deliv'ry hoss, 'n'at ole Whitey hoss ain' wuff no fo' dollah nohow! I 'uz a fool when I talk 'bout th'owin' money roun' that a-way. *I* know what *you* up to, Abalene. Man come by here li'l bit ago tole me all 'bout white man try to 'rest you, ovah on the avvynoo. Yessuh; he say white man tryin' to fine out who you *is*. He say, nemmine, he'll know Whitey ag'in, even

117

if he don' know you! He say he ketch you by the hoss; so you come roun' tryin' fix me up with Whitey so white man grab me, th'ow *me* in 'at jail. G'on 'way f'um hyuh, you Abalene! You cain' sell an' you cain' give Whitey to no cullud man 'n 'is town. You go an' drowned 'at ole hoss, 'cause you sutny goin' to jail if you git ketched drivin' him."

The substance of this advice seemed good to Abalene, especially as the seventeen dollars and sixty cents in his pocket lent sweet colours to life out of jail at this time. At dusk he led Whitey to a broad common at the edge of town, and spoke to him finally.

"G'on, 'bout you biz'nis," said Abalene; "you ain' *my* hoss. Don' look roun' at me, 'cause *I* ain' got no 'quaintance wif you. I'm a man o' money, an' I got my own frien's; I'm a-lookin' fer bigger cities, hoss. You got you' biz'nis an' I got mine. Mista' Hoss, good-night!"

Whitey found a little frosted grass upon the common and remained there all night. In the morning he sought the shed where Abalene had kept him, but that was across the large and busy town, and Whitey was hopelessly lost. He had but one eye, a feeble one, and his legs were not to be depended upon; but he managed to cover a great deal of ground, to have many painful little adventures, and to get monstrously hungry and thirsty before he happened to look in upon Penrod and Sam.

When the two boys chased him up the alley they had no intention to cause pain; they had no intention at all. They were no more cruel than Duke, Penrod's little old dog, who followed his own instincts, and, making his appearance hastily through a hole in the back fence, joined the pursuit with sound and fury. A boy will nearly always run after anything that is running, and his first impulse is to throw a stone at it. This is a survival of primeval man, who must take every chance to get his dinner. So, when Penrod and Sam drove the hapless Whitey up the alley, they were really responding to an impulse thousands and thousands of years old — an impulse founded upon the primordial observation that whatever runs is likely to prove edible. Penrod and Sam were not "bad"; they were never that. They were something which was not their fault; they were historic.

At the next corner Whitey turned to the right into the cross-street; thence, turning to the right again and still warmly pursued, he zig-zagged down a main thoroughfare until he reached another cross-street, which ran alongside the Schofields' yard and brought him to the foot of the alley he had left behind in his flight. He entered the alley, and there his dim eye fell upon the open door he had previously investigated. No memory of it remained, but the place had a look associated in his mind with hay, and as Sam and Penrod turned the corner of the alley in panting yet still vociferous

119

pursuit, Whitey stumbled up the inclined platform before the open doors, staggered thunderously across the carriage-house and through another open door into a stall, an apartment vacant since the occupancy of Mr. Schofield's last horse, now several years deceased.

The two boys shrieked with excitement as they beheld the coincidence of this strange return. They burst into the stable, making almost as much noise as Duke, who had become frantic at the invasion. Sam laid hands upon a rake.

"You get out o' there, you ole horse, you!" he bellowed. "I ain't afraid to drive him out. I —"

"*Wait* a minute!" shouted Penrod. "Wait till I — "

Sam was manfully preparing to enter the stall.

"You hold the doors open," he commanded, "so's they won't blow shut and keep him in here. I'm goin' to hit him with — "

"Quee-*yut!*" Penrod shouted, grasping the handle of the rake so that Sam could not use it. "Wait a *minute*, can't you?" He turned with ferocious voice and gestures upon Duke. "*Duke!*" And Duke, in spite of his excitement, was so impressed that he prostrated himself in silence, and then unobtrusively withdrew from the stable. Penrod ran to the alley doors and closed them.

"My gracious!" Sam protested. "What you goin' to do?"

"I'm goin' to keep this horse," said Penrod, whose face showed the strain of a great idea.

"What *for?*"

"For the reward," said Penrod simply.

Sam sat down in the wheelbarrow and stared at his friend almost with awe.

"My gracious," he said, "I never thought o' that. How — how much do you think we'll get, Penrod?"

Sam's thus admitting himself to a full partnership in the enterprise met no objection from Penrod, who was absorbed in the contemplation of Whitey.

"Well," he said judicially, "we might get more and we might get less."

Sam rose and joined his friend in the doorway opening upon the two stalls. Whitey had preëmpted the nearer, and was hungrily nuzzling the old frayed hollows in the manger.

"Maybe a hundred dollars — or sumpthing?" Sam asked in a low voice.

Penrod maintained his composure and repeated the new-found expression which had sounded well to him a moment before. He recognized it as a symbol of the non-committal attitude that makes people looked up to. "Well" — he made it slow, and frowned — "We might get more and we might get less."

"More'n a hundred *dollars?*" Sam gasped.

"Well," said Penrod, "we might get more

121

and we might get less." This time, however, he felt the need of adding something. He put a question in an indulgent tone, as though he were inquiring, not to add to his own information but to discover the extent of Sam's. "How much do you think horses are worth, anyway?"

"I don't know," said Sam frankly, and unconsciously, he added, "They might be more and they might be less."

"Well, when our ole horse died," said Penrod, "papa said he wouldn't take five hundred dollars for him. That's how much *horses* are worth!"

"My gracious!" Sam exclaimed. Then he had a practical afterthought. "But maybe he was a better horse than this'n. What colour was he?"

"He was bay. Looky here, Sam" — and now Penrod's manner changed from the superior to the eager — "you look what kind of horses they have in a circus, and you bet a circus has the *best* horses, don't it? Well, what kind of horses do they have in a circus? They have some black and white ones, but the best they have are white all over. Well, what kind of a horse is this we got here? He's perty near white right now, and I bet if we washed him off and got him fixed up nice he *would* be white. Well, a bay horse is worth five hundred dollars, Because that's what papa said, and this horse — "

Sam interrupted rather timidly.

"He — he's awful bony, Penrod. You don't guess that'd make any — "

Penrod laughed contemptuously.

"Bony! All he needs is a little food and he'll fill right up and look good as ever. You don't know much about horses, Sam, I expect. Why, *our* ole horse —"

"Do you expect he's hungry now?" asked Sam, staring at Whitey.

"Let's try him,' said Penrod. "Horses like hay and oats the best, but they'll eat most anything."

"I guess they will. He's tryin' to eat that manger up right now, and I bet it ain't good for him."

"Come on," said Penrod, closing the door that gave entrance to the stalls. "We got to get this horse some drinkin'-water and some good food."

They tried Whitey's appetite first with an autumnal branch which they wrenched from a hardy maple in the yard. They had seen horses nibble leaves, and they expected Whitey to nibble the leaves of this branch, but his ravenous condition did not allow him time for cool discrimination. Sam poked the branch at him from the passageway, and Whitey after one backward movement of alarm, seized it venomously.

"Here! You stop that!" Sam shouted. "You stop that, you ole horse, you!"

"What's the matter?" called Penrod from the

123

hydrant, where he was filling a bucket. "What's he doin' now?"

"Doin'! He's eatin' the wood part, too! He's chewin' up sticks as big as baseball bats! He's crazy!"

Penrod rushed to see this sight, and stood aghast.

"Take it away from him, Sam!" he commanded sharply.

"Go on, take it away from him yourself!" was the prompt retort of his comrade.

"You had no biz'nuss to give it to him," said Penrod. "Anybody with any sense ought to know it'd make him sick. What'd you want to go and give it to him for?"

"Well, you didn't say not to."

"Well, what if I didn't? I never said I did, did I? You go on in that stall and take it away from him."

"*Yes,* I will!" Sam returned bitterly. Then, as Whitey had dragged the remains of the branch from the manger to the floor of the stall, Sam scrambled to the top of the manger and looked over. "There ain't much left to *take* away! He's swallered it all except some splinters. Better give him the water to try and wash it down with." And, as Penrod complied, "My gracious, look at that horse *drink!*"

They gave Whitey four buckets of water, and then debated the question of nourishment. Obviously, this horse could not be trusted with branches, and, after getting their knees black

124

and their backs sodden, they gave up trying to pull enough grass to sustain him. Then Penrod remembered that horses like apples, both "cooking-apples" and "eating-apples," and Sam memtioned the fact that every autumn his father received a barrel of "cooking-apples" from a cousin who owned a farm. That barrel was in the Williamses' cellar now, and the cellar was providentially supplied with "outside doors," so that it could be visited without going through the house. Sam and Penrod set forth for the cellar.

They returned to the stable bulging, and, after a discussion of Whitey's digestion (Sam claiming that eating the core and seeds, as Whitey did, would grow trees in his inside), they went back to the cellar for supplies again — and again. They made six trips, carrying each time a capacity cargo of apples, and still Whitey ate in a famished manner. They were afraid to take more apples from the barrel, which began to show conspicuously the result of their raids, wherefore Penrod made an unostentatious visit to the cellar of his own house. From the inside he opened a window and passed vegetables out to Sam, who placed them in a bucket and carried them hurriedly to the stable, while Penrod returned in a casual manner through the house. Of his *sang-froid* under a great strain it is sufficient to relate that, in the kitchen, he said suddenly to Della, the cook, "Oh, look behind you!" and by the time Della discovered that there was nothing unusual behind, Penrod was gone, and a loaf of bread from the kitchen table was gone with him.

Whitey now ate nine turnips, two heads of lettuce, one cabbage, eleven raw potatoes, and the loaf of bread. He ate the loaf of bread last and he was a long time about it; so the boys came to a not unreasonable conclusion.

"Well, sir, I guess we got him filled up at last!" Said Penrod. "I bet he wouldn't eat a saucer of ice-cream now, if we'd give it to him!"

"He looks better to me," said Sam, staring critically at Whitey. "I think he's kind of begun to fill out some. I expect he must like us, Penrod; we been doin' a good deal for this horse."

"Well, we got to keep it up," Penrod insisted rather pompously. "Long as *I* got charge o' this horse, he's going to get good treatment."

"What we better do now, Penrod?"

Penrod took on the outward signs of deep thought.

"Well, there's plenty to *do*, all right. I got to think."

Sam made several suggestions, which Penrod — maintaining his air of preoccupation — dismissed with mere gestures.

"Oh, *I* know!" Sam cried finally. "We ought to wash him so's he'll look whiter'n what he does now. We can turn the hose on him acrost the manger."

"No; not yet," said Penrod. "It's too soon after his meal. You ought to know that yourself. What we got to do is to make up a bed for him — if he wants to lay down or anything."

"Make up a what for him?" Sam echoed, dumfounded. "What you talkin' about? How can — "

"Sawdust," said Penrod. "That's the way the horse we used to have used to have it. We'll make this horse's bed in the other stall, and then he can go in there and lay down whenever he wants to."

"How we goin' to do it?"

"Look, Sam; there's the hole into the sawdust-box! All you got to do is walk in there with the shovel, stick the shovel in the hole till it gets full of sawdust, and then sprinkle it around on the empty stall."

"All *I* got to do!" Sam cried. "What are you goin' to do?"

"I'm goin' to be right here," Penrod answered reassuringly. "He won't kick or anything, and it isn't goin' to take you half a second to slip around behind him to the other stall."

"What makes you think he won't kick?"

"Well, I *know* he won't, and besides, you could hit him with the shovel if he tried to. Anyhow, I'll be right here, won't I?"

"I don't care where you are," Sam said earnestly. "What difference would that make if he ki — "

"Why, you were goin' right in the stall," Penrod reminded him. "When he first came in, you were goin' to take the rake and — "

"I don't care if I was," Sam declared. "I was excited then."

"Well, you can get excited now, can't you?" his friend urged. "You can just as easy get —"

He was interrupted by a shout from Sam, who was keeping his eye upon Whitey throughout the discussion.

"Look! Looky there!" and undoubtedly renewing his excitement, Sam pointed at the long, gaunt head beyond the manger. It was disappearing from view. "Look!" Sam shouted. "He's layin' down!"

"Well, then," said Penrod, "I guess he's goin' to take a nap. If he wants to lay down without waitin' for us to get the sawdust fixed for him, that's his lookout, not ours."

On the contrary, Sam perceived a favourable opportunity for action.

"I just as soon go and make his bed up while he's layin' down," he volunteered. "You climb up on the manger and watch him, Penrod, and I'll sneak in the other stall and fix it all up nice for him, so's he can go in there any time when he wakes up, and lay down again, or anything; and if he starts to get up, you holler and I'll jump out over the other manger."

Accordingly, Penrod established himself in a position to observe the recumbent figure.

Whitey's breathing was rather laboured but regular, and, as Sam remarked, he looked "better," even in his slumber. It is not to be doubted that, although Whitey was suffering from a light attack of colic, his feelings were in the main those of contentment. After trouble, he was solaced; after exposure, he was sheltered; after hunger and thirst, he was fed and watered. He slept.

The noon whistles blew before Sam's task was finished, but by the time he departed for lunch there was made a bed of such quality that Whitey must needs have been a born faultfinder if he complained of it. The friends parted, each urging the other to be prompt in returning, but Penrod got into threatening difficulties as soon as he entered the house.

"Penrod," said his mother, "what did you do with that loaf of bread Della says you took from the table?"

"Ma'am? *What* loaf o' bread?"

"I believe I can't let you go outdoors this afternoon," Mrs. Schofield said severely. "If you were hungry, you know perfectly well all you had to do was to — "

"But I wasn't hungry; I — "

"You can explain later," said Mrs. Schofield. "You'll have all afternoon."

Penrod's heart grew cold.

"I *can't* stay in," he protested. "I've asked Sam Williams to come over."

"I'll telephone Mrs. Williams."

"Mamma!" Penrod's voice became agonized. "I *had* to give that bread to a — to a poor ole man. He was starving and so were his children and his wife. They were all just *starving* — and they couldn't wait while I took time to come and ask you, mamma. I *got* to go outdoors this afternoon. I *got* to! Sam's — "

She relented.

In the carriage-house, half an hour later, Penrod gave an account of the episode.

"Where'd we been, I'd just like to know," he concluded, "if I hadn't got out here this afternoon?"

"Well, I guess I could managed him all right," said Sam. "I was in the passageway, a minute ago, takin' a look at him. He's standin' up again, I expect he wants more to eat."

"Well, we got to fix about that," said Penrod. "But what I mean — if I'd had to stay in the house, where would we been about the most important thing in the whole biz'nuss?"

"What you talkin' about?"

"Well, why can't you wait till I tell you?" Penrod's tone had become peevish. For that matter, so had Sam's; they were developing one of the little differences, or quarrels, that composed the very texture of their friendship.

"Well, why don't you tell me, then?"

"Well, how can I?" Penrod demanded. "You keep talkin' every minute."

"I'm not talkin' *now*, am I?" Sam protested.

"You can tell me *now*, can't you? I'm not talk —"

"You are too!" shouted Penrod. "You talk all the time — "

He was interrupted by Whitey's peculiar cough. Both boys jumped and forgot their argument.

"He means he wants some more to eat, I bet," said Sam.

"Well, if he does, he's got to wait," Penrod declared. "We got to get the most important thing of all fixed up first."

"What's that, Penrod?"

"The reward," said Penrod mildly. "That's what I was tryin' to tell you about, Sam, if you'd ever give me half a chance."

"Well, I *did* give you a chance. I kept *tellin'* you to tell me, but — "

"You never! You kept sayin' — "

They renewed this discussion, protracting it indefinitely; but as each persisted in clinging to his own interpretation of the facts, the question still remained unsettled. It was abandoned, or rather, it merged into another during the later stages of the debate, this other being concerned with which of the debaters had the least "sense." Each made the plain statement that if he were more deficient than his opponent in that regard, self-destruction would be his only refuge. Each declared that he would "rather die than be talked to death"; and then, as the two approached a point bluntly recriminative, Whitey coughed again, whereupon they were miraculously silent, and went into the passageway in a perfectly amiable manner.

"I got to have a good look at him, for once," said Penrod, as he stared frowningly at Whitey. "We got fix up about that reward."

"I want to take a good ole look at him myself," said Sam.

After supplying Whitey with another bucket of water, they returned to the carriage-house and seated themselves thoughtfully. In truth, they were something a shade more than thoughtful; the adventure to which they had committed themselves was beginning to be a little over-powering. If Whitey had been a dog, a goat, a fowl, or even a stray calf, they would have felt equal to him; but now that the earlier glow of their wild daring had disappeared, vague apprehensions stirred. Their "good look" at Whitey had not reassured them — he seemed large, Gothic, and unusual.

Whisperings within them began to urge that for boys to undertake an enterprise connected with so huge an animal as an actual horse was perilous. Beneath the surface of their musings, dim but ominous prophecies moved; both boys began to have the feeling that, somehow, this affair was going to get beyond them and that they would be in heavy trouble before it was over — they knew not why. They knew why no more than they knew why they felt it imperative to keep the fact of Whitey's presence in the stable a secret from their respective families, but they did begin to realize that keeping a secret of that size was going to be attended with some difficulty. In brief, their sensations were becoming comparable to those of the man who stole a house.

Nevertheless, after a short period given to unspoken misgivings, they returned to the subject of the reward. The money-value of bay horses, as compared to white, was again discussed, and each announced his certainty that nothing less than "a good ole hundred dollars" would be offered for the return of Whitey.

But immediately after so speaking they fell into another silence, due to sinking feelings. They had spoken loudly and confidently, and yet they knew, somehow, that such things were not to be. According to their knowledge, it was perfectly reasonable to suppose that they would receive this fortune, but they frightened themselves in speaking of it; they knew that they *could* not have a hundred dollars for their own. An oppression, as from something awful and criminal, descended upon them at intervals.

Presently, however, they were warmed to a little cheerfulness again by Penrod's suggestion that they should put a notice in the paper. Neither of them had the slightest idea how to get it there, but such details as that were beyond the horizon; they occupied themselves with the question of what their advertisement ought to "say." Finding that they differed irreconcilably, Penrod went to a cache of his in the sawdust-box and brought two pencils and a supply of paper. He gave one of the pencils and several sheets to Sam; then both boys bent themselves in silence to the labour of practical composition. Penrod produced the briefer paragraph. (See Fig. I.) Sam's was more ample. (See Fig. II.)

Fig I

Reward:
  White horse in Schofields ally finders got him in Schofields stable and will let him taken away by by ~~pay~~ paying for good food he has aten while ~~wat w~~ while ~~wat~~ waiting and Reward of ~~$100 $20 $15 $5~~ $10

Fig II

FOND
  Horse on Saturdy morning orwer can get him by ~~alpr~~ aplying at stable bhind Mr Schofield. You will have to proove he is your horse he is whit with kind of brown ~~speel~~ speks and worout ~~tail~~ tale, he is geting good care and food, reword ~~$100 $20~~ seventyfive cent's to each one or we will keep him loked up.

Neither Sam nor Penrod showed any interest in what the other had written, but both felt

134

that something praiseworthy had been accomplished. Penrod exhaled a sigh, as of relief, and, in a manner he had observed his father use sometimes, he said:

"Thank goodness, *that's* off my mind, anyway!"

"What we goin' do next, Penrod?" Sam asked deferentially, the borrowed manner having some effect upon him.

"I don't know what *you're* goin' to do," Penrod returned, picking up the old cigarbox which had contained the paper and pencils. "*I'm* goin' to put mine in here, so's it'll come in handy when I haf to get at it."

"Well, I guess I'll keep mine there, too," said Sam. Thereupon he deposited his scribbled slip beside Penrod's in the cigarbox, and the box was solemnly returned to the secret place whence it had been taken.

"There, *that's* 'tended to!" said Sam, and, unconsciously imitating his friend's imitation, he gave forth audibly a breath of satisfaction and relief. Both boys felt that the financial side of their great affair had been conscientiously looked to, that the question of the reward was settled, and that everything was proceeding in a businesslike manner. Therefore, they were able to turn their attention to another matter.

This was the question of Whitey's next meal. After their exploits of the morning, and the consequent imperilment of Penrod, they decided that nothing more was to be done in apples, vegetables, or bread; it was evident that Whitey must be fed from the bosom of nature.

"We couldn't pull enough o' that frostbit ole grass in the yard to feed him," Penrod said gloomily. "We could work a week and not get enough to make him swaller more'n about twice. All we got this morning, he blew most of it away. He'd try to scoop it in toward his teeth with his lip, and then he'd haf to kind of blow out his breath, and after that all the grass that'd be left was just some wet pieces stickin' to the outsides of his face. Well, and you know how he acted about that maple branch. We can't trust him with branches."

Sam jumped up.

"*I* know!" he cried. "There's lots of leaves left on the branches. We can give them to him."

"I just said —"

"I don't mean the branches," Sam explained. "We'll leave the branches on the trees, but just pull the leaves off the branches and put 'em in the bucket and feed 'em to him out the bucket."

Penrod thought this plan worth trying, and for three-quarters of an hour the two boys were busy with the lower branches of various trees in the yard. Thus they managed to supply Whitey with a fair quantity of wet leaves, which he ate in a perfunctory way, displaying little of his earlier enthusiasm. And the work of his purveyors might have been more tedious if it had been less damp, for a boy is seldom bored by anything that involves his staying-out in the rain without protection. The drizzle had thickened; the leaves were heavy with water, and at every jerk the branches sent fat drops over the two collectors. They attained a noteworthy state of sogginess.

Finally, they were brought to the attention of the authorities indoors, and Della appeared upon the back porch.

"Musther Penrod," she called, "y'r mamma says ye'll c'm in the house this minute an' change y'r shoes an' stockin's an' erythun' else ye got on! D'ye hear me?"

Penrod, taken by surprise and unpleasantly alarmed, darted away from the tree he was depleting and ran for the stable.

"You tell her I'm dry as toast!" he shouted over his shoulder.

Della withdrew, wearing the air of a person gratuitously insulted; and a moment later she issued from the kitchen, carrying an umbrella. She opened it and walked resolutely to the stable.

"She says I'm to bring ye in the house," said Della, "an' I'm goin' to bring ye!"

Sam had joined Penrod in the carriage-house, and, with the beginnings of an unnamed terror, the two beheld this grim advance. But they did not stay for its culmination. Without a word to each other they hurriedly tiptoed up the stairs to the gloomy loft, and there they paused, listening.

They heard Della's steps upon the carriage-house floor.

"Ah, there's plenty places t'hide in," they heard her say; "but I'll show ye! She tole me to bring ye, and I'm —"

She was interrupted by a peculiar sound — loud, chilling, dismal, and unmistakably not of human origin. The boys knew it for Whitey's cough, but Della had not their experience. A smothered shriek reached their ears; there was a scurrying noise, and then, with horror, they heard Della's footsteps in the passageway that ran by Whitey's manger. Immediately there came a louder shriek, and even in the anguish of knowing their secret discovered, they were shocked to hear distinctly the words, "O Lard in hivvin!" in the well-known voice of Della. She shrieked again, and they heard the rush of her footfalls across the carriage-house floor. Wild words came from the outer air, and the kitchen door slammed violently. It was all over. She had gone to "tell."

Penrod and Sam plunged down the stairs and out of the stable. They climbed the back fence and fled up the alley. They turned into Sam's yard, and, without consultation, headed for the cellar doors, nor paused till they found themselves in the farthest, darkest, and gloomiest recess of the cellar. There, perspiring, stricken with fear, they sank down upon the earthen floor, with their moist backs against the stone wall.

Thus with boys. The vague apprehensions that had been creeping upon Penrod and Sam all afternoon had become monstrous; the unknown was before them. How great their crime would turn out to be (now that it was in the hands of grown people), they did not know, but, since it concerned a horse, it would undoubtedly be considered of terrible dimensions.

Their plans for a reward, and all the things that had seemed both innocent and practical in the morning, now staggered their minds as manifestations of criminal folly. A new and terrible light seemed to play upon the day's exploits; they had chased a horse belonging to strangers, and it would be said that they deliberately drove him into the stable and there concealed him. They had, in truth, virtually stolen him, and they had stolen food for him. The waning light through the small window above them warned Penrod that his inroads upon the vegetables in his own cellar must soon be discovered. Della, that Nemesis, would seek them in order to prepare them for dinner, and she would find them not. But she would recall his excursion to the cellar, for she had seen him when he came up; and also the truth would be known concerning the loaf of bread. Altogether, Penrod felt that his case was worse than Sam's — until Sam offered a suggestion which roused such horrible possibilities concerning the principal item of their offense that all thought of the smaller indictments disappeared.

"Listen, Penrod," Sam quavered: "What — what if that — what if that ole horse maybe b'longed to a — policeman!" Sam's imagination was not of the comforting kind. "What'd they — do to us, Penrod, if it turned out he was some policeman's horse?"

Penrod was able only to shake his head. He did not reply in words, but both boys thenceforth considered it almost inevitable that Whitey *had* belonged to a policeman, and in their sense of so ultimate a disaster, they ceased for a time to brood upon what their parents would probably do to them. The penalty for stealing a policeman's horse would be only a step short of capital, they were sure. They would not be hanged; but vague, looming sketches of something called the penitentiary began to flicker before them.

It grew darker in the cellar, so that finally they could not see each other.

"I guess they're huntin' for us by now," Sam said huskily. "I don't — I don't like it much down here, Penrod."

Penrod's hoarse whisper came from the profound gloom:

"Well, who ever said you did?"

"Well —" Sam paused; then he said plaintively, "I wish we'd never *seen* that dern ole horse."

"It was every bit his fault," said Penrod. "*We* didn't do anything. If he hadn't come stickin' his ole head in our stable, it'd never happened at all. Ole fool!" He rose. "I'm goin' to get out of here; I guess I've stood about enough for one day."

"Where — where you goin', Penrod? You aren't goin' *home,* are you?"

"No; I'm not! What you take me for? You think I'm crazy?"

"Well, where *can* we go?"

How far Penrod's desperation actually would have led him is doubtful, but he made this statement:

"I don't know where *you're* goin', but *I'm* goin' to walk straight out in the country till I come to a farmhouse and say my name's George and live there!"

"I'll do it, too," Sam whispered eagerly. "I'll say my name's Henry."

"Well, we better get started," said the executive Penrod. "We got to get away from here, anyway."

But when they came to ascend the steps leading to the "outside doors," they found that those doors had been closed and locked for the night.

"It's no use," Sam lamented, "and we can't bust 'em, 'cause I tried to, once before. Fanny always locks 'em about five o'clock — I forgot. We got to go up the stairway and try to sneak out through the house."

They tiptoed back, and up the inner stairs. They paused at the top, then breathlessly

141

stepped out into a hall which was entirely dark. Sam touched Penrod's sleeve in warning, and bent to listen at a door.

Immediately that door opened, revealing the bright library, where sat Penrod's mother and Sam's father.

It was Sam's mother who had opened the door.

"Come into the library, boys," she said. "Mrs. Schofield is just telling us about it."

And as the two comrades moved dumbly into the lighted room, Penrod's mother rose, and, taking him by the shoulder, urged him close to the fire.

"You stand there and try to dry off a little, while I finish telling Mr. and Mrs. Williams about you and Sam," she said. "You'd better make Sam keep near the fire, too, Mrs. Williams, because they both got wringing wet. Think of their running off just when most people would have wanted to stay! Well, I'll go on with the story, then. Della told me all about it, and what the cook next door said *she'd* seen, how they'd been trying to pull grass and leaves for the poor old thing all day — and all about the apples they carried from *your* cellar, and getting wet and working in the rain as hard as they could — and they'd given him a loaf of bread! Shame on you, Penrod!" She paused to laugh, but there was a little moisture round her eyes, even before she laughed. "And they'd fed him on potatoes and lettuce and cabbage and turnips out of *our* cellar! And I wish you'd see the sawdust bed they made for him! Well, when I'd telephoned, and the Humane Society man got there, he said it was the most touching thing he ever knew. It seems he *knew* this horse, and had been looking for him. He said ninety-nine boys out of a hundred would have chased the poor old thing away, and he was going to see to it that this case didn't go unnoticed, because the local branch of the society gives little silver medals for special acts like this. And the last thing he said before he led the poor old horse away was that he was sure Penrod and Sam each would be awarded one at the meeting of the society next Thursday night."

. . . On the following Saturday morning a yodel sounded from the sunny sidewalk in front of the Schofields' house, and Penrod, issuing forth, beheld the familiar figure of Samuel Williams in waiting.

Upon Sam's breast there glittered a round bit of silver suspended by a white ribbon from a bar of the same metal. Upon the breast of Penrod was a decoration precisely similar.

" 'Lo, Penrod," said Sam. "What you goin' to do?"

"Nothin'."

"I got mine on," said Sam.

"I have, too," said Penrod. "I wouldn't take a hunderd dollars for mine."

"I wouldn't take two hunderd for mine,"

said Sam.

Each glanced pleasantly at the other's medal. They faced each other without shame. Neither had the slightest sense of hypocrisy either in himself or in his comrade. On the contrary!

Penrod's eyes went from Sam's medal back to his own; thence they wandered, with perhaps a little disappointment, to the lifeless street and to the empty yards and spectatorless windows of the neighbourhood. Then he looked southward toward the busy heart of the town, where multitudes were.

"Let's go down and see what time it is by the court-house clock," said Penrod.

Humor's Golden Age

Father has Trouble with the Land of Egypt

Clarence Day, Jr.

One winter when most of us boys were away, Mother was invited to go to Egypt with Mrs. Tytus and two or three others. Mrs. Tytus's son, Bob, was in charge of the party. They were going to sail up the Nile in a houseboat, they would see Luxor and Memphis, and altogether it seemed to be an ideal opportunity. Mother loved travel. She was eager to see any place that was new to her, even a place that was comparatively near-by like the Whitneys' camp up in Maine, and as Egypt was ten times as far away it seemed ten times as attractive.

She explained to Father what a wonderful chance it was. He was not impressed. He said she wanted to go anywhere, always, and he had never seen such a woman. Most women were glad to have a home, he said, and knew enough to appreciate it, but the only thing Mother seemed to want was to be on the go.

He went on to say that he himself had some sense, however, and that he would no more

147

think of going to Egypt than to the North Pole. In a year or two, if he could get away from business, they might go to London and Paris once more, but not one of the Day family had even set foot in Egypt and nobody else he knew had, either, except Charlie Bond, who was one of those restless fellows anyhow and was always doing queer things. He said it was a wild and entirely unsuitable country, and that never in any circumstances whatever would he take Mother to Egypt.

"But that's just why I want to go, Clare, dear. You don't understand."

Father stared at her, and said, "What! What's why you want to go? Of course I don't understand."

"Why, because you don't like it. I thought it would please you."

The veins in Father's forehead began to swell. "You thought it would *please me?*"

"Oh Clare, dear, don't be stupid. I knew you wouldn't want to take me over to Egypt yourself, but don't you see, if Mrs. Tytus takes me, you won't ever have to."

This theory that Mother was only trying to save him trouble by getting on a ship and going to Egypt completely dumbfounded Father. But Mother clung firmly to it. She said of course she hated to have him miss seeing the Pyramids, but still she wouldn't enjoy dragging him off there if he was so unwilling, so he could just stay home and be comfortable in his own way while she went quietly over with Mrs. Tytus and hurried straight back.

To help clinch the matter, she brought Mrs. Tytus to see him. She brought young Bob Tytus, too. She told Father how much her letter of credit should be, and when he protested, she said she was saving him money, because it would be nearly twice as much if he took her himself.

When Father said violently that he wished her to remain at his side, she said everybody had to go away sometimes, and Dr. Markoe had warned her she must.

Dr. Markoe was a man Father liked. Mrs. Tytus was tactful and beautiful. Mother was pertinacious. Between them all, they actually bore Father down, and on the appointed day Mother got aboard the ship, letter of credit and all, with Father swearing that now he would have to worry about her all winter, and he wouldn't be happy for a minute until she got back.

"Goodbye, darling," she said. "Do be quiet and nice while I'm gone."

"I won't!" he shouted, kissing her, and he marched stiffly off, saying, "I hope you are satisfied," and then turned back at the foot of the gangplank, calling loudly, "Dear Vinnie!" Mother waved her hand, the whistles blew hoarsely, and the crowds swirled and jostled, hiding these two from each other as the ship slid away.

Father began looking for letters the very next morning, and when none came he cursed the pilot and the postman, and said that he had a bad headache. But a letter did arrive in a few days, when the pilot had had time to mail it, and after the first three or four weeks we heard from Mother often.

Some of the letters told us how she was constantly meeting people she knew, not only on the ship but at every port where Mrs. Tytus and she went ashore. "Your mother has the damnedest number of friends I ever heard of," said Father. "She's everlastingly meeting some old friend or other wherever she goes. I never see people I know when I'm traveling. But there isn't a city in Europe where your mother wouldn't spot a friend in five minutes." And when a letter came saying she had just climbed Mt. Vesuvius and had found old Mr. and Mrs. Quintard of Rye at the top, peering down into the crater, Father said that upon his soul he never knew anyone like her.

Other letters were full of household advice and instructions about menus, or warnings to Father to keep an eye on the rubber tree and to speak about washing the curtains. Others abused the bad habits of foreigners and the inconveniences and troubles she met. "Well, why doesn't she stay home, then?" Father demanded triumphantly. Though he swore at every foreigner who dared to inconvenience her, he relished the complaints in these letters.

But when Mother left civilization behind her, even a far outpost like Cairo, and went off up the Nile in a thing called a dahabeah, manned by native boatmen, and when letters came from queer-sounding ancient cities in the interior, Father got nervous. He said it was a wild, harum-scarum thing to do. Moreover, it was entirely needless. He said he could see all of Egypt he wanted to without leaving New York — there were enough musty old mummies in the Museum to satisfy anybody. "But your mother wouldn't look at them; no, they weren't dead enough for her; she had to go traipsing off to see a mummy on its native heath. Why, somebody even brought an obelisk over here at great expense," he went on, "and left it to crumble away in the Park, where people can see it for nothing, but for some reason or other it isn't crumbly enough for your mother."

There were letters about the strange range of hills back of Thebes, and the great colonnades at Karnak, and the statues and tombs, which Father pished at impatiently; and there were letters about fleas, and moonlight and Nubian songs, and finally letters with snapshots. Father said he hated these photographs. He spent a great deal of time staring at them in deep disapproval. There was one in particular of Mother looking very roguish and chic in her voluminous dress, sitting way up on top of a tall and insolent camel, with two big black men in white turbans standing off at one side. No

151

other member of the party around. Not a soul in sight but the black men and Mother. Father looked at that photograph often and groaned about it at night, and kept shouting things to himself about "the ends of the earth."

Soon after that, Mother turned around and headed for home. Father grew more and more eager to have her back, every day. Up to this time he had been comparatively quiet, for him, but the nearer the day of her return came the more noisy and impatient he got. Even at the pier, he made indignant remarks about how slow the ship was getting in.

He forgot this mood, however, the minute he hugged her, and he instantly took charge of her things — all except her black bag, which she would never let anyone touch — and he ordered all the customs inspectors around and got Mother through in a jiffy, and he found a man to shoulder her trunk and he picked out the best hackman, and as the carriage rattled off over the cobblestones, Mother said she was glad to be back.

Father had taken particular pains to have everything in the house in its place, so that when Mother came in the door, she would say that home was just the way she had left it. Instead, what she actually said was "Oh, this poor room! Why, I never!" and she put down the black bag and began setting the chairs at different angles and moving her favorite ornaments affectionately as she straightened them out. "Poor things," she said, as she patted them, "didn't anybody know enough to turn you around the way you belong?" Father followed her, looking puzzled at these minute changes, and calling her attention to the rubber tree, which had grown half a foot. "Well," Mother said. "of all the forlorn objects, with those dead leaves left hanging there!" But when Father's face fell and she saw how disappointed he looked, she smiled at him to console him and said, "You did the best you could, darling." And she climbed upstairs to unpack.

The letter of credit had been very much on Father's mind. He had never before given Mother the management of any such sum. He was so happy to have her back that he said nothing about this at first. He was waiting for Mother to speak of it. But she said nothing either.

He had two expectations about it, and he didn't know which to trust. One was hopeful but slightly unreal. The other, based on long experience, was pessimistic.

It had been a large letter of credit, not as much as Mrs. Tytus had recommended but still, he felt, generous. He felt he had a right to expect that Mother hadn't spent all of it, but had left a substantial balance undrawn which he could now restore to his bank account. His other and realer expectation was that she had spent every cent and had possibly even had to borrow from Mrs. Tytus besides. The fact that she was avoiding the subject pointed to this latter outcome.

One night, after she had gone up to bed, she came back down for a moment to hand him some papers. "You might be going over these, Clare," she said. "I couldn't keep track of everything for you; I tried my best but I couldn't. But I saved all the bills." And she went off to bed again.

Father checked them over, one by one, carefully. They were full of strange-looking details:

CAIRO, FEB. 24, 1900

MRS. DAY,
  Room 195, Shepheard's Hotel.
To 1 Passage to Second Cataract £ 23. 0.0.
To 60 days on Dahabeah Tih   £ 85.16.0.
                                  £108.16.0.

"Second Cataract!" Father muttered to himself vehemently. What would such a woman do next?

These bills supplied Father with more details than he had hoped to keep track of, and there was none of them that he felt much inclined to dispute. But as there were still several hundred dollars unaccounted for, he waited for Mother to confess what she had done with the balance.

Day after day went by without her saying one word. He began to fear that things must be serious. He became so alarmed that it would have been a relief to him to know the worst and be done with it. But do what he could — without direct questioning — he could get nothing out of her.

Mother had noticed his fumbling hints of course, and she did have a confession to make. But first she went and had a long talk with a young girl she was fond of — a girl whose name was Wilhelmine Johnson, whom George afterward married. Mother confided to Wilhelmine in secret that the situation was this: she hadn't spent all her letter of credit but she hated to give up the balance. It was wicked of her to feel that way, she supposed, but she meant to keep it herself.

Wilhelmine instantly took a strong stand about this. She said that on no account should Mother hand over that money to Father. Mother had always wanted to have some money of her own, Wilhelmine reminded her, and now here was her chance.

As Mother listened to this advice she felt happy, but she also felt frightened. It seemed to her far more daring to hang onto that money than it had been to ride on a camel. But while she was away all those months she had had a taste of what independence was like, and she was reluctant to drop back into her Victorian role.

When at last she nerved herself to tell Father, he felt better at once, but he smilingly reproved her for not having come to him sooner; and as to her keeping the money he said that that was all nonsense. He said that she was home now, thank God, and as he always paid all her bills at home she had no use for this money.

"Yes I have too," Mother said.

"Well, what will you use it for, then?" Father asked.

Mother didn't wish to explain. As a matter of fact she had no very definite ideas as to what she wanted some cash of her own for — she only knew that she wanted it. She said, "Oh, there are lots of little things I could use it for, Clare. Things I'd like to get when I need them, without so much talk."

This seemed unconvincing to Father. He demanded the balance. He felt that he was the natural custodian of any such fund and the only safe place for it was in his bank account, as Mother, of course, didn't have one. But Mother insisted on hiding it away in her own bureau drawer. Father pointed out how reckless this was, but he could do nothing with her. That voyage to Egypt had changed her; she was always much harder to manage after that sail up the Nile.

As a gracious concession, however, she presented Father with a large pale blue scarab, mounted to use as a scarfpin, which she said she hadn't really meant to let him have until Christmas. Father looked at this object without enthusiasm and asked what it was. When he was told that it was the image of a sacred beetle, he immediately pushed it away. He didn't want any dead beetles in his scarf, he declared. He told Mother she could send it right back to the tomb it had come from. He said that he begged to inform her that he was not a mummy.

Father Sews on a Button

Clarence Day, Jr.

It must have been hard work to keep up with the mending in our house. Four boys had to be kept in repair besides Father, and there was no special person to do it. The baby's nurse did some sewing, and Cousin Julie turned to and did a lot when she was around, but the rest of it kept Mother busy and her work basket was always piled high.

Looking back, I wonder now how she managed it. I remember her regularly going off to her room and sewing on something right after dinner or at other idle moments, when she might have sat around with the rest of us. My impression as a boy was that this was like going off to do puzzles — it was a form of amusement, or a woman's way of passing the time.

There was more talk about Father's socks and shirts than anything else. Most of this talk was by Father, who didn't like things to disappear for long periods, and who wanted them brought promptly back and put in his bureau drawer where they belonged. This was particularly true of his favorite socks. Not the plain white ones which he wore in the evening, because they were all alike, but the colored socks that were supplied to him by an English harberdasher in Paris.

These colored socks were the one outlet of something in Father which ran contrary to that religion of propriety to which he adhered. In that day of somber hues for men's suits and quiet tones for men's neckties, most socks were as dark and severe as the rest of one's garments; but Father's, hidden from the public eye by his trousers and his high buttoned shoes, had a really astonishing range both of color and fancy. They were mostly in excellent taste, but in a distinctly French way, and Wilhelmine used to tease him about them. She called them his "secret joys."

Father got holes in his socks even oftener than we boys did in our stockings. He had long athletic toes, and when he lay stretched out on his sofa reading and smoking, or absorbed in talking to anyone, these toes would begin stretching and wiggling in a curious way by themselves, as though they were seizing on this chance to live a life of their own. I often stared in fascination at their leisurely twistings and turnings, when I should have been listening to Father's instructions about far different matters. Soon one and then the other slipper would fall off, always to Father's surprise, but without interrupting his talk, and little later his busy great toe would peer out at me through a new hole in his sock.

Mother felt that it was a woman's duty to mend things and sew, but she hated it. She rather liked to embroider silk lambrequins, as a feat of womanly prowess, but her darning of Father's socks was an impatient and not-too-skillful performance. She said there were so many of them that they made the back of her neck ache.

Father's heavily starched shirts, too, were a problem. When he put one on, he pulled it down over his head, and thrust his arms blindly out right and left in a hunt for the sleeves. A new shirt was strong enough to survive these strains without splitting, but life with Father rapidly weakened it, and the first thing he knew he would hear it beginning to tear. That disgusted him. He hated any evidence of weakness, either in people or things. In his wrath he would strike out harder than ever as he felt around for the sleeve. Then would come a sharp crackling noise as the shirt ripped open, and a loud wail from Mother.

Buttons were Father's worst trial, however, from his point of view. Ripped shirts and socks with holes in them could still be worn, but drawers with their buttons off couldn't. The speed with which he dressed seemed to discourage his buttons and make them desert

Father's service. Furthermore, they always gave out suddenly and at the wrong moment.

He wanted help and he wanted it promptly at such times, of course. He would appear at Mother's door with a waistcoat in one hand and a disloyal button in the other, demanding that it be sewn on at once. If she said she couldn't just then, Father would get as indignant as though he had been drowning and a life-guard had informed him he would save him tomorrow.

When his indignation mounted high enough to sweep aside his good judgment, he would say in a stern voice, "Very well, I'll sew it on myself," and demand a needle and thread. This announcement always caused consternation. Mother knew only too well what it meant. She would beg him to leave his waistcoat in her work basket and let her do it next day. Father was inflexible. Moreover, his decision would be strengthened if he happened to glance at her basket and see how many of his socks were dismally waiting there in that crowded exile.

"I've been looking for those blue polka-dotted socks for a month," he said angrily one night before dinner. "Not a thing is done for a man in this house. I even have to sew on my own buttons. Where is your needle and thread?"

Mother reluctantly gave these implements to him. He marched off, sat on the edge of his sofa in the middle of his bedroom, and got ready to work. The gaslight was better by his bureau, but he couldn't sit on a chair when he sewed. It had no extra room on it. He laid his scissors, the spool of thread, and his waistcoat down on the sofa beside him, wet his fingers, held the needle high up and well out in front, and began poking the thread at the eye.

Like every commander, Father expected instant obedience, and he wished to deal with trained troops. The contrariness of the needle and the limp obstinacy of the thread made him swear. He stuck the needle in the sofa while he wet his fingers and stiffened the thread again. When he came to take up his needle, it had disappeared. He felt around everywhere for it. He got up, holding fast to his thread, and turned around, facing the sofa to see where it was hiding. This jerked the spool off onto the floor, where it rolled away and unwound.

The husbands of two of Mother's friends had had fits of apoplexy and died. It frightened her horribly when this seemed about to happen to Father. At the sound of his roars, she rushed in. There he was on the floor, as she had feared. He was trying to get his head under the sofa and he was yelling at something, and his face was such a dark red and his eyes so bloodshot that Mother was terrified. Pleading with him to stop only made him more apoplectic. He said he'd be damned if he'd stop. He stood up presently, tousled but triumphant, the spool in his hand. Mother ran to get a new needle. She threaded it for him and he at least started sewing.

Father sewed on the button in a violent manner, with vicious haulings and jabs. Mother said she couldn't bear to see him — but she couldn't bear to leave the room, either. She stood watching him, hypnotized and appalled, itching to sew it herself, and they talked at each other with vehemence. Then the inevitable accident happened: the needle came forcibly up through the waistcoat, it struck on the button, Father pushed at it harder, and it burst through the hole and stuck Father's finger.

He sprang up with a howl. To be impaled in this way was not only exasperating, it was an affront. He turned to me, as he strode about on the rug, holding onto his finger, and said wrathfully, "It was your mother."

"Why, Clare!" Mother cried.

"Talking every minute," Father shouted at her, "and distracting a man! How the devil can I sew on a button with this gibbering and buzz in my ears? Now see what you made me do!" he added suddenly. "Blood on my good waistcoat! Here! Take the damned thing. Give me a handkerchief to tie up my finger with. Where's the witch-hazel?"

archy and mehitabel

Don Marquis

i the coming of archy

Dobbs Ferry possesses a rat which slips out of his lair at night and runs a typewriting machine in a garage. Unfortunately, he has always been interrupted by the watchman before he could produce a complete story.

It was at first thought that the power which made the typewriter run was a ghost, instead of a rat. It seems likely to us that it was both a ghost and a rat. Mme. Blavatsky's ego went into a white horse after she passed over, and someone's personality has undoubtedly gone into this rat. It is an era of belief in communications from the spirit land.

And since this matter had been reported in the public prints and seriously received we are no longer afraid of being ridiculed, and we do not mind making a statement of something that happened to our own typewriter only a couple of weeks ago.

164

We came into our room earlier than usual in the morning, and discovered a gigantic cockroach jumping about upon the keys.

He did not see us, and we watched him. He would climb painfully upon the framework of the machine and cast himself with all his force upon a key, head downward, and his weight and the impact of the blow were just sufficient to operate the machine, one slow letter after another. He could not work the capital letters, and he had a great deal of difficulty operating the mechanism that shifts the paper so that a fresh line may be started. We never saw a cockroach work so hard or perspire so freely in all our lives before. After about an hour of this frightfully difficult literary labor he fell to the floor exhausted, and we saw him creep feebly into a nest of the poems which are always there in profusion.

Congratulating ourself that we had left a sheet of paper in the machine the night before so that all this work had not been in vain, we made an examination, and this is what we found:

expression is the need of my soul
i was once a vers libre bard
but i died and my soul went into the body
   of a cockroach
it has given me a new outlook upon life
i see things from the under side now
thank you for the apple peelings in the

wastepaper basket
but your paste is getting so stale i cant eat
    it
there is a cat here called mehitabel i wish
    you would have
removed she nearly ate me the other night
    why dont she
catch rats that is what she is supposed to be
    for
there is a rat here she should get without
    delay

most of these rats here are just rats
but this rat is like me he has a human soul
    in him
he used to be a poet himself
night after night i have written poetry for
    you
on your typewriter
and this big brute of a rat who used to be a
    poet
comes out of his hole when it is done
and reads it and sniffs at it
he is jealous of my poetry
he used to make fun of it when we were
    both human
he was a punk poet himself
and after he has read it he sneers
and then he eats it

i wish you would have mehitabel kill that
    rat

or get a cat that is onto her job
and i will write you a series of poems
    showing how things look
to a cockroach
that rats name is freddy
the next time freddy dies i hope he wont be
    a rat
but something smaller i hope i will be a rat
in the next transmigration and freddy a
    cockroach
i will teach him to sneer at my poetry then
dont you ever eat any sandwiches in your
    office
i havent had a crumb of bread for i dont
    know how long
or a piece of ham or anything but apple
    parings
and paste leave a piece of paper in your
    machine
every night you can call me archy

        ii mehitabel was once cleopatra

boss i am disappointed in
some of your readers they
are always asking how does
archy work the shift so as to get a
new line or how does archy do
this or do that they
are always interested in technical
details when the main question is

whether the stuff is
literature or not
i wish you would leave
that book of george moores on
the floor

mehitabel the cat and i want to
read it i have discovered that
mehitabel s soul formerly inhabited a
human also at least that
is what mehitabel is claiming these
days it may be she got jealous of
my prestige anyhow she and
i have been talking it over in a
friendly way who were you
mehitabel i asked her i was
cleopatra once she said well i said i
suppose you lived in a palace you bet
she said and what lovely fish dinners
we used to have and licked her chops

mehitabel would sell her soul for
a plate of fish any day i told her i thought
you were going to say you were
the favorite wife of the emperor
valerian he was some cat nip eh
mehitabel but she did not get me
                                    archy

From Nuts to Soup

Will Rogers

A couple of weeks ago I wrote the following: "If Mrs. John William Davis, wife of the Democratic presidential candidate, ever gets into the White House, we will have a mistress whom no titled European visitor can embarrass by doing the right thing first. She will never tip her soup plate, even if she can't get it all."

Now comes along an old friend of mine, Percy Hammond, a theatrical critic on the Chicago Tribune and the New York Tribune (pardon me, Percy, for having to tell them who you are, but my readers are mostly provincial). He takes up a couple of columns, part of which follows:

For years I have been tipping my soup plate, but never until Mr. Rogers instructed me, did I know that I was performing a social error. Consultation with the polished and urbane head waiters of the Middle West, where I spent my boyhood, taught me, I

169

believed, to eat soup. One wonders if Mr. Rogers has given as much thought to soup as he has to the lariat. Perhaps he does not know, being recently from Oklahoma, that in many prominent Eastern dining rooms one may tip one's soup plate, without losing his social standing. I regard Mr. Rogers' interference as prairie, impudent and unofficial. The stewards of the Dutch Treat Club assure me that it is proper to tip one's plate, provided (and here is the subtlety that escapes Mr. Rogers), provided that one tips one's soup plate from, and not toward.

Mr. Rogers might well observe the modesty in such matters that adorns Mr. Tom Mix, his fellow ex-cowman. Mr. Mix, telling of a dinner given in his honor at the Hotel Astor, said: I et for two hours and didn't recognize a thing I et, except an olive.

Them are Percy's words (you notice I call you Percy, because if I keep saying "Mr. Hammond, Mr. Hammond," all through my article, it might possibly appear too formal). Percy, I thought you were a theatrical critic. Now I find you are only a soup critic. Instead of going, as is customary, from soup to nuts, you have gone from nuts to soup. Now, Percy, I have just read your article on "My Ignorance of Etiquette" (I don't know if that etiquette thing is spelled right, or not; if it is not, it will give you a chance for another article on my bad spelling). Now you do not have to write articles on my lack of etiquette, my ignorance, my bad English, or a thousand and one other defects. All the people that I ever met, or any one who ever read one of my articles, know that. It's too well known to comment on. Besides, I admit it.

Percy, I am just an old country boy in a big town trying to get along. I have been eating pretty regular, and the reason I have been, is because I have stayed an old country boy. Now I wrote that article, and technically I admit I may have been wrong, but the newspapers paid me a lot of money for it, and I never had a complaint. And, by the way, I will get the same this week for writing about you as I got for writing about soup. Now both articles may be wrong. But if you can show me how I can get any more money by writing them right, why, I will split with you.

Now you took my soup article apart to see what made it float. I will see if we can't find some small technicalities in your literary masterpiece. You say I came recently from Oklahoma, while you came from the Middle West and "by consultation with the head waiters have learned the proper way to eat soup." I thought Oklahoma was in the Middle West. Your knowledge of geography is worse than my etiquette. You say you learned to eat soup from a head waiter in the Middle West. Well, I admit my ignorance again: I never saw a head waiter eat soup.

Down in Oklahoma, where I come from, we won't let a head waiter eat at our table, even if we had a head waiter, which we haven't. If I remember right, I think it was my mother who taught me what little she knew of how I should eat, because if we had had to wait until we sent and got a head waiter to show us, we would have all starved to death. If a head waiter taught you to eat soup, Percy, I suppose you were sent to Borden's to learn how to drink milk.

Then you state: "The stewards of the Dutch Treat Club assured me that it is proper to tip one's plate." Now if you had learned properly from the great social head waiters of the urbane Middle West, why did you have to consult the stewards of the Dutch Treat Club? Could it be that after arriving in N.Y. you couldn't rely on the information of the polished head waiters of your phantom Middle West? Now I was in the Dutch Treat Club once, but just as a guest of honor at a luncheon, and of course had no chance to get into any intimate conversation with the stewards. At the time, the place did not impress me as being one where you might learn the last word in etiquette.

And as for your saying that "anything of subtlety would escape me," that I also admit. I attribute it to my dumbness. But as for me being too dumb to get the idea of "the soup plate being tipped away and not toward one," that's not etiquette; that's just self-protection.

As bad as you plate tippers want all you can get, you don't want it in your lap. Custom makes manners, and while I know that it is permissible to tip plates, I still say that it is not a universal custom.

Manners are nothing more than common sense, and a person has no more rights to try and get every drop of soup out of his plate than he has to take a piece of bread and try and harvest all the gravy in his plate. If you are that hungry, they ought to feed you out of a nose bag. So, "prairie impudence," or no "prairie impudence," I claim there are lots of them that don't do it, even if it is permissible, head waiters and Dutch stewards to the contrary. It's permissible to get drunk, but we still have a few that don't.

Now, Percy, suppose they all did as permitted. Picture a big dinner with everybody with their soup plates all balanced up on edge, rounding up what little soup was left. If that was the universal custom, I would invent a triangle that could be pushed under the plate, so it would permit you to have one hand free, if by chance you might want to use a napkin.

So don't ask head waiters and stewards what to do, Percy, look around yourself. You will find hundreds of them that are satisfied with just what soup they can get on the level. Why, I bet you are a fellow, Percy, if you took castor oil, you would want to lick the spoon.

You know, Percy, I might know more about

etiquette than you think I do. I wrote a review on Emily Post's Book on Etiquette, and it was recopied in the Literary Digest. Now have you or any of your Mid-Western head waiters or retinue of stewards, ever been asked to write a criticism on such an authoritative work as that? So you see, I am somewhat of a critic myself. I am the Hammond of the Etiquette book business.

Another thing, Percy, I spoke of a particular case; I mentioned Mrs. Davis. Well, I happened to see the lady in question eat soup, and she did not try and corral the whole output. She perhaps knew it was permissible, still she did not seem eager to take advantage of it.

Now you speak of my friend Tom Mix, where he says, "He et two hours and did not recognize anything he et but an olive." Now that is bad grammar, even I will admit, but it's mighty good eating. Don't you kinder envy him that he can eat two hours? I bet you that you would trade your knowledge of the English language, for his constitution. Tipping that soup plate at all your meals for years, is what put that front on you, Percy. Leave some! And the fact that Tom has done something to be given a dinner for, should make him immune from attacks from the press table.

Personally, I don't think his word "et" on Mix's part will seriously affect the drawing power of his films. You see, Percy, Tom said "et" but you know better than him what to say. Still, if a western picture was to be made to amuse the entire world, I would trust Tom's judgement to yours. Percy, everybody is ignorant, only on different subjects.

So Percy, you string with the high brows, I am going to stick to the low brows, because I know I am at home with them. For remember, if it was not for us low brows, you high brows would have no one to discuss. But God love you, Percy, and if you ever want to leave them and come back to us where you started, we will all be glad to welcome you, even if you do feel like you are slumming. You must remember, Percy, that the question of the world today is not how to eat soup, but how to get soup to eat.

Convention Afterthoughts

Will Rogers

All I know is just what I read in the papers, and what I can remember of days that passed lately at — what was, for lack of better names — Political Conventions.

It kinder made you wonder, Are we doing all this progressing that we talk about all the time? They say that practice makes perfect at anything. But I tell you, 'tain't so! No nation that was ever invented under the sun does as much practicing "talking," as we do, and if you think we are perfect at it, you just listen over the radio, or worse still, in person, to the speeches at the Political Conventions.

I am just getting over it. Two weeks straight of applesauce. "These are momentous times!" "The eyes of the world are on us!" "Let us act with foresight and deliberation!" Now you heard that by every speaker. Now just take 'em apart and see why they fall over, if you try and let 'em stand alone.

"These are momentous times!" Now what is

momentous about 'em? Time is time, momentous things happen to individuals, not to everybody at once. What might be momentous to one, would just be wasting time to another. They are momentous times with the speaker. For if justice gets its due, it's the last time he will ever get to address a National Convention. The only guy a Convention is momentous with, is the bird that gets the nomination.

Then the prize bromo of all: "The eyes of the world are upon us!" Now if that is not insulting your intelligence! Whose eyes are on who? What's the world care what we are doing? What do we care what the world is doing? The eyes of the world are cockeyed as far as we are concerned. Why, the eyes of our own country are not even on us. They know the thing is just an ordinary routine. Somebody is going to be President. It don't make any difference who is in. None of them, from any party, are going to purposely ruin the country. They will do the best they can. If weather and crops, and no wars, and a fair share of prosperity is with them, they will go out of office having had a good administration. So the world is not paying any attention to us; the world is shortsighted as far as we are concerned.

Our public men take themselves so serious. It just looks like they are stoop-shouldered from carrying our country on their backs. And the women, poor souls, when they speak it seems they have paid more attention to the material in the dress, than they have to the material in the speech. They mean well and act awful sincere. It gets 'em out and gives 'em a chance to get away from home, but it just seems like they haven't added anything constructive to the art of politics. They haven't been able to harrow much of a row as far as cleaning up our national pastime is concerned. I think they take it too serious. I believe they would get further if they kinder ridiculed and kidded the men. They can do that in everything else, so why can't they do it in politics?

Personally, I think the camera has done more harm for politics than any other one faction. Everybody would rather get their picture than their ideas in the paper. What does the platform of a political party amount to compared to the photography? There are 10 cameras to every plank in the platform. There was more film wasted on the two Conventions than was wasted making "King of Kings." Speakers get up early in the morning, not to find out how their speech was received by the press, but how the pictures turned out.

And some means should be worked out whereby you could keep track of the same things said by various speakers over and over again. Each man just stands and repeats what has been said a thousand times before, and generally better than he is saying it.

The most terrible things were the nominating speeches. Every man would talk for half the time about what his state had done. For instance, a Wisconsin man gabbed for an hour, telling what Wisconsin had accomplished, including the milk and butter fat per cow. Now what's that got to do with Al Smith?

Another guy, one from Tennessee, was nominating somebody from perhaps Vermont, or Arizona — I forget which — and he went on for an age about what Andrew Jackson had done for the Commonwealth, and the records and traditions of his state. As a matter of fact, about all old Andrew was responsible for, was the system that made us all have to sit there and listen to such junk. Andrew was the one that said: "If you don't get out and work for the Party, you don't get in on the gravy after election!" So all these guys were lined up at the feed trough.

One thing these nominators dwelled on was their candidate's honesty. You would think — from the nominating speeches — that that was their outstanding qualification, honesty. They didn't exactly say so, but they casually insinuated that the candidate on the other side will perhaps steal the White House, if he is not carefully watched.

We did think that the Democratic Convention at Houston would improve on the Republicans at Kansas City. For we did think that the one thing that a Democrat had on a Republican, was that he was a better talker. For he, being out of office more, had more time to think up reasons why he should be in. But it's just as I told you, the speeches at the Democratic wake blew up higher than the Kansas City orgy.

One speaker started his speech with: "As I look into this sea of faces. . ." So that shows you about how far speech making has advanced. It was Noah, that first pulled that line when he looked over the bunch just before pulling in the gang plank.

Then the Democrats especially harped on "Corruption." Now they made that their battle slogan four years ago, when all the corruption and Tea Pot Dome oil scandal was at its height — and they were then beaten by eight million. So how can they win with it this year, when we are more used to corruption than we was four years ago?

In fact, what these nominators should say, is: "The man I am about to name, needs no naming!" Then he would have it right. The ones that were named, needed no naming. They should have been left to their own solitude. And the ones that did the nominating, just where do they dig them up? And do the men that are being nominated know of it in advance? I don't believe they do, or they would never allow them to go on. These nominators can't be friends of the men being nominated, or they would never go on and handicap them as they do.

You see, here is what has made bad speeches stand out so over what they used to be. Maybe in the old days speeches were just as idea-less.

180

But they were only listened to by the delegates. And the man making the speech was a delegate, so he only had to appeal to intelligence as high as his own. But nowadays, this radio thing has changed all that. They are not just talking to a lot of politicians — they are talking to the world. And people are getting wise to the type of man that is supposed to be saving our country. Right away he compares the intelligence of their talk with the talk that he hears in other lines of business, and it just don't stand up. So the old radio is just about to give us a true line on our public servants. But speech making was never at a lower ebb in the history of the world than it is today here in America. A speech nowadays is just like bootleg liquor. Nobody knows what all the junk is they put in it, but it tastes terrible and sounds worse.

But it's a great game, this Convention game is. I don't suppose there is a show in the world with as much sameness in it. You know exactly what each speaker is going to say before he says it. You know before you go who will be nominated. The platform will always be the same: promise everything, deliver nothing! You cuss yourself for sitting day in and day out, listening to such nonsense. So let's don't hold another Convention till some one can think of a new speech.

Brief Gust of Glory

H. L. Mencken

When I was a boy in the Aurignacian Epoch of Baltimore, the favorite bivouac and chapel-of-ease of all healthy males of tender years was the neighborhood livery stable. I have since learned, by a reading in the social sciences, that the American livery stables of that era were seminaries of iniquity, with a curriculum embracing cursing and swearing, gambling, cigarette-smoking, tobacco-chewing, the classical or Abraham Lincoln répertoire of lewd anecdotes, the design and execution of dirty pictures, and even the elements of seduction, burglary, and delirium tremens. It may have been true, for all I know, in the pathological small towns that all social scientists appear to hail from, but certainly it was not true in West Baltimore, a sedate and sequestered section of a great American seaport. I was a regular student at Reveille's stable in Stricker Street from the beginning of my seventh year to the end of my nonage, and a special student at

Coblens's stable in Paca Street, off and on, for most of the same period, but so far as I can recall I never heard a word uttered in either of them, or beheld any human act, transaction, or phenomenon, that might not have been repeated before a bench of archbishops.

On the contrary, they were both schools of decorum, operated by proud and even haughty men, and staffed by blackamoors of a generally high tone. No palpably dipsomaniacal or larcenous coon could survive more than a few days in any such establishment. There were too many valuable horses and rigs on hand to be trusted to the former, and too many valuable carriage robes, buggy whips, hassocks, etc., to be exposed to the latter. My father's No. 1 whip, hung up by the snapper in Mr. Reveille's office, had a gold band around the handle engraved with the insigne of the Ancient Arabic Order of Nobles of the Mystic Shrine, and in Mr. Coblens's office, where my father commonly kept his No. 2 whip, there was also a buffalo robe that he set great store by, although I should add that its hair had pretty well played out, and that after his death I gave it freely to the poor.

Mr. Coblens was a man of erect bearing, reserved manner, and great dignity. He wore none of the loud checks associated with his vocation, but was always clad in plain colors, and not infrequently appeared in a black cutaway. His only concession to the public expectation was a gray derby, very high in the crown. If you can imagine a Jewish colonel of a swagger cavalry regiment, then you have got him to the life. My father had a high regard for him, and often paused to discuss horses with him — a subject about which he knew everything and my father next to nothing. Mr. Coblens seldom descended from his heights to speak to my brother or me. He knew us very well and would indicate by a vague flicker of his eyes that he was aware of our presence, but it was not often that he said anything.

His cousin Felix was a far more cordial fellow. Felix was a bachelor in those days, and apparently a somewhat gay one, for more than once I saw him set out of an afternoon in a buggy shining like a hundred-dollar coffin, with sometimes a blonde lady beside him and sometimes a brunette. My brother and I, boylike, regarded his ease and success at gallantry with great respect. He was, indeed, one of our heroes, and also one of our friends. He was never too busy to explain to us, with the use of living models paraded by his blackamoors, the points of a harness horse, and he also had illuminating ideas about buggy architecture. When I was eight years old and my brother six, my father gave us a pony named Frank, and it was Mr. Felix who taught us how to handle it — no mean art, I assure you, for Shetland ponies not only kick like mules but also bite like dogs, and no doubt would scratch like cats if they had claws. To this day I have a scar on my bosom, often passing for a war wound, that proves how effectively Frank could use his teeth.

In 1890 or thereabout my father traded two cases of leaf tobacco and a Swiss repeater watch for a gelding bearing the strange name (for a horse) of John. John was a trotter, and supposedly of some speed in harness, but my father could never get it out of him. The two did so badly together, indeed, that my father concluded that John must have rheumatism, and thereafter, for a year or so, the poor beast was the patient of a veterinarian who sent in large bottles of a fiery, suffocating liniment and even larger bills, but never did John any good. Mr. Felix, it appeared, had suspected all the while that the trouble was predominantly in the driver rather than in the horse, and eventually he volunteered to go out with my father some afternoon and make a scientific review of his driving. He returned downcast. "Your pa," he said to me the next time I dropped in, "is hopeless. It would take him two or three hundred years to learn to drive a cart horse, let alone a trotter. He holds the lines like a man dealing cards. If he ever got John to really stepping, he would fall out of the buggy and break his neck."

A few days later, as if reminded by conscience that he might have been hasty in dismissing his duty to the family, he amazed and delighted me by offering to give *me* a few lessons. It was a colossal opportunity to a boy of eleven, for Mr. Felix was an eminent figure in the trotting world of Baltimore and seldom condescended to pedagogy. I had, as I recall it, only four or five lessons, but when they were over, Mr. Felix was so complimentary that I developed on the spot a complacency which still survives after nearly fifty years, protecting me like an undershirt of concrete from the contumely of mankind. Indeed, he said flatly, and I believe he meant it, that I had in me the makings of a really smart harness driver. "By the time you begin to shave," he concluded, "you'll be showing 'em."

By that time, alas, I had turned from equestrology to chemistry, and a little while later I abandoned chemistry (to my sneaking regret on many a rainy day) for the kind of beautiful letters on tap in newspaper offices. But for two or three years I drove John every day, and so gradually improved and mellowed my technique. On summer afternoons, when my father and I were driving home to the country, and the clomp-clomp of a trotter's scissoring hooves began to sound behind us on the Pimlico Road, he would silently hand me the reins and settle back to be torn between parental pride and personal humiliation. I seemed to hear him groan now and then, but he never said anything. When John, who was really very fast, had left the other nag behind, and the brush was over, my father would quietly revive his cigar with a few sad puffs and resume the reins. He never complimented me: it would have been ruinous to his dignity as a harness driver. Despite the unction to my vanity that flowed out of these episodes, there was also melancholy in them, and they implanted in me a lifelong conviction that children, taking one day with another, must de damned pests.

It was not the Coblens stable, however, but the Reveille stable that was my chief haunt in boyhood. The Coblens stable was downtown near my father's place of business; the Reveille stable was only two blocks from our home on Hollins Street. My brother and I spent many happy hours there, watching the blackamoors currying and feeding the horses, plaiting their tails, excavating and blacking their hooves, dosing them with Glauber's salts and condition powders, and treating their lampas (pronounced "lampers") with red-hot pokers. This last was a horrifying spectacle, for lampas is an overgrowth of tissue behind the upper incisor teeth, and burning it out involved thrusting the poker into the poor horse's gaping mouth. But I learned before long that horses have very little sense of pain, if indeed any at all; and years afterward I saw one, with a leg cut off by a trolley car, munching the grass between the cobblestones as it lay on a Baltimore street, waiting for a cop to shoot it.

Mr. Reveille was a Frenchman who seemed venerable and even ancient to my brother and me, for he wore a straggling beard and always had on a black coat. He had two grown sons, both stout and hearty fellows, but like their father, very dignified. There was a period when both the trotter John and our pony Frank were quartered in the Reveille stable, along with two buggies, a pony cart, and several other rigs, so my brother and I had plenty of excuse for hanging about. The Reveilles always welcomed us gravely, and let us warm up, in winter, in their tiny office, which was so filled with robes that there was scarcely room for the stove, always verging on white-hot. We admired especially the rack of whips, which included some virtuoso pieces by the Baltimore master craftsmen of the time. A good whip might cost as much as $25. We figured that the whole lot must be worth at least $1,000, and toyed for a while with a plan to break in some dark night, smouch them all, sell them to the cattleherders at the Calverton stockyards, and go West with the proceeds to fight the Indians. What the herders would do with puny buggy whips we never paused to figure out. In the end, we abandoned the scheme as probably unlawful.

The colored brethren who pontificated at Reveille's have all faded, with the flight of the years, into a brown smudge — all, that is, save Old Jim. Jim was the carriage-washer, and a fellow of vast size and unparalleled amiability.

He was coal-black and built like a battleship, and when he got into his hip-high rubber boots and put on his long rubber apron he had the imposing presence of an emperor in Hell. Jim's atelier was a skylighted space at the rear of the carriage house, paved with cobblestones and always flowing with water. He got to work at six in the morning, and was sometimes still going hard at nine at night. He had the care of fifty or more buggies, and of perhaps as many other vehicles, and he kept them clean and shining. His hardest time came on Sunday morning, when he had to wash and polish all the buggies in preparation for the pleasure jaunts of the afternoon. For this business he brought out his newest sponges and cleanest chamois skins. Also, he put on a black derby, never worn on weekdays.

In the intervals of his washing and polishing, Jim took out rigs to the homes of clients of the stable, and thereby sometimes acquired quiet brannigans, for it was the custom to reward him not with money but with drinks. My father kept a special jug for the purpose. It was shared by the iceman, but Jim got most of it, for in view of his great bulk he was given a much larger drink than the iceman. He always downed it at a gulp, and after it was down he would blink his eyes, rub his belly, and say "Ah-h-h-h-h!" This ritual was a Baltimore custom of the time, practiced by most of the nobility and gentry and imitated by serving

189

folk. Sometimes Jim also got a cigar. He would light it at once and stalk back to Reveille's smoking it at an angle of forty-five degrees. Smoking was forbidden to the faculty at the stable and when he reached there he would choke it carefully and deposit it on a high ledge in the brick wall. Some of its other members had sharp eyes for likely stumps and the cigar was out of their reach there, but not out of his.

My brother and I greatly admired Jim, and delighted in watching him at work. He had a way of spinning buggy wheels that was really magnificent, and he worked with larger sponges and broader chamois skins than any other carriage-washer in West Baltimore. The buggies of those days all had carpets, and when there was nothing else to do he would get out a dozen or so of them and beat them. Sometimes he would find a nickel or a dime under one of them. It always went into his pocket, for it was the theory among the colored proletariat of Baltimore in those days that whatever a white person lost or mislaid he really didn't want. If he wanted it, he would ask for it, and probably raise hell about it. Jim's income from this source was not large, for he found a great many more pins than nickels. He always laid them aside and then threw them into the manure pit, for a pin in the frog of a horse's hoof might bring on calamity.

One day my brother and I were astonished to

find Jim missing; it seemed almost as strange as finding Mr. Reveille missing, or the stable itself. His *locum tenens*, a short, spotty colored man named Browny, ordinarily a hostler, told us the sad news. Jim's youngest son, a youth of sixteen, had been blown up by an explosion in a one-horse soda-pop factory up a nearby alley, and Jim was off for the day, arranging for the interment of the few fragments that had been recovered. We had never heard of this son, but we were full of sympathy, and when Jim returned we tried to tell him so in the shy manner of boys. He replied that it was God's deliberate act and will, and that he did not repine. The son, he added judicially, was not really bad, at least as sons went in an age of moral chaos, but nevertheless there was some worry in him, for now and then, like any other high-spirited colored boy, he got into trouble with the cops, and when that wasn't going on he wasted his substance on trashy yallah gals. Now he was far, far away, riding some cloud or rainbow, and hence safe from the hangman forever. He had even escaped, by the unusual manner of his death, the body-snatchers.

Two or three days later we saw a brisk-looking white man in a short yellow overcoat talking to Jim, and the day following, Jim again disappeared. We heard from Browny that the brisk-looking man was a lawyer and that the talk had been of damages. Another talk, he said, was proceeding downtown. Jim was gone a week, and then suddenly reappeared, but not to resume work. He showed up one morning in a stovepipe hat and a long-tailed black coat, carrying an ebony cane with a bone head in the shape of a horse with widely distended nostrils tinted red, and green gems for eyes. His right-hand coat pocket was bulging with at least a quarter's worth of peanuts, and he invited all his old colleagues to thrust in their paws and help themselves. In his other coat pocket he had half a dozen apples for horses he especially liked, including our pony Frank but not the trotter John, and in the hand unburdened by the cane he carried a two-pound bag of lump sugar. In all four pockets of his white waistcoat were rows of five-cent cigars, standing up like cartridges in a belt. He offered the cigars freely and recommended them as the best in West Baltimore. He even offered one to Mr. Peter Reveille. His hip pockets were stuffed with chewing tobacco.

Such was Jim in the full tide of his bereavement. Mr. Peter Reveille told us that the lawyer had offered Jim $250, but that he had stuck out for $300, and got it. He let it be known that he had demanded the money in one-dollar bills, but where he kept them we didn't know until later. Some of the hostlers were of the opinion that he had sneaked into the stable loft by night and hidden them in the hay, and for a week or so a vain search for them went on. Browny insisted that they were in Jim's stovepipe hat. He knew, as all of us knew, that policemen always kept their valuables in their helmets; ergo, why not Jim? But this theory blew up when Jim dropped in, a week or so later, without his hat and complaining that two bad niggers from Boot Alley had knocked it off with clubs and run away with it. The hat was gone, but Jim continued in funds for a long while afterward — indeed, for fully a month. He visited the stable almost daily, and never failed to distribute cigars, peanuts, and chewing tobacco, with sugar and apples for the horses. He appeared, at different times, in no less than five hats, and was often mildly in liquor. But he never brought any liquor on the premises, and so the Reveilles, who had a large experience with the darker races, tolerated him patiently.

They knew that he would be back in his long boots and rubber apron soon or late, and he was. One morning early they found him at work, somewhat trembly and with a cut over his left eye, but otherwise as he had been in the days before wealth corrupted him. He had not been seen during the preceding week, and for a while his final adventures were unknown, for neither then nor thereafter did he ever mention them. But the other colored men gradually assembled and disgorged the story, and the cop on the beat helped out with a fact or two. It was really very simple. Jim, a decent widower, had been ganged and undone by the massed yallah gals of three alleys. They had all tackled him singly and failed, but when they tackled him in a body he succumbed.

The ensuing party raged for four days and four nights, with continuous music by banjos, mouth organs, and bones. It began in a little saloon that was the G.H.Q. of one of the alleys, but gradually spread over the whole block, and ended at last in a loft over an empty stable. There was no hint whatever of carnality; the thing was purely alcoholic. After the first few hours each of the yallah gals sent for her regular fellow, and beginning with the second day, all sorts of gate-crashers barged in. Thereafter there was a flow in and a flow out. Every hour or two some guest would collapse and roll home, and another would make the gate. Only Jim himself and a yallah gal named Mildred survived for more than forty-eight hours. Mildred, on the last day, was in the first stages of *mania à potu*, and the cop on the beat, looking in, ordered her off the job, but Jim was still going strong.

Alas, he didn't go long, for a little while later the saloonkeeper's son Otto came in to say that time was called on the party. Otto and his brother Hermann had been hauling booze for it for four days and four nights and both were badly used up. Hermann, in fact, had had to be put to bed. But it wasn't fatigue that made Otto call time; it was the fact that Jim's last dollar bill had been devoured. The father of Otto and Hermann was known to be a determined man, with the cops always on his side, so no one questioned the fiat. One by one, they simply faded away, leaving only Jim. He rolled himself in his long-tailed coat and lay down to a prodigal's dreams. He slept all the rest of that day and all of the ensuing night to 5 A.M. Then he shuffled off to Reveille's stable and resumed his station in life.

It was not until long afterward that my brother and I learned where Jim had kept his fortune while it oozed away. Mr. Reveille, worming the story out of the blackamoors, told my father, who told it to a neighbor, Mr. Glaser, whose boy Harold, lurking about, overheard the telling and brought it to us. The money had been in the care and custody of the saloonkeeper all the while. He doled it out to Jim dollar by dollar, marking the score on a blackboard behind his bar. He charged Jim a dollar a day "interest" for keeping it. When the final orgies began, he charged a dollar for every day and a dollar for every night.

The Glaser boy reported that, in telling about this "interest," my father swore in a hair-raising manner. He had, in fact, little use for saloonkeepers. He would often say that while he knew and respected some upright men among them, only too many were disgraces to a humane and even noble profession.

How to Swat a Fly

Will Cuppy

Being as sound in mind and body as I am ever likely to be, I have decided to release my notes on Fly-swatting made from time to time during many years of active service at my Long Island beach cottage, Chez Cuppy. (It's the same old place I used to call Tobacco Road, but I think the new name sort of lends a tone — and, besides, it's a change.) In the belief that Fly-swatting is here to stay for awhile, DDT and other squirts to the contrary notwithstanding, I am passing on the torch in Ten Easy Lessons, as follows:

1. Get set. Be sure you're not going to fall off your chair backwards in the act of swatting. Here as elsewhere, style is everything.

2. Still, don't take too much time with the preliminaries. The Fly won't wait there forever. He has other things to do with his time.

3. Try to ascertain in some unobtrusive way whether the object you're after is actually a Fly

or a nail head, such as often occurs in the woodwork of country homes. Don't go poking at the thing to see which it is. When in doubt, swat.

Little situations like this are bound to occur in every swatter's routine. For instance, there is a small black spot on the ceiling of my bedroom that has embarrassed me dozens of times, it looks so exactly like a Fly of some large and vicious species. If I have crept up on it once — Oh, well! Stalking an imperfection in the paint and swinging one's heart out at a nail head are not things one likes to remember, but perhaps they have their place in the give and take of daily living. We can't be heroes to ourselves every instant.

4. In any case, never flirt your swatter back and forth past a Fly before swatting, expecting to get him your next time around. When you finally make up your mind to hit him, he will not be there. The Fly who hesitates is lost. He knows this and acts accordingly.

5. Take aim quickly but carefully. A complete miss is not good for the morale, either yours or the Fly's.

6. If possible, fix him with the first swat. Failure to do so may be serious. For one thing, you didn't get him. That alone is bad. Secondly, conditions will never be quite the same again, since you are now dealing with an alert and disillusioned Fly. He is never going to trust you as he did before. He will avoid

you in future.

That was one of the many faults of my dear Aunt Etta's swatting. She never hit her Fly the first time and she seldom came anywhere near him on repeated attempts, partly because she employed that worst of all swatting techniques, the folded newspaper, or slow motion, method. She would lunge at the Fly again and yet again with her antiquated weapon in a free-for-all that left her exhausted and the Fly in the best of health and spirits. A folded newspaper is only about 17 per cent efficient in anybody's hands, and Aunt Etta's form was nothing to boast of. Her batting average must have been something incredible. I'm glad to state that she often thought she had won. Her eyesight wasn't so good, either.

I assure you that Aunt Etta was one of the kindest persons I have ever known though not so soft about Flies as my Uncle Toby, who did so much in his day to encourage the spread of typhoid fever and other diseases. There was certainly no sadistic urge in her swatting activities. She never engaged a Fly in hand-to-hand combat until after she and we children had staged a ceremonious Fly-drive with kitchen aprons and dish towels, then a second and often a third to chase the last one out the open screen door. It was only the Fly or Flies who failed to respect these rites that she tackled, and it always amazed me that there would be any such. If we thought Aunt Etta had one of her headaches, or felt a nap coming on, or couldn't stand such a racket — in which case she would tell us so in no uncertain terms — we disappeared. We vanished utterly, with the usual gift of cookies. But Flies are not brought up that way, apparently. They cannot take a hint.

The family would want me to add that Aunt Etta's house was no more Fly-ridden than any other home of the period. In fact, it was less so than most, as it was thoroughly screened. Which reminds me that she never did, to my knowledge, solve the riddle of how they got in. She was always saying there wasn't a crack where they could squeeze through. All right, then, how did the Mouse get in?

7. Don't mind a little incidental breakage around the house. Aunt Etta was much too careful of her bric-a-brac. She wouldn't strike within yards of her whatnot when a Fly took sanctuary there. For the cause I would smash anything in Chez Cuppy to smithereens, except possibly my shaving mirror. I'm not having seven years of bad luck for any Fly.

8. Cultivate patience. It is a beautiful thing in itself, and when you are after a Fly who will not light, you will need it. Eventually that Fly will light, and ten to one it will be in some dark, inaccessible corner, down behind the stove.

The Fly who absolutely refuses to settle is a problem for advanced swatters, and not an easy one. Talk about a watched pot! Do not stalk such a Fly too openly, but try to act as though you were interested in something else altogether. This involves looking wall-eyed at the Fly while gazing fixedly in the other direction, but it can be done, with practice. It is my opinion that a Fly will not settle while you are looking straight at him with a swatter in your fist. At any rate, he won't while you are following him around the room, making passes at him. Believe me, he knows what you are up to.

I would go so far as to say that a Fly knows the exact moment when you start looking for a swatter, if you should be caught without one. Edge yourself ever so casually in the general direction of a swatter, and notice what happens. Other persons who may be present will simply wonder why you are hitching your chair along in that insane fashion or tiptoeing across the room with one groping hand outstretched and a haunted look in your eyes. They won't have the faintest notion of what goes on, but the Fly will. He has already figured out his first five moves and several of yours.

This does not necessarily prove that the Fly is more intelligent than you are. If such things could be measured — and they will be, some day — I have little doubt that you, gentle swatter, would be found to have a higher I.Q. than the average Fly. You may be slow on the uptake, while the Fly is unbelievably fast. His sheer brilliance in planning and executing maneuvers of every sort on the ground and in the air amounts to genius, and you have all you can do to keep from falling over your feet. You cannot make quick decisions, or, if you do, you are generally dead wrong, as everybody at the office knows but yourself. The Fly's decisions are mostly right. They have to be.

Yet on the whole, taking it by and large, and allowing for individual exceptions, you are smarter that the Fly. You know more than he does about more things. Above all, you possess the power of abstract reasoning, a faculty which distinguishes mankind from the merely brute creation, such as Flies. You can listen to the radio, look at television, and go to the movies. You can read mystery stories and try to guess who done it. Keep your chin up and always remember that if you are not the Fly's superior in every single respect one might mention, you are at least his equal, mentally. Since you are fighting on practically even terms, then, when you are after a Fly who will not light you must seek for a flaw in his intellectual equipment if you hope to regain the initiative, and I can help you there. The key is his imperfect memory. You can remember as far back as yesterday. The Fly cannot. He forgets. The particular Fly of whom we were speaking will be out of his dark corner in a few brief moments, and you can begin the whole show all over again.

9. Check up on yourself occasionally. Ask yourself, "Am I a better swatter than I was last

year?" The correct answer is No.

10.   Don't be discouraged at a few failures. I don't always get them myself, but I give them pause. It makes 'em think.

Butch Minds the Baby

Damon Runyon

One evening along about seven o'clock I am sitting in Mindy's restaurant putting on the gefillte fish, which is a dish I am very fond of, when in comes three parties from Brooklyn wearing caps as follows: Harry the Horse, Little Isadore and Spanish John.

Now these parties are not such parties as I will care to have much truck with, because I often hear rumors about them that are very discreditable, even if the rumors are not true. In fact, I hear that many citizens of Brooklyn will be very glad indeed to see Harry the Horse, Little Isadore and Spanish John move away from there, as they are always doing something that is considered a knock to the community, such as robbing people, or maybe shooting or stabbing them, and throwing pineapples, and carrying on generally.

I am really much surprised to see these parties on Broadway, as it is well known that the Broadway coppers just naturally love to shove such parties around, but here they are in Mindy's, and there I am, so of course I give them a very large hello, as I never wish to seem inhospitable, even to Brooklyn parties. Right away they come over to my table and sit down, and Little Isadore reaches out and spears himself a big hunk of my gefillte fish with his fingers, but I overlook this, as I am using the only knife on the table.

Then they all sit there looking at me without saying anything, and the way they look at me makes me very nervous indeed. Finally I figure that maybe they are a little embarrassed being in a high-class spot such as Mindy's, with legitimate people around and about, so I say to them, very polite: "It is a nice night."

"What is nice about it?" asks Harry the Horse, who is a thin man with a sharp face and sharp eyes.

Well, now that it is put up to me in this way, I can see there is nothing so nice about the night, at that, so I try to think of something else jolly to say, while Little Isadore keeps spearing at my gefillte fish with his fingers, and Spanish John nabs one of my potatoes.

"Where does Big Butch live?" Harry the Horse asks.

"Big Butch?" I say, as if I never hear the name before in my life, because in this man's town it is never a good idea to answer any question without thinking it over, as some time you may give the right answer to the wrong guy, or the wrong answer to the right guy. "Where does Big Butch live?" I ask them again.

"Yes, where does he live?" Harry the Horse says, very impatient. "We wish you to take us to him."

"Now wait a minute, Harry," I say, and I am now more nervous than somewhat. "I am not sure I remember the exact house Big Butch lives in, and furthermore I am not sure Big Butch will care to have me bringing people to see him, especially three at a time, and especially from Brooklyn. You know Big Butch has a very bad disposition, and there is no telling what he may say to me if he does not like the idea of me taking you to him."

"Everything is very kosher," Harry the Horse says. "You need not be afraid of anything whatever. We have a business proposition for Big Butch. It means a nice score for him, so you take us to him at once, or the chances are I will have to put the arm on somebody around here."

Well, as the only one around there for him to put the arm on at this time seems to be me, I can see where it will be good policy for me to take these parties to Big Butch, especially as the last of my gefillte fish is just going down Little Isadore's gullet, and Spanish John is finishing up my potatoes, and is dunking a piece of rye bread in my coffee, so there is nothing more for me to eat.

So I lead them over into West Forty-ninth

Street, near Tenth Avenue, where Big Butch
lives on the ground floor of an old brownstone-
front house, and who is sitting out on the stoop
but Big Butch himself. In fact, everybody in
the neighborhood is sitting out on the front
stoops over there, including women and children, because sitting out on the front stoops is
quite a custom in this section.

Big Butch is peeled down to his undershirt
and pants, and he has no shoes on his feet, as
Big Butch is a guy who likes his comfort.
Furthermore, he is smoking a cigar, and laid
out on the stoop beside him on a blanket is a
little baby with not much clothes on. This baby
seems to be asleep, and every now and then
Big Butch fans it with a folded newspaper to
shoo away the mosquitoes that wish to nibble
on the baby. These mosquitoes come across the
river from the Jersey side on hot nights and
they seem to be very fond of babies.

"Hello, Butch," I say, as we stop in front of
the stoop.

"Sh-h-h-h!" Butch says, pointing at the baby,
and making more noise with his shush than an
engine blowing off steam. Then he gets up and
tiptoes down to the sidewalk where we are
standing, and I am hoping that Butch feels all
right, because when Butch does not feel so
good he is apt to be very short with one and
all. He is a guy of maybe six foot two and a
couple of feet wide, and he has big hairy hands
and a mean look.

In fact, Big Butch is known all over this man's town as a guy you must not monkey with in any respect, so it takes plenty of weight off of me when I see that he seems to know the parties from Brooklyn, and nods at them very friendly, especially at Harry the Horse. And right away Harry states a most surprising proposition to Big Butch.

It seems that there is a big coal company which has an office in an old building down in West Eighteenth Street, and in this office is a safe, and in this safe is the company pay roll of twenty thousand dollars cash money. Harry the Horse knows the money is there because a personal friend of his who is the paymaster for the company puts it there late this very afternoon.

It seems that the paymaster enters into a dicker with Harry the Horse and Little Isadore and Spanish John for them to slug him while he is carrying the pay roll from the bank to the office in the afternoon, but something happens that they miss connections on the exact spot, so the paymaster has to carry the sugar on to the office without being slugged, and there it is now in two fat bundles.

Personally it seems to me as I listen to Harry's story that the paymaster must be a very dishonest character to be making deals to hold still while he is being slugged and the company's sugar taken away from him, but of course it is none of my business, so I take no part in the conversation.

Well, it seems that Harry the Horse and Little Isadore and Spanish John wish to get the money out of the safe, but none of them knows anything about opening safes, and while they are standing around over in Brooklyn talking over what is to be done in this emergency Harry suddenly remembers that Big Butch is once in the business of opening safes for a living.

In fact, I hear afterwards that Big Butch is considered the best safe opener east of the Mississippi River in his day, but the law finally takes to sending him to Sing Sing for opening these safes, and after he is in and out of Sing Sing three different times for opening safes Butch gets sick and tired of the place, especially as they pass what is called the Baumes Law in New York, which is a law that says if a guy is sent to Sing Sing four times hand running, he must stay there for the rest of his life, without any argument about it.

So Big Butch gives up opening safes for a living, and goes into business in a small way, such as running beer, and handling a little Scotch now and then, and becomes an honest citizen. Furthermore, he marries one of the neighbor's children over on the West Side by the name of Mary Murphy, and I judge the baby on this stoop comes of this marriage between Big Butch and Mary because I can see that it is a very homely baby, indeed. Still, I never see many babies that I consider rose geraniums for looks, anyway.

Well, it finally comes out that the idea of Harry the Horse and Little Isadore and Spanish John is to get Big Butch to open the coal company's safe and take the payroll money out, and they are willing to give him fifty percent of the money for his bother, taking fifty percent for themselves for finding the plant, and paying all the overhead, such as the paymaster, out of their bit, which strikes me as a pretty fair sort of deal for Big Butch. But Butch only shakes his head.

"It is old-fashioned stuff," Butch says. "Nobody opens pete boxes for a living any more. They make the boxes too good, and they are all wired up with alarms and are a lot of trouble generally. I am in a legitimate business now and going along. You boys know I cannot stand another fall, what with being away three times already, and in addition to this I must mind the baby. My old lady goes to Mrs. Clancy's wake tonight up in the Bronx, and the chances are she will be there all night, as she is very fond of wakes, so I must mind little John Ignatius Junior."

"Listen, Butch," Harry the Horse says, "this is a very soft pete. It is old-fashioned, and you can open it with a toothpick. There are no wires on it, because they never put more than a dime in it before in years. It just happens they have to put the twenty G's in it tonight because my pal the paymaster makes it a point not to get back from the jug with the scratch in time to pay off today, especially after he sees we miss out on him. It is the softest touch you will ever know, and where can a guy pick up ten G's like this?"

I can see that Big Butch is thinking the ten G's over very seriously, at that, because in these times nobody can afford to pass up ten G's, especially a guy in the beer business, which is very, very tough just now. But finally he shakes his head again and says like this:

"No," he says, "I must let it go, because I must mind the baby. My old lady is very, very particular about this, and I dast not leave little John Ignatius Junior for a minute. If Mary comes home and finds I am not minding the baby she will put the blast on me plenty. I like to turn a few honest bobs now and then as well as anybody, but," Butch says, "John Ignatius Junior comes first with me."

Then he turns away and goes back to the stoop as much as to say he is through arguing, and sits down beside John Ignatius Junior again just in time to keep a mosquito from carrying off one of John's legs. Anybody can see that Big Butch is very fond of this baby, though personally I will not give you a dime a dozen for babies, male and female.

Well, Harry the Horse and Little Isadore and Spanish John are very much disappointed, and stand around talking among themselves, and paying no attention to me, when all of a sudden

Spanish John, who never has much to say up to this time, seems to have a bright idea. He talks to Harry and Isadore, and they get all pleasured up over what he has to say, and finally Harry goes to Big Butch.

"Sh-h-h-h!" Big Butch says, pointing to the baby as Harry opens his mouth.

"Listen, Butch," Harry says in a whisper, "we can take the baby with us, and you can mind it and work, too."

"Why," Big Butch whispers back, "this is quite an idea indeed. Let us go into the house and talk things over."

So he picks up the baby and leads us into his joint, and gets out some pretty fair beer, though it is needled a little, at that, and we sit around the kitchen chewing the fat in whispers. There is a crib in the kitchen, and Butch puts the baby in his crib, and it keeps on snoozing away first rate while we are talking. In fact, it is sleeping so sound that I am commencing to figure that Butch must give it some of the needled beer he is feeding us, because I am feeling a little dopey myself.

Finally Butch says that as long as he can take John Ignatius Junior with him he sees no reason why he shall not go and open the safe for them, only he says he must have five percent more to put in the baby's bank when he gets back, so as to round himself up with his ever-loving wife in case of a beef from her over keeping the baby out in the night air. Harry the Horse says he considers this extra five percent a little strong, but Spanish John, who seems to be a very square guy, says that after all it is only fair to cut the baby in if it is to be with them when they are making the score, and Little Isadore seems to think this is all right, too. So Harry the Horse gives in, and says five percent it is.

Well, as they do not wish to start out until after midnight, and as there is plenty of time, Big Butch gets out some more needled beer, and then he goes looking for the tools with which he opens safes, and which he says he does not see since the day John Ignatius Junior is born, and he gets them out to build the crib.

Now this is a good time for me to bid one and all farewell, and what keeps me there is something I cannot tell you to this day, because personally I never before have any idea of taking part in a safe opening, especially with a baby, as I consider such actions very dishonorable. When I come to think things over afterwards, the only thing I can figure is the needled beer, but I wish to say I am really very much surprised at myself when I find myself in a taxicab along about one o'clock in the morning with these Brooklyn parties and Big Butch and the baby.

Butch has John Ignatius Junior rolled up in a blanket, and John is still pounding his ear. Butch has a satchel of tools, and what looks to me like a big flat book, and just before we leave the house Butch hands me a package and tells me to be very careful with it. He gives Little Isadore a smaller package, which Isadore shoves into his pistol pocket, and when Isadore sits down in the taxi something goes wa-wa, like a sheep, and Big Butch becomes very indignant because it seems Isadore is sitting on John Ignatius Junior's doll, which says "Mamma" when you squeeze it.

It seems Big Butch figures that John Ignatius Junior may wish something to play with in case he wakes up, and it is a good thing for Little Isadore that the mamma doll is not squashed so it cannot say "Mamma" any more, or the chances are Little Isadore will get a good bust in the snoot.

We let the taxicab go a block away from the spot we are headed for in West Eighteenth Street, between Seventh and Eighth Avenues, and walk the rest of the way two by two. I walk with Big Butch, carrying my package, and Butch is lugging the baby and his satchel and the flat thing that looks like a book. It is so quiet down in West Eighteenth Street at such an hour that you can hear yourself think, and in fact I hear myself thinking very plain that I am a big sap to be on a job like this, especially with a baby, but I keep going just the same, which shows you what a very big sap I am, indeed.

There are very few people in West Eighteenth Street when we get there, and one of them is a fat guy who is leaning against a building almost in the center of the block, and who takes a walk for himself as soon as he sees us. It seems that this fat guy is the watchman at the coal company's office and is also a personal friend of Harry the Horse, which is why he takes the walk when he sees us coming.

It is agreed before we leave Big Butch's house that Harry the Horse and Spanish John are to stay outside the place as lookouts, while Big Butch is inside opening the safe, and that Little Isadore is to go with Butch. Nothing whatever is said by anybody about where I am to be at any time, and I can see that, no matter where I am, I will still be an outsider, but, as Butch gives me the package to carry, I figure he wishes me to remain with him.

It is no bother at all getting into the office of the coal company, which is on the ground floor, because it seems the watchman leaves the front door open, this watchman being a most obliging guy, indeed. In fact he is so obliging that by and by he comes back and lets Harry the Horse and Spanish John tie him up good and tight, and stick a handkerchief in his mouth and chuck him in an areaway next to the office, so nobody will think he has anything to do with opening the safe in case anybody comes around asking.

The office looks out on the street, and the safe that Harry the Horse and Little Isadore and Spanish John wish Big Butch to open is standing up against the rear wall of the office facing the street windows. There is one little electric light burning very dim over the safe so that when anybody walks past the place outside, such as a watchman, they can look in through the window and see the safe at all times, unless they are blind. It is not a tall safe, and it is not a big safe, and I can see Big Butch grin when he sees it, so I figure this safe is not much of a safe, just as Harry the Horse claims.

Well, as soon as Big Butch and the baby and Little Isadore and me get into the office, Big Butch steps over to the safe and unfolds what I think is the big flat book, and what is it but a sort of screen painted on one side to look exactly like the front of a safe. Big Butch stands this screen up on the floor in front of the real safe, leaving plenty of space in between, the idea being that the screen will keep anyone passing in the street outside from seeing Butch while he is opening the safe, because when a man is opening a safe he needs all the privacy he can get.

Big Butch lays John Ignatius Junior down on the floor on the blanket behind the phony safe front and takes his tools out of the satchel and starts to work opening the safe, while Little Isadore and me get back in a corner where it is dark, because there is not room for all of us back of the screen. However, we can see what Big Butch is doing, and I wish to say while I never before see a professional safe opener at work, and never wish to see another, this Butch handles himself like a real artist.

He starts drilling into the safe around the combination lock, working very fast and very quiet, when all of a sudden what happens but John Ignatius Junior sits up on the blanket and lets out a squall. Naturally this is most disquieting to me, and personally I am in favor of beaning John Ignatius Junior with something to make him keep still, because I am nervous enough as it is. But the squalling does not seem to bother Big Butch. He lays down his tools and picks up John Ignatius Junior and starts whispering, "There, there, there, my itty oddleums. Da-dad is here."

Well, this sounds very nonsensical to me in such a situation, and it makes no impression whatever on John Ignatius Junior. He keeps on squalling, and I judge he is squalling pretty loud because I see Harry the Horse and Spanish John both walk past the window and look in very anxious. Big Butch jiggles John Ignatius Junior up and down and keeps whispering baby talk to him, which sounds very undignified coming from a high-class safe opener, and finally Butch whispers to me to hand him the package I am carrying.

He opens the package, and what is in it but a baby's nursing bottle full of milk. Moreover, there is a little tin stew pan, and Butch hands the pan to me and whispers to me to find a water tap somewhere in the joint and fill the

216

pan with water. So I go stumbling around in the dark in a room behind the office and bark my shins several times before I find a tap and fill the pan. I take it back to Big Butch, and he squats there with the baby on one arm, and gets a tin of what is called canned heat out of the package, and lights this canned heat with his cigar lighter, and starts heating the pan of water with the nursing bottle in it.

Big Butch keeps sticking his finger in the pan of water while it is heating, and by and by he puts the rubber nipple of the nursing bottle in his mouth and takes a pull at it to see if the milk is warm enough, just like I see dolls who have babies do. Apparently the milk is okay, as Butch hands the bottle to John Ignatius Junior, who grabs hold of it with both hands and starts sucking on the business end. Naturally he has to stop squalling, and Big Butch goes to work on the safe again, with John Ignatius Junior sitting on the blanket, pulling on the bottle and looking wiser than a treeful of owls.

It seems the safe is either a tougher job than anybody figures, or Big Butch's tools are not so good, what with being old and rusty and used for building baby cribs, because he breaks a couple of drills and works himself up into quite a sweat without getting anywhere. Butch afterwards explains to me that he is one of the first guys in this country to open safes without explosives, but he says to do this work properly you have to know the safes so as to drill to the tumblers of the lock just right, and it seems that this particular safe is a new type to him, even if it is old, and he is out of practice.

Well, in the meantime John Ignatius Junior finishes his bottle and starts mumbling again, and Big Butch gives him a tool to play with, and finally Butch needs this tool and tries to take it away from John Ignatius Junior, and the baby lets out such a squawk that Butch has to let him keep it until he can sneak it away from him, and this causes more delay.

Finally Big Butch gives up trying to drill the safe open, and he whispers to us that he will have to put a little shot in it to loosen up the lock, which is all right with us, because we are getting tired of hanging around and listening to John Ignatius Junior's glug-glugging. As far as I am personally concerned, I am wishing I am home in bed.

Well, Butch starts pawing through his satchel looking for something and it seems that what he is looking for is a little bottle of some kind of explosive with which to shake the lock on the safe up some, and at first he cannot find this bottle, but finally he discovers that John Ignatius Junior has it and is gnawing at the cork, and Butch has quite a battle making John Ignatius Junior give it up.

Anyway, he fixes the explosive in one of the holes he drills near the combination lock on the safe, and then he puts in a fuse, and just before he touches off the fuse Butch picks up John Ignatius Junior and hands him to Little Isadore, and tells us to go into the room behind the office. John Ignatius Junior does not seem to care for Little Isadore, and I do not blame him, at that, because he starts to squirm around quite some in Isadore's arms and lets out a squall, but all of a sudden he becomes very quiet indeed, and, while I am not able to prove it, something tells me that Little Isadore has his hand over John Ignatius Junior's mouth.

Well, Big Butch joins us right away in the back room, and sound comes out of John Ignatius Junior again as Butch takes him from Little Isadore, and I am thinking that it a good thing for Isadore that the baby cannot tell Big Butch what Isadore does to him.

"I put in just a little bit of a shot," Big Butch says, "and it will not make any more noise than snapping your fingers."

But a second later there is a big whoom from the office, and the whole joint shakes, and John Ignatius Junior laughs right out loud. The chances are he thinks it is the Fourth of July.

"I guess maybe I put in too big a charge," Big Butch says, and then he rushes into the office with Little Isadore and me after him, and John Ignatius Junior still laughing very heartily for a small baby. The door of the safe is swinging loose, and the whole joint looks somewhat wrecked, but Big Butch loses no time in getting his dukes into the safe and grabbing out two big bundles of cash money, which he sticks inside his shirt.

As we go into the street Harry the Horse and Spanish John come running up much excited, and Harry says to Big Butch like this:

"What are you trying to do," he says, "wake up the whole town?"

"Well," Butch says, "I guess maybe the charge is too strong, at that, but nobody seems to be coming, so you and Spanish John walk over to Eighth Avenue, and the rest of us will walk to Seventh, and if you go along quiet, like people minding their own business, it will be all right."

But I judge Little Isadore is tired of John Ignatius Junior's company by this time, because he says he will go with Harry the Horse and Spanish John, and this leaves Big Butch and John Ignatius Junior and me to go the other way. So we start moving, and all of a sudden two cops come tearing around the corner toward which Harry and Isadore and Spanish John are going. The chances are the cops hear the earthquake Big Butch lets off and are coming to investigate.

But the chances are, too, that if Harry the Horse and the other two keep on walking along very quietly like Butch tells them to, the coppers will pass them up entirely, because it is not likely that coppers will figure anybody to be opening safes with explosives in this neighborhood. But the minute Harry the Horse sees the coppers he loses his nut, and he outs with the old equalizer and starts blasting away, and what does Spanish John do but get his out, too, and open up.

The next thing anybody knows, the two coppers are down on the ground with slugs in them, but other coppers are coming from every which direction, blowing whistles and doing a little blasting themselves, and there is plenty of excitement, especially when the coppers who are not chasing Harry the Horse and Little Isadore and Spanish John start poking around the neighborhood and find Harry's pal, the watchman, all tied up nice and tight where Harry leaves him, and the watchman explains that some scoundrels blow open the safe he is watching.

All this time Big Butch and me are walking in the other direction toward Seventh Avenue, and Big Butch has John Ignatius in his arms, and John Ignatius is now squalling very loud, indeed. The chances are he is still thinking of the big whoom back there which tickles him so and is wishing to hear some more whooms. Anyway, he is beating his own best record for squalling, and as we go walking along Big Butch says to me like this:

"I dast not run," he says, "because if any coppers see me running they will start popping at me and maybe hit John Ignatius Junior, and besides running will joggle the milk up in him and make him sick. My old lady always warns me never to joggle John Ignatius Junior when he is full of milk."

"Well, Butch," I say, "there is no milk in me, and I do not care if I am joggled up, so if you do not mind, I will start doing a piece of running at the next corner."

But just then around the corner of Seventh Avenue toward which we are headed comes two or three coppers with a big fat sergeant with them, and one of the coppers, who is half out of breath as if he has been doing plenty of sprinting, is explaining to the sergeant that somebody blows a safe down the street and shoots a couple of coppers in the getaway.

And there is Big Butch, with John Ignatius Junior in his arms and twenty G's in his shirt front and a tough record behind him, walking right up to them.

I am feeling very sorry, indeed, for Big Butch, and very sorry for myself, too, and I am saying to myself that if I get out of this I will never associate with anyone but ministers of the gospel as long as I live. I can remember thinking that I am getting a better break than Butch, at that, because I will not have to go to Sing Sing for the rest of my life, like him, and I also remember wondering what they will give John Ignatius Junior, who is still tearing off these squalls, with Big Butch saying: "There, there, there, Daddy's itty woogleums." Then I hear one of the coppers say to the fat sergeant: "We better nail these guys. They may be in on this."

Well, I can see it is good-by to Butch and John Ignatius Junior and me, as the fat sergeant steps up to Big Butch, but instead of putting the arm on Butch, the fat sergeant only points at John Ignatius Junior and asks very sympathetic: "Teeth?"

"No," Big Butch says. "Not teeth. Colic. I just get the doctor here out of bed to do something for him, and we are going to a drug store to get some medicine."

Well, naturally I am very much surprised at this statement, because of course I am not a doctor, and if John Ignatius Junior has colic it serves him right, but I am only hoping they do not ask for my degree, when the fat sergeant says: "Too bad. I know what it is. I got three of them at home. But," he says, "it acts more like it is teeth than colic."

Then as Big Butch and John Ignatius Junior and me go on about our business I hear the fat sergeant say to the copper, very sarcastic: "Yea, of course a guy is out blowing safes with a baby in his arms! You will make a great detective, you will!"

I do not see Big Butch for several days after I learn that Harry the Horse and Little Isadore and Spanish John get back to Brooklyn all right, except they are a little nicked up here and there from the slugs the coppers toss at them, while the coppers they clip are not damaged so very much. Furthermore, the chances are I will not see Big Butch for several years, if it is left to me, but he comes looking for me one night, and he seems to be all pleasured up about something.

"Say," Big Butch says to me, "you know I never give a copper credit for knowing any too much about anything, but I wish to say that this fat sergeant we run into the other night is a very, very smart duck. He is right about it being teeth that is ailing John Ignatius Junior, for what happens yesterday but John cuts in his first tooth."

The Busher's Honeymoon

Ring Lardner

Chicago, Illinois, October 17.
FRIEND AL: Well Al it looks as if I would not be writeing so much to you now that I am a married man. Yes Al I and Florrie was married the day before yesterday just like I told you we was going to be and Al I am the happyest man in the world though I have spent $30 in the last 3 days incluseive. You was wise Al to get married in Bedford where not nothing is nearly half so dear. My expenses was as follows:

License	$2.00	Show tickets	3.00
Preist	3.50	Flowers	.50
Haircut and		Candy	.30
shave	.35	Hotel	4.50
Shine	.05	Tobacco	
Carfair	.45	both kinds	.25
New suit	14.50		

You see Al it costs a hole lot of money to get married here. The sum of what I have wrote

225

down is $29.40 but as I told you I have spent $30 and I do not know what I have did with that other $0.60. My new brother-in-law Allen told me I should ought to give the preist $5 and I thought it should be about $2 the same as the license so I split the difference and give him $3.50. I never seen him before and probily won't never see him again so why should I give him anything at all when it is his business to marry couples? But I like to do the right thing. You know me Al.

I thought we would be in Bedford by this time but Florrie wants to stay here a few more days because she says she wants to be with her sister. Allen and his wife is thinking about takeing a flat for the winter instead of going down to Waco Texas where they live. I don't see no sense in that when it costs so much to live here but it is none of my business if they want to throw their money away. But I am glad I got a wife with some sense though she kicked because I did not get no room with a bath which would cost me $2 a day instead of $1.50. I says I guess the clubhouse is still open yet and if I want a bath I can go over there and take the shower. She says Yes and I suppose I can go and jump in the lake. But she would not do that Al because the lake here is cold at this time of the year.

When I told you about my expenses I did not include in it the meals because we would be eating them if I was getting married or not getting married only I have to pay for six meals a day now instead of three and I didn't used to eat no lunch in the playing season except once in a while when I knowed I was not going to work that afternoon. I had a meal ticket which had not quite ran out over to a resturunt on Indiana Ave and we eat there for the first day except at night when I took Allen and his wife to the show with us and then he took us to a chop suye resturunt. I guess you have not never had no chop suye Al and I am here to tell you you have not missed nothing but when Allen was going to buy the supper what could I say? I could not say nothing.

Well yesterday and to-day we been eating at a resturunt on Cottage Grove Ave near the hotel and at the resturunt on Indiana that I had the meal ticket at only I do not like to buy no new meal ticket when I am not going to be round here no more than a few days. Well Al I guess the meals has cost me all together about $1.50 and I have eat very little myself. Florrie always wants desert ice cream or something and that runs up into money faster than regular stuff like stake and ham and eggs.

Well Al Florrie says it is time for me to keep my promise and take her to the moveing pictures which is $0.20 more because the one she likes round here costs a dime apeace. So I must close for this time and will see you soon.

Your pal, JACK

AL: Just a note Al to tell you why I have not yet came to Bedford yet where I expected I would be long before this time. Allen and his wife have took a furnished flat for the winter and Allen's wife wants Florrie to stay here untill they get settled. Meentime it is costing me a hole lot of money at the hotel and for meals besides I am paying $10 a month rent for the house you got for me and what good am I getting out of it? But Florrie wants to help her sister and what can I say? Though I did make her promise she would not stay no longer than next Saturday at least. So I guess Al we will be home on the evening train Saturday and then may be I can save some money.

I know Al that you and Bertha will like Florrie when you get acquainted with her spesially Bertha though Florrie dresses pretty swell and spends a hole lot of time fusing with her face and her hair.

She says to me to-night Who are you writeing to and I told her Al Blanchard who I have told you about a good many times. She says I bet you are writeing to some girl and acted like as though she was kind of jealous. So I thought I would tease her a little and I says I don't know no girls except you and Violet and Hazel. Who is Violet and Hazel? she says. I kind of laughed and says Oh I guess I better not tell you and then she says I guess you will tell me. That made me kind of mad because no girl can't tell me what to do. She says Are you going to tell me? and I says No.

Then she says If you don't tell me I will go over to Marie's that is her sister Allen's wife and stay all night. I says Go on and she went downstairs but I guess she probily went to get a soda because she has some money of her own that I give her. This was about two hours ago and she is probily down in the hotel lobby now trying to scare me by makeing me believe she has went to her sister's. But she can't fool me Al and I am now going out to mail this letter and get a beer. I won't never tell her about Violet and Hazel if she is going to act like that.

Yours truly, JACK.

Chicago, Illinois, October 24.
FRIEND AL: I guess I told you Al that we would be home Saturday evening. I have changed my mind. Allen and his wife has a spair bedroom and wants us to come there and stay a week or two. It won't cost nothing except they will probily want to go out to the moving pictures nights and we will probily have to go along with them and I am a man Al that wants to pay his share and not be cheap.

I and Florrie had our first quarrle the other night. I guess I told you the start of it but I don't remember. I made some crack about Violet and Hazel just to tease Florrie and she wanted to know who they was and I would not tell her. So she gets sore and goes over to Marie's to stay all night. I was just kidding Al and was willing to tell her about them two poor girls whatever she wanted to know except that I don't like to brag about girls being stuck on me. So I goes over to Marie's after her and tells her all about them except that I turned them down cold at the last minute to marry her because I did not want her to get all swelled up. She made me sware that I did not never care nothing about them and that was easy because it was the truth. So she come back to the hotel with me just like I knowed she would when I ordered her to.

They must not be no mistake about who is the boss in my house. Some men lets their wife run all over them but I am not that kind. You know me Al.

I must get busy and pack my suitcase if I am going to move over to Allen's. I sent three collars and a shirt to the laundrey this morning so even if we go over there to-night I will have to take another trip back this way in a day or two. I won't mind Al because they sell my kind of beer down to the corner and I never seen it sold nowheres else in Chi. You know the kind it is, eh Al? I wish I was lifting a few with you to-night.

Your pal, JACK.

Chicago, Illinois, October 28.
DEAR OLD AL: Florrie and Marie has went

downtown shopping because Florrie thinks she has got to have a new dress though she has got two changes of cloths now and I don't know what she can do with another one. I hope she don't find none to suit her though it would not hurt none if she got something for next spring at a reduckshon. I guess she must think I am Charles A. Comiskey or somebody. Allen has went to a colledge football game. One of the reporters give him a pass. I don't see nothing in football except a lot of scrapping between little slobs that I could lick the whole bunch of them so I did not care to go. The reporter is one of the guys that travled round with our club all summer. He called up and said he hadn't only the one pass but he was not hurting my feelings none because I would not go to no rotten football game if they payed me.

The flat across the hall from this here one is for rent furnished. They want $40 a month for it and I guess they think they must be lots of suckers running round loose. Marie was talking about it and says Why don't you and Florrie take it and then we can be right together all winter long and have some big times? Florrie says It would be all right with me. What about it Jack? I says What do you think I am? I don't have to live in no high price flat when I got a home in Bedford where they ain't no people trying to hold everybody up all the time. So they did not say no more about it when they seen I was in ernest. Nobody cannot tell me where I am going to live sister-in-law or no sister-in-law. If I was to rent the rotten old flat I would be paying $50 a month rent includeing the house down in Bedford. Fine chance Al.

Well Al I am lonesome and thirsty so more later.

Your pal, JACK

Chicago, Illinois, November 2.
FRIEND AL: Well Al I got some big news for you. I am not comeing to Bedford this winter after all except to make a visit which I guess will be round Xmas. I changed my mind about that flat across the hall from the Allens and decided to take it after all. The people who was in it and owns the furniture says they would let us have it till the 1 of May if we would pay $42.50 a month which is only $2.50 a month more than they would of let us have it for for a short time. So you see we got a bargain because it is all furnished and everything and we won't have to blow no money on furniture besides the club goes to California the middle of Febuery so Florrie would not have no place to stay while I am away.

The Allens only subleased their flat from some other people till the 2 of Febuery and when I and Allen goes West Marie can come over and stay with Florrie so you see it is best all round. If we should of boughten furniture it would cost us in the neighborhod of $100 even without no piano and they is a piano in

232

this here flat which makes it nice because Florrie plays pretty good with one hand and we can have lots of good times at home without it costing us nothing except just the bear liveing expenses. I consider myself lucky to of found out about this before it was too late and somebody else had of gotten the tip.

Now Al old pal I want to ask a great favor of you Al. I all ready have payed one month rent $10 on the house in Bedford and I want you to see the old man and see if he won't call off that lease. Why should I be paying $10 a month rent down there and $42.50 up here when the house down there is not no good to me because I am liveing up here all winter? See Al? Tell him I will gladly give him another month rent to call off the lease but don't tell him that if you don't have to. I want to be fare with him.

If you will do this favor for me, Al, I won't never forget it. Give my kindest to Bertha and tell her I am sorry I and Florrie won't see her right away but you see how it is Al.

Yours, JACK.

Chicago, Illinois, November 30.
FRIEND AL: I have not wrote for a long time have I Al but I have been very busy. They was not enough furniture in the flat and we have been buying some more. They was enough for some people maybe but I and Florrie is the kind that won't have nothing but the best. The

233

furniture them people had in the liveing room was oak but they had a bookcase bilt in in the flat that was mohoggeny and Florrie would not stand for no joke combination like that so she moved the oak chairs and table in to the spair bedroom and we went downtown to buy some mohoggeny. But it costs to much Al and we was feeling pretty bad about it when we seen some Sir Cashion walnut that was prettier even than the mohoggeny and not near so expensive. It is not no real Sir Cashion walnut but it is just as good and we got it reasonable. Then we got some mission chairs for the dining room because the old ones was just straw and was no good and we got a big lether couch for $9 that somebody can sleep on if we get to much company.

I hope you and Bertha can come up for the holidays and see how comfertible we are fixed. That is all the new furniture we have boughten but Florrie set her heart on some old Rose drapes and a red table lamp that is the biggest you ever seen Al and I did not have the heart to say no. The hole thing cost me in the neighborhood of $110 which is very little for what we got and then it will always be ourn even when we move away from this flat though we will have to leave the furniture that belongs to the other people but their part of it is not no good anyway.

I guess I told you Al how much money I had when the season ended. It was $1400 all told includeing the city serious money. Well Al I got in the neighborhood of $800 left because I give $200 to Florrie to send down to Texas to her other sister who had a bad egg for a husband that managed a club in the Texas Oklahoma League and this was the money she had to pay to get the divorce. I am glad Al that I was lucky enough to marry happy and get a good girl for my wife that has got some sense and besides if I have got $800 left I should not worry as they say.

Your pal, JACK.

Chicago, Illinois, December 7.
DEAR OLD AL: No I was in ernest Al when I says that I wanted you and Bertha to come up here for the holidays. I know I told you that I might come to Bedford for the holidays but that is all off. I have gave up the idea of comeing to Bedford for the holidays and I want you to be sure and come up here for the holidays and I will show you a good time. I would love to have Bertha come to and she can come if she wants to only Florrie don't know if she would have a good time or not and thinks maybe she would rather stay in Bedford and you come alone. But be sure and have Bertha come if she wants to come but maybe she would not injoy it. You know best Al.

I don't think the old man give me no square deal on that lease but if he wants to stick me all right. I am grateful to you Al for trying to fix it up but maybe you could of did better if you had of went at it in a different way. I am not finding no fault with my old pal though. Don't think that. When I have a pal I am the man to stick to him threw thick and thin. If the old man is going to hold me to that lease I guess I will have to stand it and I guess I won't starv to death for no $10 a month because I am going to get $2800 next year besides the city serious money and maybe we will get into the World Serious too. I know we will if Callahan will pitch me every 3d day like I wanted him to last season. But if you had of approached the old man in a different way maybe you could of fixed it up. I wish you would try it again Al if it is not no trouble.

We had Allen and his wife here for thanksgiveing dinner and the dinner cost me better than $5. I thought we had enough to eat to last a week but about six o'clock at night Florrie and Marie said they was hungry and we went downtown and had dinner all over again and I payed for it and it cost me $5 more. Allen was all ready to pay for it when Florrie said No this day's treat is on us so I had to pay for it but I don't see why she did not wait and let me do the talking. I was going to pay for it any way.

Be sure and come and visit us for the holidays Al and of coarse if Bertha wants to come bring her along. We will be glad to see you both. I won't never go back on a friend and pal. You know me Al.

Your old pal, JACK.

FRIEND AL: I don't see what can be the matter with Bertha because you know Al we would not care how she dressed and would not make no kick if she come up here in a night gown. She did not have no license to say we was to swell for her because we did not never think of nothing like that. I wish you would talk to her again Al and tell her she need not get sore on me and that both her and you is welcome at my house any time I ask you to come. See if you can't make her change her mind Al because I feel like as if she must of took offense at something I may of wrote you. I am sorry you and her are not comeing but I suppose you know best. Only we was getting all ready for you and Florrie said only the other day that she wished the holidays was over but that was before she knowed you was not comeing. I hope you can come Al.

Well Al I guess there is not no use talking to the old man no more. You have did the best you could but I wish I could of came down there and talked to him. I will pay him his rotten old $10 a month and the next time I come to Bedford and meet him on the street I will bust his jaw. I know he is a old man Al but I don't like to see nobody get the best of me and I am sorry I ever asked him to let me off. Some of them old skinflints has no heart

237

Al but why should I fight with a old man over chicken feed like $10? Florrie says a star pitcher like I should not ought never to scrap about little things and I guess she is right Al so I will pay the old man his $10 a month if I have to.

Florrie says she is jealous of me writeing to you so much and she says she would like to meet this great old pal of mine. I would like to have her meet you to Al and I would like to have you change your mind and come and visit us and I am sorry you can't come Al.

Yours truly, JACK.

Chicago, Illinois, December 27.
OLD PAL: I guess all these lefthanders is alike though I thought this Allen had some sense. I thought he was different from the most and was not no rummy but they are all alike Al and they are all lucky that somebody don't hit them over the head with a ax and kill them but I guess at that you could not hurt no lefthanders by hitting them over the head. We was all down on State St. the day before Xmas and the girls was all tired out and ready to go home but Allen says No I guess we better stick down a while because now the crowds is out and it will be fun to watch them. So we walked up and down State St. about a hour longer and finally we come in front of a big jewlry store window and in it was a swell dimond ring that was marked $100. It was a ladies' ring so Marie says to Allen Why don't you buy that for me?

238

And Allen says Do you really want it? And she says she did.

So we tells the girls to wait and we goes over to a saloon where Allen has got a friend and gets a check cashed and we come back and he bought the ring. Then Florrie looks like as though she was getting all ready to cry and I asked her what was the matter and she says I had not boughten her no ring not even when we was engaged. So I and Allen goes back to the saloon and I gets a check cashed and we come back and bought another ring but I did not think the ring Allen had boughten was worth no $100 so I gets one for $75. Now Al you know I am not makeing no kick on spending a little money for a present for my own wife but I had allready boughten her a rist watch for $15 and a rist watch was just what she had wanted. I was willing to give her the ring if she had not of wanted the rist watch more than the ring but when I give her the ring I kept the rist watch and did not tell her nothing about it.

Well I come downtown alone the day after Xmas and they would not take the rist watch back in the store where I got it. So I am going to give it to her for a New Year's present and I guess that will make Allen feel like a dirty doose. But I guess you cannot hurt no left-hander's feelings at that. They are all alike. But Allen has not got nothing but a dinky curve ball and a fast ball that looks like my slow one. If Comiskey was not good hearted he would of sold him long ago.

I sent you and Bertha a cut glass dish Al which was the best I could get for the money and it was pretty high pricet at that. We was glad to get the pretty pincushions from you and Bertha and Florrie says to tell you that we are well supplied with pincushions now because the ones you sent makes a even half dozen. Thanks Al for remembering us and thank Bertha too though I guess you paid for them.

Your pal, JACK.

Chicago, Illinois, January 3.

OLD PAL: Al I been pretty sick ever since New Year's eve. We had a table at 1 of the swell resturunts downtown and I never seen so much wine drank in my life. I would rather of had beer but they would not sell us none so I found out that they was a certain kind that you can get for $1 a bottle and it is just as good as the kind that has got all them fancy names but this lefthander starts ordering some other kind about 11 oclock and it was $5 a bottle and the girls both says they liked it better. I could not see a hole lot of difference myself and I would of gave $0.20 for a big stine of my kind of beer. You know me Al. Well Al you know they is not nobody that can drink more than your old pal and I was all O. K. at one oclock but I seen the girls was getting kind of sleepy so I says we better go home.

Then Marie says Oh, shut up and don't be no quiter. I says You better shut up yourself and not be telling me to shut up, and she says What will you do if I don't shut up? And I says I would bust her in the jaw. But you know Al I would not think of busting no girl. Then Florrie says You better not start nothing because you had to much to drink or you would not be talking about busting girls in the jaw. Then I says I don't care if it is a girl I bust or a lefthander. I did not mean nothing at all Al but Marie says I had insulted Allen and he gets up and slaps my face. Well Al I am not going to stand that from nobody not even if he is my brother-in-law and a lefthander that has not got enough speed to brake a pin of glass.

So I give him a good beating and the waiter butts in and puts us all out for fighting and I and Florrie comes home in a taxi and Allen and his wife don't get in till about 5 oclock so I guess she must of had to of took him to a doctor to get fixed up. I been in bed ever since till just this morning kind of sick to my stumach. I guess I must of eat something that did not agree with me. Allen come over after breakfast this morning and asked me was I all right so I guess he is not sore over the beating I give him or else he wants to make friends because he has saw that I am a bad guy to monkey with.

Florrie tells me a little while ago that she paid the hole bill at the resturunt with my money because Allen was broke so you see what kind of a cheap skate he is Al and some day I am going to bust his jaw. She won't tell me how much the bill was and I won't ask her to no more because we had a good time outside of the fight and what do I care if we spent a little money?

Yours truly, JACK.

Chicago, Illinois, January 20.

FRIEND AL: Allen and his wife have gave up the flat across the hall from us and come over to live with us because we got a spair bedroom and why should they not have the bennifit of it? But it is pretty hard for the girls to have to cook and do the work when they is four of us so I have a hired girl who does it all for $7 a week. It is great stuff Al because now we can go round as we please and don't have to wait for no dishes to be washed or nothing. We generally almost always has dinner downtown in the evening so it is pretty soft for the girl too. She don't generally have no more than one meal to get because we generally run round downtown till late and don't get up till about noon.

That sounds funny don't it Al, when I used to get up at 5 every morning down home. Well Al I can tell you something else that may sound funny and that is that I lost my taste for beer. I don't seem to care for it no more and I found I can stand allmost as many drinks of other stuff as I could of beer. I guess Al they is not nobody ever lived can drink more and stand up better under it than me. I make the girls and Allen quit every night.

I only got just time to write you this short note because Florrie and Marie is giving a big party to-night and I and Allen have got to beat it out of the house and stay out of the way till they get things ready. It is Marie's berthday and she says she is 22 but say Al if she is 22 Kid Gleason is 30. Well Al the girls says we must blow so I will run out and mail this letter.

Yours truly, JACK.

Chicago, Illinois, January 31.

AL: Allen is going to take Marie with him on the training trip to California and of course Florrie has been at me to take her along. I told her postivly that she can't go. I can't afford no stunt like that but still I am up against it to know what to do with her while we are on the trip because Marie won't be here to stay with her. I don't like to leave her here all alone but they is nothing to it Al I can't afford to take her along. She says I don't see why you can't take me if Allen takes Marie. And I says That stuff is all O. K. for Allen because him and Marie has been grafting off of us all winter. And then she gets mad and tells me I should not ought to say her sister was no grafter. I did not mean nothing like that Al but you don't never know when a woman is going to

243

take offense.

If our furniture was down in Bedford everything would be all O. K. because I could leave her there and I would feel all O. K. because I would know that you and Bertha would see that she was getting along O. K. But they would not be no sense in sending her down to a house that has not no furniture in it. I wish I knowed somewheres where she could visit Al. I would be willing to pay her bord even.

Well Al enough for this time.

Your old pal, JACK.

Chicago, Illinois, Febuery 4.

FRIEND AL: You are a real old pal Al and I certainly am greatful to you for the invatation. I have not told Florrie about it yet but I am sure she will be tickled to death and it is certainly kind of you old pal. I did not never dream of nothing like that. I note what you say Al about not excepting no bord but I think it would be better and I would feel better if you would take something say about $2 a week.

I know Bertha will like Florrie and that they will get along O. K. together because Florrie can learn her how to make her cloths look good and fix her hair and fix up her face. I feel like as if you had took a big load off of me Al and I won't never forget it.

If you don't think I should pay no bord for Florrie all right. Suit yourself about that old pal.

244

We are leaveing here the 20 of Febuery and if you don't mind I will bring Florrie down to you about the 18. I would like to see the old bunch again and spesially you and Bertha.

Yours, JACK.

P. S. We will only be away till April 14 and that is just a nice visit. I wish we did not have no flat on our hands.

Chicago, Illinois, Febuery 9.

OLD PAL: I want to thank you for asking Florrie to come down there and visit you Al but I find she can't get away. I did not know she had no engagements but she says she may go down to her folks in Texas and she don't want to say that she will come to visit you when it is so indefanate. So thank you just the same Al and thank Bertha too.

Florrie is still at me to take her along to California but honest Al I can't do it. I am right down to my last $50 and I have not payed no rent for this month. I owe the hired girl 2 weeks' salery and both I and Florrie needs some new cloths.

Florrie has just came in since I started writing this letter and we have been talking some more about California and she says maybe if I would ask Comiskey he would take her along as the club's guest. I had not never thought of that Al and maybe he would because he is a pretty good scout and I guess I will go and see him about it. The league has its skedule meeting here tomorrow and may be I can see him down to the hotel where they meet at. I am so worried Al that I can't write no more but I will tell you how I come out with Comiskey.

Your pal, JACK.

Chicago, Illinois, Febuery 11.

FRIEND AL: I am up against it right Al and I don't know where I am going to head in at. I went down to the hotel where the league was holding its skedule meeting at and I seen Comiskey and got some money off the club but I owe all the money I got off of them and I am still wondering what to do about Florrie.

Comiskey was busy in the meeting when I went down there and they was not no chance to see him for a while so I and Allen and some of the boys hung round and had a few drinks and fanned. This here Joe Hill the busher that Detroit has got that Violet is hooked up to was round the hotel. I don't know what for but I felt like busting his jaw only the boys told me I had better not do nothing because I might kill him and any way he probily won't be in the league much longer. Well finally Comiskey got threw the meeting and I seen him and he says Hello young man what can I do for you? And I says I would like to get $100 advance money. He says Have you been takeing care of youself down in Bedford? And I told him I had been liveing here all winter and it did not seem to make no hit with him though I don't see

246

what business if is of hisn where I live.

So I says I had been takeing good care of myself. And I have Al. You know that. So he says I should come to the ball park the next day which is today and he would have the secretary take care of me but I says I could not wait and so he give me $100 out of his pocket and says he would have it charged against my salery. I was just going to brace him about the California trip when he got away and went back to the meeting.

Well Al I hung round with the bunch waiting for him to get threw again and we had some more drinks and finally Comiskey was threw again and I braced him in the lobby and asked him if it was all right to take my wife along to California. He says Sure they would be glad to have her along. And then I says Would the club pay her fair? He says I guess you must of spent that $100 buying some nerve: He says Have you not got no sisters that would like to go along to? He says Does your wife insist on the drawing room or will she take a lower birth? He says Is my special train good enough for her?

Then he turns away from me and I guess some of the boys must of heard the stuff he pulled because they was laughing when he went away but I did not see nothing to laugh at. But I guess he ment that I would have to pay her fair if she goes along and that is out of the question Al. I am up against it and I don't know where I am going to head in at.

Your pal, JACK.

Chicago, Illinois, Febuery 12.
DEAR OLD AL: I guess everything will be all
O. K. now at least I am hopeing it will. When
I told Florrie about how I come out with
Comiskey she bawled her head off and I thought
for a while I was going to have to call a doctor
or something but pretty soon she cut it out and
we sat there a while without saying nothing.
Then she says If you could get your salery
razed a couple of hundred dollars a year would
you borrow the money ahead somewheres and
take me along to California? I says Yes I would
if I could get a couple hundred dollars more
salery but how could I do that when I had
signed a contract for $2800 last fall allready?
She says Don't you think you are worth more
than $2800? And I says Yes of coarse I was
worth more than $2800. She says Well if you
will go and talk the right way to Comiskey I
believe he will give you $3000 but you must be
sure you go at it the right way and don't go
and ball it all up.

Well we argude about it a while because I
don't want to hold nobody up Al but finally I
says I would. It would not be holding nobody
up anyway because I am worth $3000 to the
club if I am worth a nichol. The papers is all
saying that the club has got a good chance to
win the pennant this year and talking about the

248

pitching staff and I guess they would not be no pitching staff much if it was not for I and one or two others — about one other I guess.

So it looks like as if everything will be all O. K. now Al. I am going to the office over to the park to see him the first thing in the morning and I am pretty sure that I will get what I am after because if I do not he will see that I am going to quit and then he will see what he is up against and not let me get away.

I will let you know how I come out.

Your pal, JACK.

Chicago, Illinois, Febuery 14.

FRIEND AL: Al old pal I have got a big supprise for you. I am going to the Federal League. I had a run in with Comiskey yesterday and I guess I told him a thing or 2. I guess he would of been glad to sign me at my own figure before I got threw but I was so mad I would not give him no chance to offer me another contract.

I got out to the park at 9 oclock yesterday morning and it was a hour before he showed up and then he kept me waiting another hour so I was pretty sore when I finally went in to see him. He says Well young man what can I do for you? I says I come to see about my contract. He says Do you want to sign up for next year all ready? I says No I am talking about this year. He says I thought I and you talked business last fall. And I says Yes but now I think I am worth more money and I want to sign a contract for $3000. He says If you behave yourself and work good this year I will see that you are took care of. But I says That won't do because I have got to be sure I am going to get $3000.

Then he says I am not sure you are going to get anything. I says What do you mean? And he says I have gave you a very fare contract and if you don't want to live up to it that is your own business. So I give him a awful call Al and told him I would jump to the Federal League. He says Oh, I would not do that if I was you. They are having a hard enough time as it is. So I says something back to him and he did not say nothing to me and I beat it out of the office.

I have not told Florrie about the Federal League business yet as I am going to give her a big supprise. I bet they will take her along with me on the training trip and pay her fair but even if they don't I should not worry because I will make them give me a contract for $4000 a year and then I can afford to take her with me on all the trips.

I will go down and see Tinker to-morrow morning and I will write you to-morrow night Al how much salery they are going to give me. But I won't sign for no less than $4000. You know me Al.

Yours, JACK.

Chicago, Illinois, Febuery 15.

OLD PAL: It is pretty near midnight Al but I been to bed a couple of times and I can't get no sleep. I am worried to death Al and I don't know where I am going to head in at. Maybe I will go out and buy a gun Al and end it all and I guess it would be better for everybody. But I cannot do that Al because I have not got the money to buy a gun with.

I went down to see Tinker about signing up with the Federal League and he was busy in the office when I come in. Pretty soon Buck Perry the pitcher that was with Boston last year come out and seen me and as Tinker was still busy we went out and had a drink together. Buck shows me a contract for $5000 a year and Tinker had allso gave him a $500 bonus. So pretty soon I went up to the office and pretty soon Tinker seen me and called me into his private office and asked what did I want. I says I was ready to jump for $4000 and a bonus. He says I thought you was signed up with the White Sox. I says Yes I was but I was not satisfied. He says That does not make no difference to me if you are satisfied or not. You ought to of came to me before you signed a contract. I says I did not know enough but I know better now. He says Well it is to late now. We cannot have nothing to do with you because you have went and signed a contract with the White Sox. I argude with him a while and asked him to come out and have a drink

251

so we could talk it over but he said he was busy so they was nothing for me to do but blow.

So I am not going to the Federal League Al and I will not go with the White Sox because I have got a raw deal. Comiskey will be sorry for what he done when his team starts the season and is up against it for good pitchers and then he will probily be willing to give me anything I ask for but that don't do me no good now Al. I am way in debt and no chance to get no money from nobody. I wish I had of stayed with Terre Haute Al and never saw this league.

Your pal, JACK.

Chicago, Illinois, Febuery 17.

FRIEND AL: Al don't ever let nobody tell you that these here lefthanders is right. This Allen my own brother-in-law who married sisters has been grafting and spongeing on me all winter Al. Look what he done to me now Al. You know how hard I been up against it for money and I know he has got plenty of it because I seen it on him. Well Al I was scared to tell Florrie I was cleaned out and so I went to Allen yesterday and says I had to have $100 right away because I owed the rent and owed the hired girl's salery and could not even pay no grocery bill. And he says No he could not let me have none because he has got to save all his money to take his wife on the trip to California. And here he has been liveing on me all winter and maybe I could of took my wife to California

252

if I had not of spent all my money takeing care of this no good lefthander and his wife. And Al honest he has not got a thing and ought not to be in the league. He gets by with a dinky curve ball and has not got no more smoke than a rabbit or something.

Well Al I felt like busting him in the jaw but then I thought No I might kill him and then I would have Marie and Florrie both to take care of and God knows one of them is enough besides paying his funeral expenses. So I walked away from him without takeing a crack at him and went into the other room where Florrie and Marie was at. I says to Marie I says Marie I wish you would go in the other room a minute because I want to talk to Florrie. So Marie beats it into the other room and then I tells Florrie all about what Comiskey and the Federal League done to me. She bawled something awful and then she says I was no good and she wished she had not never married me. I says I wisht it too and then she says Do you mean that and starts to cry.

I told her I was sorry I says that because they is not no use fusing with girls Al specially when they is your wife. She says No California trip for me and then she says What are you going to do? And I says I did not know. She says Well if I was a man I would do something. So then I got mad and I says I will do something. So I went down to the corner salloon and started in to get good and drunk but I could

253

not do it Al because I did not have the money.

Well old pal I am going to ask you a big favor and it is this I want you to send me $100 Al for just a few days till I can get on my feet. I do not know when I can pay it back Al but I guess you know the money is good and I know you have got it. Who would not have it when they live in Bedford? And besides I let you take $20 in June 4 years ago Al and you give it back but I would not have said nothing to you if you had of kept it. Let me hear from you right away old pal.

Yours truly, JACK.

Chicago, Illinois, Febuery 19.

AL: I am certainly greatful to you Al for the $100 which come just a little while ago. I will pay the rent with it and part of the grocery bill and I guess the hired girl will have to wait a while for hern but she is sure to get it because I don't never forget my debts. I have changed my mind about the White Sox and I am going to go on the trip and take Florrie along because I don't think it would not be right to leave her here alone in Chi when her sister and all of us is going.

I am going over to the ball park and up in the office pretty soon to see about it. I will tell Comiskey I changed my mind and he will be glad to get me back because the club has not got no chance to finish nowheres without me. But I won't go on no trip or give the club my services without them giveing me some more advance money so as I can take Florrie along with me because Al I would not go without her.

Maybe Comiskey will make my salery $3000 like I wanted him to when he sees I am willing to be a good fellow and go along with him and when he knows that the Federal League would of gladly gave me $4000 if I had not of signed no contract with the White Sox.

I think I will ask him for $200 advance money Al and if I get it may be I can send part of your $100 back to you but I know you cannot be in no hurry Al though you says you wanted it back as soon as possible. You could not be very hard up Al because it don't cost near so much to live in Bedford as it does up here.

Anyway I will let you know how I come out with Comiskey and I will write you as soon as I get out to Paso Robles if I don't get no time to write you before I leave.

Your pal, JACK.

P. S. I have took good care of myself all winter Al and I guess I ought to have a great season.

P. S. Florrie is tickled to death about going along and her and I will have some time together out there on the Coast if I can get some money somewheres.

Chicago, Illinois, Febuery 21.
FRIEND AL: I have not got the heart to write

255

this letter to you Al. I am up here in my $42.50 a month flat and the club has went to California and Florrie has went too. I am flat broke Al and all I am asking you is to send me enough money to pay my fair to Bedford and they and all their leagues can go to hell Al.

I was out to the ball park early yesterday morning and some of the boys was there allready fanning and kidding each other. They tried to kid me to when I come in but I guess I give them as good as they give me. I was not in no mind for kidding Al because I was there on business and I wanted to see Comiskey and get it done with.

Well the secretary come in finally and I went up to him and says I wanted to see Comiskey right away. He says The boss was busy and what did I want to see him about and I says I wanted to get some advance money because I was going to take my wife on the trip. He says This would be a fine time to be telling us about it even if you was going on the trip.

And I says What do you mean? And he says You are not going on no trip with us because we have got wavers on you and you are sold to Milwaukee.

Honest Al I thought he was kidding at first and I was waiting for him to laugh but he did not laugh and finally I says What do you mean? And he says Cannot you understand no English? You are sold to Milwaukee. Then I says I want to see the boss. He says It won't do you no good to see the boss and he is to busy to see you. I says I want to get some money. And he says You cannot get no money from this club and all you get is your fair to Milwaukee. I says I am not going to no Milwaukee anyway and he says I should not worry about that. Suit yourself.

Well Al I told some of the boys about it and they was pretty sore and says I ought to bust the secretary in the jaw and I was going to do it when I thought No I better not because he is a little guy and I might kill him.

I looked all over for Kid Gleason but he was not nowheres round and they told me he would not get into town till late in the afternoon. If I could of saw him Al he would of fixed me all up. I asked 3 or 4 of the boys for some money but they says they was all broke.

But I have not told you the worst of it yet Al. When I come back to the flat Allen and Marie and Florrie was busy packing up and they asked me how I come out. I told them and Allen just stood there stareing like a big rummy but Marie and Florrie both begin to cry and I almost felt like as if I would like to cry to only I am not no baby Al.

Well Al I told Florrie she might as well quit packing and make up her mind that she was not going nowheres till I got money enough to go to Bedford where I belong. She kept right on crying and it got so I could not stand it no more so I went out to get a drink because I still had just about a dollar left yet.

It was about 2 oclock when I left the flat and pretty near 5 when I come back because I had ran in to some fans that knowed who I was and would not let me get away and besides I did not want to see no more of Allen and Marie till they was out of the house and on their way.

But when I come in Al they was nobody there. They was not nothing there except the furniture and a few of my things scattered round. I sit down for a few minutes because I guess I must of had to much to drink but finally I seen a note on the table addressed to me and I seen it was Florrie's writeing.

I do not remember just what was there in the note Al because I tore it up the minute I read it but it was something about I could not support no wife and Allen had gave her enough money to go back to Texas and she was going on the 6 oclock train and it would not do me no good to try and stop her.

Well Al they was not no danger of me trying to stop her. She was not no good Al and I wisht I had not of never saw either she or her sister or my brother-in-law.

For a minute I thought I would follow Allen and his wife down to the deepo where the special train was to pull out of and wait till I see him and punch his jaw but I seen that would not get me nothing.

So here I am all alone Al and I will have to stay here till you send me the money to come home. You better send me $25 because I have got a few little debts I should ought to pay before I leave town. I am not going to Milwaukee Al because I did not get no decent deal and nobody cannot make no sucker out of me.

Please hurry up with the $25 Al old friend because I am sick and tired of Chi and want to get back there with my old pal.

Yours, JACK.

P. S. Al I wish I had of took poor little Violet when she was so stuck on me.

Mr. and Mrs. Fix-It

Ring Lardner

They're certainly a live bunch in this town. We ain't only been here three days and had calls already from people representin' four different organizations — the Chamber of Commerce, Kiwanis, and I forget who else. They wanted to know if we was comfortable and did we like the town and is they anything they can do for us and what to be sure and see.

And they all asked how we happened to come here instead of goin' somewheres else. I guess they keep a record of everybody's reasons for comin' so as they can get a line of what features tourists is most attracted by. Then they play up them features in next year's booster advertisin'.

Well, I told them we was perfectly comfortable and we like the town fine and they's nothin' nobody can do for us right now and we'll be sure and see all the things we ought to see. But when they asked me how did we happen to come here, I said it was just a kind

260

of a accident, because the real reason makes too long a story.

My wife has been kiddin' me about my friends ever since we was married. She says that judgin' by the ones I've introduced her to, they ain't nobody in the world got a rummier bunch of friends than me. I'll admit that the most of them ain't, well, what you might call hot; they're different somehow than when I first hung around with them. They seem to be lost without a brass rail to rest their dogs on. But of course they're old friends and I can't give 'em the air.

We have 'em to the house for dinner every little w'ile, they and their wives, and what my missus objects to is because they don't none of them play bridge or mah jong or do cross-word puzzles or sing or dance or even talk, but just set there and wait for somebody to pour 'em a fresh drink.

As I say, my wife kids me about 'em and they ain't really nothin' I can offer in their defense. That don't mean, though, that the shoe is all on one foot. Because w'ile the majority of her friends may not be quite as dumb as mine, just the same they's a few she's picked out who I'd of had to be under the ether to allow anybody to introduce 'em to me in the first place.

Like the Crandalls, for instance. Mrs. Crandall come from my wife's home town and they didn't hardly know each other there, but they

261

met again in a store in Chi and it went from bad to worse till finally Ada asked the dame and her husband to the house.

Well, the husband turns out to be the fella that win the war, w'ile it seems that Mrs. Crandall was in Atlantic City once and some movin' picture company was makin' a picture there and they took a scene of what was supposed to be society people walkin' up and down the Boardwalk and Mrs. Crandall was in the picture and people that seen it when it come out, they all said that from the way she screened, why if she wanted to go into the business, she could make Gloria Swanson look like Mrs. Gump.

Now it ain't only took me a few words to tell you these things, but when the Crandalls tells their story themselves, they don't hardly get started by midnight and no chance of them goin' home till they're through even when you drop 'em a hint that they're springin' it on you for the hundred and twelfth time.

That's the Crandalls, and another of the wife's friends is the Thayers. Thayer is what you might call a all-around handy man. He can mimic pretty near all the birds and beasts and fishes, he can yodel, he can play a ocarena, or he can recite Kipling or Robert H. Service, or he can do card tricks, and strike a light without no matches, and tie all the different knots.

And besides that, he can make a complete radio outfit and set it up, and take pictures as good as the best professional photographers and a whole lot better. He collects autographs. And he never had a sick day in his life.

Mrs. Thayer gets a headache playin' bridge, so it's mah jong or rhum when she's around. She used to be a teacher of elocution and she still gives readin's if you coax her, or if you don't, and her hair is such a awful nuisance that she would get it cut in a minute only all her friends tells her it would be criminal to spoil that head of hair. And when she talks to her husband, she always talks baby talk, maybe because somebody has told her that she'd be single if he wasn't childish.

And then Ada has got still another pal, a dame named Peggy Flood who is hospital mad and ain't happy unless she is just goin' under the knife or just been there. She's had everything removed that the doctors knew the name of and now they're probin' her for new giblets.

Well, I wouldn't mind if they cut her up into alphabet soup if they'd only do such a good job of it that they couldn't put her together again, but she always comes through O.K. and she spends the intermission at our place, describin' what all they done or what they're plannin' to do next.

But the cat's nightgown is Tom Stevens and his wife. There's the team that wins the Olympics! And they're Ada's team, not mine.

Ada met Belle Stevens on the elevated. Ada was invited to a party out on the North Side and didn't know exactly where to get off and Mrs. Stevens seen her talkin' to the guard and horned in and asked her what was it she wanted to know and Ada told her, and Mrs. Stevens said she was goin' to get off the same station Ada wanted to get off, so they got off together.

Mrs. Stevens insisted on goin' right along to the address where Ada was goin' because she said Ada was bound to get lost if she wasn't familiar with the neighborhood.

Well, Ada thought it was mighty nice of her to do so much for a stranger. Mrs. Stevens said she was glad to because she didn't know what would happen to her lots of times if strangers hadn't been nice and helped her out.

She asked Ada where she lived and Ada told her on the South Side and Mrs. Stevens said she was sure we'd like it better on the North Side if we'd leave her pick out a place for us, so Ada told her we had a year's lease that we had just signed and couldn't break it, so then Mrs. Stevens said her husband had studied law and he claimed they wasn't no lease that you couldn't break and some evening she would bring him out to call on us and he'd tell us how to break our lease.

Well, Ada had to say sure, come on out, though we was perfectly satisfied with our apartment and didn't no more want to break the lease than each other's jaw. Maybe not as much. Anyway, the very next night, they showed up, Belle and Tom, and when they'd gone, I give 'em the nickname — Mr. and Mrs. Fix-It.

After the introductions, Stevens made some remark about what a cozy little place we had and then he asked if I would mind tellin' what rent we paid. So I told him a hundred and a quarter a month. So he said, of course, that was too much and no wonder we wanted to break the lease. Then I said we was satisfied and didn't want to break it and he said I must be kiddin' and if I would show him the lease he would see what loopholes they was in it.

Well, the lease was right there in a drawer in the table, but I told him it was in my safety deposit box at the bank. I ain't got no safety deposit box and no more use for one than Judge Landis has for the deef and dumb alphabet.

Stevens said the lease was probably just a regular lease and if it was, they wouldn't be no trouble gettin' out of it, and meanw'ile him and his wife would see if they couldn't find us a place in the same buildin' with them.

And he was pretty sure they could even if the owner had to give some other tenant the air, because he, the owner, would do anything in the world for Stevens.

So I said yes, but suppose we want to stay where we are. So he said I looked like a man with better judgment than that and if I would just leave everything to him he would fix it so's we could move within a month. I kind of laughed and thought that would be the end of it.

He wanted to see the whole apartment so I showed him around and when we come to the bathroom he noticed my safety razor on the shelf. He said, "So you use one of them things," and I said, "Yes," and he asked me how I liked it, and I said I liked it fine and he said that must be because I hadn't never used a regular razor.

He said a regular razor was the only thing to use if a man wanted to look good. So I asked him if he used a regular razor and he said he did, so I said, "Well, if you look good, I don't want to."

But that didn't stop him and he said if I would meet him downtown the next day he would take me to the place where he bought all his razors and help me pick some out for myself. I told him I was goin' to be tied up, so just to give me the name and address of the place and I would drop in there when I had time.

But, no, that wouldn't do; he'd have to go along with me and introduce me to the proprietor because the proprietor was a great pal of his and would do anything in the world for him, and if the proprietor vouched for the razors, I could be sure I was gettin' the best razors money could buy. I told him again that I was goin' to be tied up and I managed to get him on some other subject.

Meanw'ile, Mrs. Stevens wanted to know

where Ada had bought the dress she was wearin' and how much had it cost and Ada told her and Mrs. Stevens said it was a crime. She would meet Ada downtown tomorrow morning and take her to the shop where she bought her clothes and help her choose some dresses that really was dresses.

So Ada told her she didn't have no money to spend on dresses right then, and besides, the shop Mrs. Stevens mentioned was too high priced. But it seems the dame that run the shop was just like a sister to Mrs. Stevens and give her and her friends a big reduction and not only that, but they wasn't no hurry about payin'.

Well, Ada thanked her just the same, but didn't need nothin' new just at present; maybe later on she would take advantage of Mrs. Stevens's kind offer. Yes, but right now they was some models in stock that would be just beautiful on Ada and they might be gone later on. They was nothin' for it but Ada had to make a date with her; she wasn't obliged to buy nothin', but it would be silly not to go and look at the stuff that was in the joint and get acquainted with the dame that run it.

Well, Ada kept the date and bought three dresses she didn't want and they's only one of them she's had the nerve to wear. They cost her a hundred dollars a smash and I'd hate to think what the price would of been if Mrs. Stevens and the owner of the shop wasn't so much like sisters.

I was sure I hadn't made no date with Stevens, but just the same he called me up the next night to ask why I hadn't met him. And a couple of days later I got three new razors in the mail along with a bill and a note from the store sayin' that these was three specially fine razors that had been picked out for me by Thomas J. Stevens.

I don't know yet why I paid for the razors and kept 'em. I ain't used 'em and never intended to. Though I've been tempted a few times to test their edge on Stevens's neck.

That same week, Mrs. Stevens called up and asked us to spend Sunday with them and when we got out there, the owner of the buildin' is there, too. And Stevens has told him that I was goin' to give up my apartment on the South Side and wanted him to show me what he had.

I thought this was a little too strong and I said Stevens must of misunderstood me, that I hadn't no fault to find with the place I was in and wasn't plannin' to move, not for a year anyway. You can bet this didn't make no hit with the guy, who was just there on Stevens's say-so that I was a prospective tenant.

Well, it was only about two months ago that this cute little couple come into our life, but I'll bet we seen 'em twenty times at least. They was always invitin' us to their place or invitin' themselves to our place and Ada is one of these here kind of people that just can't say no.

Which may be why I and her is married.

Anyway, it begin to seem like us and the Stevenses was livin' together and all one family, with them at the head of it. I never in my life seen anybody as crazy to run other people's business. Honest to heavens, it's a wonder they let us brush our own teeth!

Ada made the remark one night that she wished the ski jumper who was doin' our cookin' would get married and quit so's she wouldn't have to can her. Mrs. Stevens was there and asked Ada if she should try and get her a new cook, but Ada says no, the poor gal might have trouble findin' another job and she felt sorry for her.

Just the same, the next afternoon a Jap come to the apartment and said he was ready to go to work and Mrs. Stevens had sent him. Ada had to tell him the place was already filled.

Another night, Ada complained that her feet was tired. Belle said her feet used to get tired, too, till a friend of hers recommended a chiropodist and she went to him and he done her so much good that she made a regular appointment with him for once every month and paid him a flat sum and no matter how much runnin' around she done, her dogs hadn't fretted her once since this corn-husker started tendin' to 'em.

She wanted to call up the guy at his home right then and there and make a date for Ada and the only way Ada could stop her was by promisin' to go and see him the next time her feet hurt. After that, whenever the two gals met, Belle's first question was "How is your feet?" and the answer was always "Fine, thanks."

Well, I'm quite a football fan and Ada likes to go, too, when it's a big game and lots of excitement. So we decided we'd see the Illinois-Chicago game and have a look at this "Red" Grange. I warned Ada to not say nothin' about it to Tom and Belle as I felt like we was entitled to a day off.

But it happened that they was goin' to be a game up at Evanston that day and the Stevenses invited us to see that one with them. So we used the other game as a alibi. And when Tom asked me later on if I'd boughten my tickets yet, instead of sayin' yes, I told him the truth and said no.

So then he said:

"I'm glad you ain't, because I and Belle has made up our mind that the Chicago game is the one we ought to see. And we'll all go together. And don't you bother about tickets because I can get better ones than you can as Stagg and I is just like that."

So I left it to him to get the tickets and we might as well of set on the Adams Street bridge. I said to Stevens, I said:

"If these is the seats Mr. Stagg digs up for his old pals, I suppose he leads strangers twenty or thirty miles out in the country and blindfolds

270

'em and ties 'em to a tree.''

Now of course it was the bunk about he and Stagg bein' so close. He may of been introduced to him once, but he ain't the kind of a guy that Stagg would go around holdin' hands with. Just the same, most of the people he bragged about knowin', why it turned out that he really did know 'em; yes, and stood ace high with 'em, too.

Like, for instance, I got pinched for speedin' one night and they give me a ticket to show up in the Speeders' court and I told Stevens about it and he says, "Just forget it! I'll call up the judge and have it wiped off the book. He's a mighty good fella and a personal friend of mine."

Well, I didn't want to take no chances so I phoned Stevens the day before I was supposed to appear in court, and I asked him if he'd talked to the judge. He said he had and I asked him if he was sure. So he said, "If you don't believe me, call up the judge yourself." And he give me the judge's number. Sure enough, Stevens had fixed it and when I thanked the judge for his trouble, he said it was a pleasure to do somethin' for a friend of Tom Stevens's.

Now, I know it's silly to not appreciate favors like that and not warm up to people that's always tryin' to help you along, but still a person don't relish bein' treated like they was half-witted and couldn't button their shirt alone. Tom and Belle meant all right, but I and Ada got kind of tired of havin' fault found with everything that belonged to us and everything we done or tried to do.

Besides our apartment bein' no good and our clothes terrible, we learned that my dentist didn't know a bridge from a mustache cup, and the cigarettes I smoked didn't have no taste to them, and the man that bobbed Ada's hair must of been mad at her, and neither of us would ever know what it was to live till we owned a wire-haired fox terrier.

And we found out that the liquor I'd been drinkin' and enjoyin' was a mixture of bath salts and assorted paints, and the car we'd paid seventeen hundred smackers for wasn't nowhere near as much of a car as one that Tom could of got for us for eight hundred on account of knowin' a brother-in-law of a fella that used to go to school with the president of the company's nephew, and that if Ada would take up aesthetic dancin' under a dame Belle knew about, why she'd never have no more trouble with her tonsils.

Nothin' we had or nothin' we talked about gettin' or doin' was worth a damn unless it was recommended or suggested by the Stevenses.

Well, I done a pretty good business this fall and I and Ada had always planned to spend a winter in the South, so one night we figured it out that this was the year we could spare the money and the time and if we didn't go this year we never would. So the next thing was where should we go, and we finally decided on Miami. And we said we wouldn't mention nothin' about it to Tom and Belle till the day we was goin'. We'd pretend we was doin' it out of a clear sky.

But a secret is just as safe with Ada as a police dog tethered with dental floss. It wasn't more than a day or two after we'd had our talk when Tom and Belle sprang the news that they was leavin' for California right after New Year's. And why didn't we go with them.

Well, I didn't say nothin' and Ada said it sounded grand, but it was impossible. Then Stevens said if it was a question of money, to not let that bother us as he would loan it to me and I could pay it back whenever I felt like it. That was more than Ada could stand, so she says we wasn't as poor as people seemed to think and the reason we couldn't go to California was because we was goin' to Miami.

This was such a surprise that it almost struck 'em dumb at first and all Tom could think of to say, was that he'd been to Miami himself and it was too crowded and he'd lay off of it if he was us. But the next time we seen 'em they had our trip all arranged.

First, Tom asked me what road we was goin' on and I told him the Big Four. So he asked if we had our reservations and I told him yes.

"Well," he said, "we'll get rid of 'em and I'll fix you up on the C. & E. I. The general passenger agent is a friend of mine and they

273

ain't nothin' he won't do for my friends. He'll see that you're treated right and that you get there in good shape."

So I said:

"I don't want to put you to all that trouble, and besides I don't know nobody connected with the Big Four well enough for them to resent me travelin' on their lines, and as for gettin' there in good shape, even if I have a secret enemy or two on the Big Four, I don't believe they'd endanger the lives of the other passengers just to see that I didn't get there in good shape."

But Stevens insisted on takin' my tickets and sellin' 'em back to the Big Four and gettin' me fixed on the C. & E. I. The berths we'd had on the Big Four was Lower 9 and Lower 10. The berths Tom got us on the C. & E. I. was Lower 7 and Lower 8, which he said was better. I suppose he figured that the nearer you are to the middle of the car, the less chance there is of bein' woke up if your car gets in another train's way.

He wanted to know, too, if I'd made any reservations at a hotel. I showed him a wire I had from the Royal Palm in reply to a wire I'd sent 'em.

"Yes," he says, "but you don't want to stop at the Royal Palm. You wire and tell 'em to cancel that and I'll make arrangements for you at the Flamingo, over at the Beach. Charley Krom, the manager there, was born and raised in the same town I was. He'll take great care of you if he knows you're a friend of mine."

So I asked him if all the guests at the Flamingo was friends of his, and he said of course not; what did I mean?

"Well," I said, "I was just thinkin' that if they ain't, Mr. Krom probably makes life pretty miserable for 'em. What does he do, have the phone girl ring 'em up at all hours of the night, and hide their mail, and shut off their hot water, and put cracker crumbs in their beds?"

That didn't mean nothin' to Stevens and he went right ahead and switched me from one hotel to the other.

While Tom was reorganizin' my program and tellin' me what to eat in Florida, and what bait to use for barracuda and carp, and what time to go bathin' and which foot to stick in the water first, why Belle was makin' Ada return all the stuff she had boughten to wear down there and buy other stuff that Belle picked out for her at joints where Belle was so well known that they only soaked her twice as much as a stranger. She had Ada almost crazy, but I told her to never mind; in just a few more days we'd be where they couldn't get at us.

I suppose you're wonderin' why didn't we quarrel with 'em and break loose from 'em and tell 'em to leave us alone. You'd know why if you knew them. Nothin' we could do would convince 'em that we didn't want their advice and help. And nothin' we could say was a insult.

Well, the night before we was due to leave Chi, the phone rung and I answered it. It was Tom.

"I've got a surprise for you," he says. "I and Belle has give up the California idear. We're goin' to Miami instead, and on account of me knowin' the boys down at the C. & E. I., I've landed a drawin' room on the same train you're takin'. How is that for news?"

"Great!" I said, and I went back and broke it to Ada. For a minute I thought she was goin' to faint. And all night long she moaned and groaned and had hysterics.

So that's how we happened to come to Biloxi.

Ladies' Wild

Robert Benchley

In the exclusive set (no diptheria cases allowed) in which I travel, I am known as a heel in the matter of parlor games. I will drink with them and, now and again, leer at the ladies, but when they bring out the bundles of pencils and the pads of paper and start putting down all the things they can think of beginning with "W," or enumerating each other's bad qualities on a scale of 100 (no hard-feeling results, mind you — just life-long enmity), I tiptoe noisily out of the room and say: "The hell with you."

For this reason, I am not usually included in any little games that may be planned in advance. If they foresee an evening of "Consequences" coming over them, they whisper, "Get Benchley out of the house. Get him a horse to ride, or some beads to string — anything to get him out of the way." For, I forgot to tell you, not only am I a non-participant in parlor games, but I am a militant non-participant. I heckle from the sidelines. I throw stones and spit at the players. Hence the nickname: "Sweet Old Bob," or sometimes just the initials.

One night last summer, I detected, from the general stir among the ladies and more effete gents, that I was being eased out of the house. This meant that the gaming was about to begin. But instead of the usual clatter of pencils among the *croupiers,* I saw someone sneaking in with a tray of poker chips. They almost had me out the door when I discovered what was up.

"Well, so long, Bob," they said. "Good bowling to you."

"What's this?" I came back into the room. "Are those poker chips?"

"Sure, they're poker chips. It's all right to play poker, isn't it? The reform administration's gone out."

I assumed a hurt air. In fact, I didn't have to assume it, I was hurt.

"I don't suppose I'm good enough to play poker with you." I said. "All I'm good enough for is to furnish the liquor and the dancing girls."

"Why, we thought you didn't like games. You always act like such a goddamned heel whenever a game is suggested."

"My dear people," I said, trying to be calm, "there are games and games. "Twenty Questions is one game, if you will, but poker — why, poker is a man's game. It's my dish. I'm an old newspaperman, you know. Poker is the breath of life to a newspaperman." (As a matter of fact, I never played poker once when I was on a newspaper, and was never allowed to do more than kibitz at the Thanatopsis games of Broun, Adams, Kaufman, and that bunch, but poker is still my favorite game in a small way, or at least it *was*.)

Then there was a great scrambling to get me a chair, and sell me chips. "Old Bob's going to play!" was the cry. "Old Bob likes poker!" People came in from the next room to see what the commotion was, and one woman said that, if I was going to play, she had a headache. (I had ruined a game of "Who Am I?" for her once by blowing out a fuse from the coat-closet.)

As for me, I acted the part to the hilt. I took off my coat, unbuttoned my vest so that just the watch-chain connected it, lighted my pipe, and kept my hat on the back of my head.

"This is the real poker costume," I said. "The way we used to play it down on the old *Trib*. There ought to be a City News ticker over in the corner to make it seem like home."

"I'm afraid he's going to be too good for us." said one of the more timid ladies. "We play for very small stakes, you know."

"The money doesn't matter," I laughed. "It's the game. And anyway," I added modestly, "I haven't played for a long time. You'll probably take me good." (I wish now that I had made book on that prediction.)

It was to be Dealer's Choice, which should

have given me a tipoff right there, with three women at the table, one the dealer.

"This," she announced, looking up into space as if for inspiration, "is going to be 'Hay Fever.' "

"I beg pardon," I said, leaning forward.

" 'Hay Fever,' " explained one of the men. "The girls like it. One card up, two down, the last two up. One-eyed Jacks, sevens, and nines wild. High-low."

"I thought this was going to be poker," I said.

"From then on you play it just like regular poker," said the dealer.

From then on! My God! Just like regular poker!

Having established myself as an old poker-fan, I didn't want to break down and cry at the very start, so I played the hand through. I say I "played" it. I sat looking at my cards, peeking now and then just to throw a bluff that I knew what I was doing. One-eyed Jacks, sevens, and nines wild, I kept saying that to myself, and puffing very hard at my pipe. After a minute of owlish deliberation, I folded.

The next hand was to be "Whistle Up Your Windpipe," another one which the girls had introduced into the group and which the men, weak-kneed sissies that they were, had allowed to become regulation. This was seven-card stud, first and last cards up, deuces, treys, and red-haired Queens wild, high-low-and-medium. I figured out that I had a very nice straight, bet it as I would have bet a straight in the old days, and was beaten to eleven dollars and sixty cents by a royal straight flush. Amid general laughter, I was told that an ordinary straight in these games is worth no more than a pair of sixes in regular poker. A royal straight flush usually wins. Well, it usually won in the old days, too.

By the time the deal came to me, my pipe had gone out and I had taken my hat off. Between clenched teeth I announced: "And this, my frands, is going to be something *you* may have not heard of. This is going to be *old-fashioned draw-poker*, with *nothing* wild." The women had to have it explained to them, and remarked that they didn't see much fun in that. However, the hand was played. Nobody had anything (in comparison to what they had been having in the boom days), and nobody bet. The hand was over in a minute and a half, amid terrific silence.

That was the chief horror of this epidemic of "Whistle Up Your Windpipe," "Beezy-Weezy," and "Mice Afloat." It made old-fashioned stud seem tame, even to me. Every time it came to me, I elected the old game, just out of spite, but nobody's heart was in it. I became the spoil-sport of the party again, and once or twice I caught them trying to slip the deal past me, as if by mistake. Even a round of jack-pots netted nothing in the way of excitement, and even when I won one on a full-house, there was no savor to the victory, as I had to explain to the women what a full-house was. They thought that I was making up my own rules. Nothing as small as a full-house had ever been seen in that game.

The Big Newspaper Man was taken for exactly sixty-one dollars and eight cents when the game broke up at four A.M. Two of the women were the big winners. They had finally got it down to a game where everything was wild but the black nines, and everyone was trying for "low."

From now on I not only walk out on "Twenty Questions" and "Who Am I?" but, when there are ladies present (God *bless* them!), I walk out on poker. And a fine state of affairs it is when an old newspaperman has to walk out on poker!

Christmas Afternoon
(Done in the Manner, if Not the Spirit, of Dickens)

Robert Benchley

What an afternoon! Mr. Gummidge said that, in his estimation, there never had *been* such an afternoon since the world began, a sentiment which was heartily endorsed by Mrs. Gummidge and all the little Gummidges, not to mention the relatives who had come over from Jersey for the day.

In the first place, there was the *ennui*. And such *ennui* as it was! A heavy, overpowering *ennui*, such as results from a participation in eight courses of steaming, gravied food, topping off with salted nuts which the little old spinster Gummidge from Oak Hill said she never knew when to stop eating — and true enough she didn't — a dragging, devitalizing *ennui*, which left its victims strewn about the living-room in various attitudes of prostration suggestive of those of the petrified occupants in a newly unearthed Pompeiian dwelling; an *ennui* which carried with it a retinue of yawns, snarls and thinly veiled insults, and which ended in

283

ruptures in the clan spirit serious enough to last throughout the glad new year.

Then there were the toys! Three and a quarter dozen toys to be divided among seven children. Surely enough, you or I might say, to satisfy the little tots. But that would be because we didn't know the tots. In came Baby Lester Gummidge, Lillian's boy, dragging an electric grain-elevator which happened to be the only toy in the entire collection which appealed to little Norman, five-year-old son of Luther, who lived in Rahway. In came curly-headed Effie in frantic and throaty disputation with Arthur, Jr., over the possession of an articulated zebra. In came Everett, bearing a mechanical Negro which would no longer dance, owing to a previous forcible feeding by the baby of a marshmallow into its only available aperture. In came Fonlansbee, teeth buried in the hand of little Ormond, which bore a popular but battered remnant of what had once been the proud false-bosom of a hussar's uniform. In they all came, one after another, some crying, some snapping, some pulling, some pushing — all appealing to their respective parents for aid in their intramural warfare.

And the cigar smoke! Mrs. Gummidge said that she didn't mind the smoke from a good cigarette, but would they mind if she opened the windows for just a minute in order to clear the room of the heavy aroma of used cigars? Mr. Gummidge stoutly maintained that they were good cigars. His brother, George Gummidge, said that he, likewise, would say that they were. At which colloquial sally both the Gummidge brothers laughed testily, thereby breaking the laughter record for the afternoon.

Aunt Libbie, who lived with George, remarked from the dark corner of the room that it seemed just like Sunday to her. An amendment was offered to this statement by the cousin, who was in the insurance business, stating that it was worse than Sunday. Murmurings indicative of as hearty agreement with this sentiment as their lethargy would allow came from the other members of the family circle, causing Mr. Gummidge to suggest a walk in the air to settle their dinner.

And then arose such a chorus of protestations as has seldom been heard. It was too cloudy to walk. It was too raw. It looked like snow. It looked like rain. Luther Gummidge said that he must be starting along home soon, anyway, bringing forth the acid query from Mrs. Gummidge as to whether or not he was bored. Lillian said that she felt a cold coming on, and added that something they had had for dinner must have been undercooked. And so it went, back and forth, forth and back, up and down, and in and out, until Mr. Gummidge's suggestion of a walk in the air was reduced to a tattered impossibility and the entire company glowed with ill-feeling.

In the meantime, we must not forget the

children. No one else could. Aunt Libbie said that she didn't think there was anything like children to make a Christmas; to which Uncle Ray, the one with the Masonic fob, said, "No, thank God!" Although Christmas is supposed to be the season of good cheer, you (or I, for that matter) couldn't have told, from listening to the little ones, but what it was the children's Armageddon season, when Nature had decreed that only the fittest should survive, in order that the race might be carried on by the strongest, the most predatory and those possessing the best protective coloring. Although there were constant admonitions to Fonlansbee to "Let Ormond have that now; it's his," and to Arthur, Jr., not to be selfish, but to "give the kiddie-car to Effie; she's smaller than you are," the net result was always that Fonlansbee kept the whistle and Arthur, Jr., rode in permanent, albeit disputed, possession of the kiddie-car. Oh, that we mortals should set ourselves up against the inscrutable workings of Nature!

Hallo! A great deal of commotion! That was Uncle George stumbling over the electric train, which had early in the afternoon ceased to function and which had been left directly across the threshold. A great deal of crying! That was Arthur, Jr., bewailing the destruction of his already useless train, about which he had forgotten until the present moment. A great deal of recrimination! That was Arthur, Sr., and George fixing it up. And finally a great crashing! That was Baby Lester pulling over the tree on top of himself, necessitating the bringing to bear of all of Uncle Ray's knowledge of forestry to extricate him from the wreckage.

And finally Mrs. Gummidge passed the Christmas candy around. Mr. Gummidge afterward admitted that this was a tactical error on the part of his spouse. I no more believe that Mrs. Gummidge thought they wanted the cold turkey which she later suggested. My opinion is that she wanted to drive them home. At any rate, that is what she succeeded in doing. Such cries as there were of "Ugh! Don't let me see another thing to eat!" and "Take it away!" Then came hurried scramblings in the coat-closet for overshoes. There were the rasping sounds made by cross parents when putting wraps on children. There were insincere exhortations to "come and see us soon" and to "get together for lunch some time." And, finally, there were slammings of doors and the silence of utter exhaustion, while Mrs. Gummidge went about picking up stray sheets of wrapping paper.

And, as Tiny Tim might say in speaking of Christmas afternoons as an institution, "God help us, every one."

Groucho and Chico Make a Deal

George S. Kaufman and Morrie Ryskind

GROUCHO: Two beers, bartender.

CHICO: I'll take two beers, too.

GROUCHO (*drifting right into that barroom conversation*): Well, things seem to be getting better around the country.

CHICO: I don't know — I'm a stranger here myself.

GROUCHO (*looking at him curiously*): Stranger? Aren't you an Italian?

CHICO: No, no. I just look that way because my mother and father are Italian.

GROUCHO: I just remembered — I came back here looking for somebody. You don't know who it is, do you?

CHICO: Funny — it just slipped my mind.

GROUCHO (*snapping his fingers*): I remember now, the greatest tenor in the world! That's what I'm after!

CHICO: That's funny. I am his manager.

GROUCHO: Whose manager?

CHICO: The greatest tenor in the world.

GROUCHO: The fellow that sings at the opera here?

CHICO: Sure!

GROUCHO: What's his name?

CHICO: What do you care? Some Italian name — I can't pronounce it. What you want with him?

GROUCHO: Well, I'd like to offer him a job. Would he be interested?

CHICO: I don't know, but *I'm* interested. That's the main thing. What sort of job?

GROUCHO: With the New York Opera. America is waiting to hear him sing.

CHICO: Well, he can sing loud, but he can't sing that loud.

GROUCHO: Well, I think we can get America to meet him halfway. The main thing is, can he sail tomorrow night?

CHICO: If you pay him enough money, he can sail *last* night. How much you pay him?

GROUCHO *(aside):* Let's see — a thousand dollars a night. I'm entitled to a little profit.(*To* CHICO) How about ten dollars a night?

  CHICO *laughs scornfully.*

CHICO: Ten dollars! . . . (*A quick change of mood*) All right. I'll take it.

GROUCHO: That's fine. Of course, I want a ten-per-cent commission for putting the deal over.

CHICO: And I get ten per cent as his manager.

GROUCHO: Well that leaves eight dollars. Say he sings once a week — that's eight dollars a week clear profit for him.

CHICO (*considering a week*): He sends five dollars home to his mother.

GROUCHO: Well, that still leaves him three dollars.

CHICO: Three dollars. Can he live in New York on that?

GROUCHO: Like a prince — of course, he won't be able to eat but he can live like a prince. Oh, I forgot to tell you. He'll have to pay income tax on that three dollars.

CHICO: Income tax?

GROUCHO: Yes, there's a federal tax and the state tax and there may be a city tax. And, naturally, a sales tax.

CHICO: How much does that all come to?

GROUCHO: Well, I figure if he doesn't sing too often, he can break even.

CHICO: All right. We'll take it.

GROUCHO: Fine! (*He pulls out two contracts*) Now just his name there and you sign on the bottom. You don't have to read yours because it's a duplicate.

CHICO: What?

GROUCHO: A duplicate. (CHICO *looks at him*) Don't you know what duplicates are?

CHICO: Oh, sure! Those five kids up in Canada.

GROUCHO: Well, I wouldn't know about that. I haven't been in Canada for years.

CHICO: Wait a minute. Before I sign anything, what does it say?

GROUCHO: Go ahead and read it.

CHICO: (*a little reluctantly*): Well — er — you

read it. I don't like to read anything unless I know what it says.

GROUCHO (*catching on*): I see. All right, *I'll* read it to you. Can you hear?

CHICO: I haven't heard anything yet. Did you say anything?

GROUCHO: Well, I haven't said anything worth hearing.

CHICO: I guess that's why I didn't hear anything.

GROUCHO (*having the last word*): Well, that's why I didn't say anything.

(*He scans the contract, holding it near him and then far away.* CHICO *watches him suspiciously*)

CHICO: Wait a minute. Can *you* read?

GROUCHO (*holding contract farther and farther away*): I can read, but I can't see it. If my arms were a little longer, I could read it . . . . Ah, here we are. Now pay attention to this first clause. (*Reads*) "The party of the first part shall be known in this contract as the party of the first part." How do you like that. Pretty neat, eh?

CHICO: No, that'sa no good.

GROUCHO (*indignantly*): What's the matter with it?

CHICO (*conciliatorily*): I don't know — let's hear it again.

GROUCHO: "The party of the first part shall be known in this contract as the party of the first part."

CHICO: It sounds a little better this time.

GROUCHO: Well, it grows on you. Want to hear

it once more?

CHICO: Only the first part.

GROUCHO: The *party* of the first part?

CHICO: No. The *first part* of the party of the first part.

GROUCHO: Well, it says "The first part of the party of the first part shall be known in this contract" — look! Why should we quarrel about a thing like that? (*He tears off the offending clause*) We'll take it right out.

CHICO (*tearing the same clause out of his contract*): Sure, it's too long anyhow. Now what have we got left?

GROUCHO: Well, I've got about a foot and a half . . . . Now, then: "The party of the second part shall be known in this contract as the party of the second part."

CHICO: Well, I don't know. I don't like the second party, either.

GROUCHO: You should have come to the first party. We didn't get home till around four in the morning. (*Slight pause*) I was blind for three days.

CHICO: Look, couldn't the first part of the second party be the second part of the first party? Then we got something.

GROUCHO: Look! Rather than go through all that again, what do you say? (*He indicates a willingness to tear further*)

CHICO: Fine. (*They both tear off another piece*)

GROUCHO: Now, I've got something here you're *bound* to like. You'll be crazy about it.

CHICO: No, I don't like it.

GROUCHO: You don't like what?

CHICO: Whatever it is.

GROUCHO: All right. Why should we break up an old friendship over a thing like this? Ready?

CHICO: Okay. (*They both tear*) Now, the next part I don't think *you're* going to like.

GROUCHO: All right — your word's good enough for me. (*They both tear*) Now then, is *my* word good enough for *you?*

CHICO: I should say not.

GROUCHO: All right — let's go. (*They both tear,* GROUCHO *looking at the contract*) The party of the eighth part —

CHICO: No. (*They tear*)

GROUCHO: The party of the ninth part —

CHICO: No. (*They tear*) Say, how is it I got a skinnier contract than you?

GROUCHO: I don't know. You must have been out on a tear last night. Anyhow, now we're all set. Now sign right here. (*He produces a fountain pen*)

CHICO: I forgot to tell you. I can't write.

GROUCHO: That's all right. There's no ink in the pen, anyway. But, listen, it's a bargain, isn't it? We've got a contract, no matter how small it is.

CHICO (*extending hand.* GROUCHO *clasps it*): You betcha! Only one thing I want to know: what does this say? (*Showing last piece of contract left*)

GROUCHO: Oh, that's nothing. That's the usual clause in every contract. It says if any of the parties participating in the contract are shown not to be in their right mind, the contract is nullified.

CHICO: What do you call it?

GROUCHO: That's what they call a sanity clause.

CHICO: You can't fool me. There ain't no sanity clause!

The Cliché Expert Testifies on Love

Frank Sullivan

Q — Mr. Arbuthnot, as an expert in the use of the cliché, are you prepared to testify here today regarding its application in topics of sex, love, matrimony, and so on?

A — I am.

Q — Very good. Now, Mr. Arbuthnot, what is love?

A — Love is blind.

Q — Good. What does love do?

A — Love makes the world go round.

Q — Whom does a young man fall in love with?

A — With the Only Girl in the World.

Q — Whom does a young woman fall in love with?

A — With the Only Boy in the World.

Q — When do they fall in love?

A — At first sight.

Q — How?

A — Madly.

Q — They are then said to be?

A — Victims of Cupid's darts.

Q — And he?

A — Whispers sweet nothings in her ear.

Q — Who loves a lover?

A — All the world loves a lover.

Q — Describe the Only Girl in the World.

A — Her eyes are like stars. Her teeth are like pearls. Her lips are ruby. Her cheek is damask, and her form divine.

Q — Haven't you forgotten something?

A — Eyes, teeth, lips, cheek, form — no, sir, I don't think so.

Q — Her hair?

A — Oh, certainly. How stupid of me. She has hair like spun gold.

Q — Very good, Mr Arbuthnot. Now will you describe the Only Man?

A — He is a blond Viking, a he-man, and a square shooter who plays the game. There is something fine about him that rings true, and he has kept himself pure and clean so that when he meets the girl of his choice, the future mother of his children, he can look her in the eye.

Q — How?

A — Without flinching.

Q — Are all the Only Men blond Vikings?

A — Oh, no. Some of them are dark, handsome chaps who have sown their wild oats. This sort of Only Man has a way with a maid, and there is a devil in his eye. But he is not a cad; he would not play fast and loose with an Only

Girl's affections. He has a heart of gold. He is a diamond in the rough. He tells the Only Girl frankly about his Past. She understands — and forgives.

Q — And marries him?

A — And marries him.

Q — Why?

A — To reform him.

Q — Does she reform him?

A — Seldom.

Q — Seldom what?

A — Seldom, if ever.

Q — Now, Mr. Arbuthnot, when the Only Man falls in love, madly, with the Only Girl, what does he do?

A — He walks on air.

Q — Yes, I know, but what does he do? I mean, what is it he pops?

A — Oh, excuse me. The question, of course.

Q — Then what do they plight?

A — Their troth.

Q — What happens after that?

A — They get married.

Q — What is marriage?

A — Marriage is a lottery.

Q — Where are marriages made?

A — Marriages are made in Heaven.

Q — What does the bride do at the wedding?

A — She blushes.

Q — What does the groom do?

A — Forgets the ring.

Q — After the marriage, what?

A — The honeymoon.

Q — Then what?

A — She has a little secret.

Q — What is it?

A — She is knitting a tiny garment.

Q — What happens after that?

A — Oh, they settle down and raise a family and live happily ever afterward, unless —

Q — Unless what?

A — Unless he is a fool for a pretty face.

Q — And if he is?

A — Then they come to the parting of the ways.

Q — Mr. Arbuthnot, thank you very much.

A — But I'm not through yet, Mr. Untermyer.

Q — No?

A — Oh, no. There is another side to sex.

Q — There is? What side?

A — The seamy side. There are, you know, men who are wolves in sheep's clothing and there are, alas, lovely women who stoop to folly.

Q — My goodness! Describe these men you speak of, please.

A — They are snakes in the grass who do not place woman upon a pedestal. They are cads who kiss and tell, who trifle with a girl's affections and betray her innocent trust. They are cynics who think that a woman is only a woman, but a good cigar is a smoke. Their mottoes are "Love 'em and leave 'em" and "Catch 'em young, treat 'em rough, tell 'em nothing." These cads speak of "the light that lies in woman's eyes, and lies — and lies — and lies." In olden days they wore black, curling mustachios, which they twirled, and they invited innocent Gibson girls to midnight suppers, with champagne, at their bachelor apartments, and said, "Little girl, why do you fear me?" Nowadays they have black, patent-leather hair, and roadsters, and they drive up to the curb and say, "Girlie, can I give you a lift?" They are fiends in human form, who would rob a woman of her most priceless possession.

Q — What is that?

A — Her honor.

Q — How do they rob her?

A — By making improper advances.

Q — What does a woman do when a snake in the grass tries to rob her of her honor?

A — She defends her honor.

Q — How?

A — By repulsing his advances and scorning his embraces.

Q — How does she do that?

A — By saying, "Sir, I believe you forget yourself," or "Please take your arm away," or "I'll kindly thank you to remember I'm a lady," or "Let's not spoil it all."

Q — Suppose she doesn't say any of those things?

A — In that case, she takes the first false step.

Q — Where does the first false step take her?

A — Down the primrose path.

Q — What's the primrose path?

A — It's the easiest way.

Q — Where does it lead?

A — To a life of shame.

Q — What is a life of shame?

A — A life of shame is a fate worse than death.

Q — Now, after lovely woman has stooped to folly, what does she do to the gay Lothario who has robbed her of her most priceless possession?

A — She devotes the best years of her life to him.

Q — Then what does he do?

A — He casts her off.

Q — How?

A — Like an old shoe.

Q — Then what does she do?

A — She goes to their love nest, then everything goes black before her, her mind becomes a blank, she pulls a revolver, and gives the fiend in human form something to remember her by.

Q — That is called?

A — Avenging her honor.

Q — What is it no jury will do in such a case?

A — No jury will convict.

Q — Mr. Arbuthnot, your explanation of the correct application of the cliché in these matters has been most instructive, and I know that all of us cliché-users here will know exactly how to respond hereafter when, during a conversation, sex — when sex — when — ah —

A — I think what you want to say is "When

sex rears its ugly head," isn't it?

Q — Thank you, Mr. Arbuthnot. Thank you very much.

A — Thank *you*, Mr. Untermyer.

Gentlemen Prefer Blondes

Anita Loos

March 16th:

A gentleman friend and I were dining at
the Ritz last evening and he said that if I
took a pencil and a paper and put down all
of my thoughts it would make a book. This
almost made me smile as what it would really
make would be a whole row of encyclopediacs.
I mean I seem to be thinking practically all
of the time. I mean it is my favorite recreation
and sometimes I sit for hours and do not
seem to do anything else but think. So this
gentleman said a girl with brains ought to do
something else with them besides think. And
he said he ought to know brains when he
sees them, because he is in the senate and he
spends quite a great deal of time in Washington, d. c., and when he comes into contract
with brains he always notices it. So it might
have all blown over but this morning he sent
me a book. And so when my maid brought
it to me, I said to her, "Well, Lulu, here is

another book and we have not read half the ones we have got yet." But when I opened it and saw that it was all a blank I remembered what my gentleman acquaintance said, and so then I realized that it was a diary. So here I am writing a book instead of reading one.

But now it is the 16th of March and of course it is to late to begin with January, but it does not matter as my gentleman friend, Mr. Eisman, was in town practically all of January and February, and when he is in town one day seems to be practically the same as the next day.

I mean Mr. Eisman is in the wholesale button profession in Chicago and he is the gentleman who is known practically all over Chicago as Gus Eisman the Button King. And he is the gentleman who is interested in educating me, so of course he is always coming down to New York to see how my brains have improved since the last time. But when Mr. Eisman is in New York we always seem to do the same thing and if I wrote one day in my diary, all I would have to do would be to put quotation marks for all other days. I mean we always seem to have dinner at the Colony and see a show and go to the Trocadero and then Mr. Eisman shows me to my apartment. So of course when a gentleman is interested in educating a girl, he likes to stay and talk about the topics of the day until quite late, so I am quite fatigued the next day and I do not really get up until it is time to dress for dinner at the Colony.

It would be strange if I turned out to be an authoress. I mean at my home near Little Rock, Arkansas, my family all wanted me to do something about my music. Because all of my friends said I had talent and they all kept after me about practising. I mean I simply could not sit for hours and hours at a time practising just for the sake of a career. So one day I got quite tempermental and threw the old mandolin clear across the room and I have really never touched it since. But writing is different because you do not have to learn or practise and it is more tempermental because practising seems to take all the temperment out of me. So now I really almost have to smile because I have just noticed that I have written clear across two pages onto March 18th, so this will do for today and tomorrow. And it just shows how tempermental I am when I get started.

March 19th:

Well last evening Dorothy called up and Dorothy said she has met a gentleman who gave himself an introduction to her in the lobby of the Ritz. So then they went to luncheon and tea and dinner and then they went to a show and then they went to the Trocadero. So Dorothy said his name was Lord Cooksleigh but what she really calls him is Coocoo. So Dorothy said why don't you and I and Coocoo go to the Follies tonight and bring Gus along if he is in town? So then Dorothy and I had quite a little quarrel because every time that Dorothy mentions the subject of Mr. Eisman she calls Mr. Eisman by his first name, and she does not seem to realize that when a gentleman who is as important as Mr. Eisman, spends quite a lot of money educating a girl, it really does not show reverence to call a gentleman by his first name. I mean I never even think of calling Mr. Eisman by his first name, but if I want to call him anything at all, I call him "Daddy" and I do not even call him "Daddy" if a place seems to be public. So I told Dorothy that Mr. Eisman would not be in town until day after tomorrow. So then Dorothy and Coocoo came up and we went to the Follies.

So this morning Coocoo called up and he wanted me to luncheon at the Ritz. I mean these foreigners really have quite a nerve. Just because Coocoo is an Englishman and a Lord he thinks a girl can waste hours on him just for a luncheon at the Ritz, when all he does is talk about some exposition he went on to a place called Tibet and after talking for hours I found out that all they were was a lot of Chinamen. So I will be quite glad to see Mr. Eisman when he gets in. Because he always has something quite interesting to talk about, as for instants the last time he was here he presented me with quite a beautiful emerald bracelet. So next week is my birthday and he always has some delightful surprise on holidays.

I did intend to luncheon at the Ritz with Dorothy today and of course Coocoo had to spoil it, as I told him that I could not luncheon with him today, because my brother was in town on business and had the mumps, so I really could not leave him alone. Because of course if I went to the Ritz now I would bump into Coocoo. But I sometimes almost have to smile at my own imagination, because of course I have not got any brother and I have not even thought of the mumps for years. I mean it is no wonder that I can write.

So the reason I thought I would take luncheon at the Ritz was because Mr. Chaplin is at the Ritz and I always like to renew old acquaintances, because I met Mr. Chaplin once when we were both working on the same lot in Hollywood and I am sure he would remember me. Gentlemen always seem to remember blondes. I mean the only career I would like to be besides an authoress is a cinema star and I was doing quite well in the cinema when Mr. Eisman made me give it all up. Because of course when a gentleman takes such a friendly interest in educating a girl as Mr. Eisman does, you like to show that you appreciate it, and he is against a girl being in the cinema because his mother is authrodox.

March 20th:
Mr. Eisman gets in tomorrow to be here in time for my birthday. So I thought it would really be delightful to have at least one good time before Mr. Eisman got in, so last evening I had some literary gentlemen in to spend the evening because Mr. Eisman always likes me to have literary people in and out of the apartment. I mean he is quite anxious for a girl to improve her mind and his greatest interest in me is because I always seem to want to improve my mind and not waste any time. And Mr. Eisman likes me to have what the French people call a "salo" which means that people all get together in the evening and improve their minds. So I invited all of the brainy gentlemen I could think up. So I thought up a gentleman who is the proffessor of all the economics up at Columbia College, and the editor who is the famous editor of the New York Transcript and another gentleman who is a famous playright who writes very, very famous plays that are all about Life. I mean anybody would recognize his name but it always seems to slip my memory because all of we real friends of his only call him Sam. So Sam asked if he could bring a gentleman who writes novels

from England, so I said yes, so he brought him. And then we all got together and I called up Gloria and Dorothy and the gentlemen brought their own liquor. So of course the place was a wreck this morning and Lulu and I worked like proverbial dogs to get it cleaned up, but Heaven knows how long it will take to get the chandelier fixed.

March 22nd:
Well my birthday has come and gone but it was really quite depressing. I mean it seems to me a gentleman who has a friendly interest in educating a girl like Gus Eisman, would want her to have the biggest square cut diamond in New York. I mean I must say I was quite disappointed when he came to the apartment with a little thing you could hardly see. So I told him I thought it was quite cute, but I had quite a headache and I had better stay in a dark room all day and I told him I would see him the next day, perhaps. Because even Lulu thought it was quite small and she said, if she was I, she really would do something definite and she said she always believed in the old addage, "Leave them while you're looking good." But he came in at dinner time with really a very very beautiful bracelet of square cut diamonds so I was quite cheered up. So then we had dinner at the Colony and we went to a show and supper at the Trocadero as usual whenever he is in

town. But I will give him credit that he realized how small it was. I mean he kept talking about how bad business was and the button profession was full of bolshevicks who make nothing but trouble. Because Mr. Eisman feels that the country is really on the verge of the bolshevicks and I become quite worried. I mean if the bolshevicks do get in, there is only one gentleman who could handle them and that is Mr. D. W. Griffith. Because I will never forget when Mr. Griffith was directing Intolerance. I mean it was my last cinema just before Mr. Eisman made me give up my career and I was playing one of the girls that fainted at the battle when all of the gentlemen fell off the tower. And when I saw how Mr. Griffith handled all of those mobs in Intolerance I realized that he could do anything, and I really think that the government of America ought to tell Mr. Griffith to get all ready if the bolshevicks start to do it.

Well I forgot to mention that the English gentleman who writes novels seems to have taken quite an interest in me, as soon as he found out that I was literary. I mean he has called up every day and I went to tea twice with him. So he has sent me a whole complete set of books for my birthday by a gentleman called Mr. Conrad. They all seem to be about ocean travel although I have not had time to more than glance through them. I have always

309

liked novels about ocean travel ever since I posed for Mr. Christie for the front cover of a novel about ocean travel by McGrath because I always say that a girl never really looks as well as she does on board a steamship, or even a yacht.

So the English gentleman's name is Mr. Gerald Lamson as those who have read his novels would know. And he also sent me some of his own novels and they all seem to be about middle age English gentlemen who live in the country over in London and seem to ride bicycles, which seems quite different from America, except at Palm Beach. So I told Mr. Lamson how I write down all of my thoughts and he said he knew I had something to me from the first minute he saw me and when we become better acquainted I am going to let him read my diary. I mean I even told Mr. Eisman about him and he is quite pleased. Because of course Mr. Lamson is quite famous and it seems Mr. Eisman has read all of his novels going to and fro on the trains and Mr. Eisman is always anxious to meet famous people and take them to the Ritz to dinner on Saturday night. But of course I did not tell Mr. Eisman that I am really getting quite a little crush on Mr. Lamson, which I really believe I am, but Mr. Eisman thinks my interest in him is more literary.

March 30th:

At last Mr. Eisman has left on the 20th Century and I must say I am quite fatigued and a little rest will be quite welcome. I mean I do not mind staying out late every night if I dance, but Mr. Eisman is really not such a good dancer so most of the time we just sit and drink some champagne or have a bite to eat and of course I do not dance with anyone else when I am out with Mr. Eisman. But Mr. Eisman and Gerry, as Mr. Lamson wants me to call him, became quite good friends and we had several evenings, all three together. So now that Mr. Eisman is out of town at last, Gerry and I are going out together this evening and Gerry said not to dress up, because Gerry seems to like me more for my soul. So I really had to tell Gerry that if all the gentlemen were like he seems to be, Madame Frances' whole dress making establishment would have to go out of business. But Gerry does not like a girl to be nothing else but a doll, but he likes her to bring in her husband's slippers every evening and make him forget what he has gone through.

But before Mr. Eisman went to Chicago he told me that he is going to Paris this summer on professional business and I think he intends to present me with a trip to Paris as he says there is nothing so educational as traveling. I mean it did worlds of good to

Dorothy when she went abroad last spring and I never get tired of hearing her telling how the merry-go-rounds in Paris have pigs instead of horses. But I really do not know whether to be thrilled or not because, of course, if I go to Paris I will have to leave Gerry and both Gerry and I have made up our minds not to be separated from one another from now on.

March 31st:

Last night Gerry and I had dinner at quite a quaint place where we had roast beef and baked potato. I mean he always wants me to have food which is what he calls "nourishing," which most gentlemen never seem to think about. So then we took a hansom cab and drove for hours around the park because Gerry said the air would be good for me. It is really very sweet to have some one think of all those things that gentlemen hardly ever seem to think about. So then we talked quite a lot. I mean Gerry knows how to draw a girl out and I told him things that I really would not even put in my diary. So when he heard all about my life he became quite depressed and we both had tears in our eyes. Because he said he never dreamed a girl could go through so much as I, and come out so sweet and not made bitter by it all. I mean Gerry thinks that most gentlemen are brutes and hardly ever think about a girl's soul.

So it seems that Gerry has had quite a lot of trouble himself and he can not even get married on account of his wife. He and she have never been in love with each other but she was a suffragette and asked him to marry her, so what could he do? So we rode all around the park until quite late talking and philosophizing quite a lot and I finally told him that I thought, after all, that bird life was the highest form of civilization. So Gerry calls me his little thinker and I really would not be surprised if all of my thoughts will give him quite a few ideas for his novels. Because Gerry says he has never seen a girl of my personal appearance with so many brains. And he had almost given up looking for his ideal when our paths seemed to cross each other and I told him I really thought a thing like that was nearly always the result of fate.

So Gerry says that I remind him quite a lot of Helen of Troy, who was of Greek extraction. But the only Greek I know is a Greek gentleman by the name of Mr. Georgopolis who is really quite wealthy and he is what Dorothy and I call a "Shopper" because you can always call him up at any hour and ask him to go shopping and he is always quite delighted, which very few gentlemen seem to be. And he never seems to care how much anything costs. I mean Mr. Georgopolis is also quite cultured, as I know quite a few gentlemen who can speak to a waiter in French but Mr. Georgopolis can also speak to a waiter in Greek which very few gentlemen seem to be able to do.

April 1st:

I am taking special pains with my diary from now on as I am really writing it for Gerry. I mean he and I are going to read it together some evening in front of the fireplace. But Gerry leaves this evening for Boston as he has to lecture about all of his works at Boston, but he will rush right back as soon as possible. So I am going to spend all of my time improving myself while he is gone. And this afternoon we are both going to a museum on 5th Avenue, because Gerry wants to show me a very very beautiful cup made by an antique jeweler called Mr. Cellini and he wants me to read Mr. Cellini's life which is a very fine book and not dull while he is in Boston.

So the famous playright friend of mine who is called Sam called up this morning and he wanted me to go to a literary party tonight that he and some other literary gentlemen are giving to Florence Mills in Harlem but Gerry does not want me to go with Sam as Sam always insists on telling riskay stories. But personally I am quite broad minded and I always say that I do not mind a riskay story as long as it is really funny. I mean I have a

314

great sense of humor. But Gerry says Sam does not always select and choose his stories and he just as soon I did not go out with him. So I am going to stay home and read the book by Mr. Cellini instead, because, after all, the only thing I am really interested in, is improving my mind. So I am going to do nothing else but improve my mind while Gerry is in Boston. I mean I just received a cable from Willie Gwynn who arrives from Europe tomorrow, but I am not even going to bother to see him. He is a sweet boy but he never gets anywhere and I am not going to waste my time on such as him, after meeting a gentleman like Gerry.

April 2nd:

I seem to be quite depressed this morning as I always am when there is nothing to put my mind to. Because I decided not to read the book by Mr. Cellini. I mean it was quite amuseing in spots because it was really quite riskay but the spots were not so close together and I never seem to like to always be hunting clear through a book for the spots I am looking for, especially when there are really not so many spots that seem to be so amuseing after all. So I did not waste my time on it but this morning I told Lulu to let all of the house work go and spend the day reading a book entitled "Lord Jim" and then tell me all about it, so that I would improve my mind while Gerry is away. But when I got her the book I nearly made a mistake and gave her a book by the title of "The Nigger of the Narcissus" which really would have hurt her feelings. I mean I do not know why authors cannot say "Negro" instead of "Nigger" as they have their feelings just the same as we have.

Well I just got a telegram from Gerry that he will not be back until tomorrow and also some orchids from Willie Gwynn, so I may as well go to the theatre with Willie tonight to keep from getting depressed, as he really is a sweet boy after all. I mean he never really does anything obnoxious. And it is quite depressing to stay at home and do nothing but read, unless you really have a book that is worth bothering about.

April 3rd:
I was really so depressed this morning that I was even glad to get a letter from Mr. Eisman. Because last night Willie Gwynn came to take me to the Follies, but he was so intoxicated that I had to telephone his club to send around a taxi to take him home. So that left me alone with Lulu at nine o'clock with nothing to do, so I put in a telephone call for Boston to talk to Gerry but it never went through. So Lulu tried to teach me how to play mah jong, but I really could not keep my mind on it because I was so

depressed. So today I think I had better go over to Madame Frances and order some new evening gowns to cheer me up.

Well Lulu just brought me a telegram from Gerry that he will be in this afternoon, but I must not meet him at the station on account of all the reporters who always meet him at the station wherever he comes from. But he says he will come right up to see me as he has something to talk about.

April 4th:

What an evening we had last evening. I mean it seems that Gerry is madly in love with me. Because all of the time he was in Boston lecturing to the womens clubs he said, as he looked over the faces of all those club women in Boston, he never realized I was so beautiful. And he said that there was only one in all the world and that was me. But it seems that Gerry thinks that Mr. Eisman is terrible and that no good can come of our friendship. I mean I was quite surprised, as they both seemed to get along quite well together, but it seems that Gerry never wants me to see Mr. Eisman again. And he wants me to give up everything and study French and he will get a divorce and we will be married. Because Gerry does not seem to like the kind of life all of us lead in New York and he wants me to go home to papa in Arkansas and he will send me books

317

to read so that I will not get lonesome there. And he gave me his uncle's Masonic ring, which came down from the time of Soloman and which he never even lets his wife wear, for our engagement ring, and this afternoon a lady friend of his is going to bring me a new system she thought up of how to learn French. But some way I still seem to be depressed. I mean I could not sleep all night thinking of the terrible things Gerry said about New York and about Mr. Eisman. Of course I can understand Gerry being jealous of any gentleman friend of mine and of course I never really thought that Mr. Eisman was Rudolph Valentino, but Gerry said it made him cringe to think of a sweet girl like I having a friendship with Mr. Eisman. So it really made me feel quite depressed. I mean Gerry likes to talk quite a lot and I always think a lot of talk is depressing and worries your brains with things you never even think of when you are busy. But so long as Gerry does not mind me going out with other gentlemen when they have something to give you mentally, I am going to luncheon with Eddie Goldmark of the Goldmark Films who is always wanting me to sign a contract to go into the cinema. Because Mr. Goldmark is madly in love with Dorothy and Dorothy is always wanting me to go back in the cinema because Dorothy says that she will go if I will go.

April 6th:

Well I finally wrote Mr. Eisman that I was going to get married and it seems that he is coming on at once as he would probably like to give me his advice. Getting married is really quite serious and Gerry talks to me for hours and hours about it. I mean he never seems to get tired of talking and he does not seem to even want to go to shows or dance or do anything else but talk, and if I don't really have something definite to put my mind on soon I will scream.

April 7th:

Well Mr. Eisman arrived this morning and he and I had quite a long talk, and after all I think he is right. Because here is the first real opportunity I have ever really had. I mean to go to Paris and broaden out and improve my writing, and why should I give it up to marry an author, where he is the whole thing and all I would be would be the wife of Gerald Lamson? And on top of that I would have to be dragged into the scandal of a divorce court and get my name smirched. So Mr. Eisman said that opportunities come to seldom in a girls life for me to give up the first one I have really ever had. So I am sailing for France and London on Tuesday and taking Dorothy with me and Mr. Eisman says that he will see us there later. So Dorothy knows all of the ropes and she can get along in Paris just as though she knew French and besides she knows a French gentleman who was born and raised there, and speaks it like a native and knows Paris like a book. And Dorothy says that when we get to London nearly everybody speaks English anyway. So it is quite lucky that Mr. Lamson is out lecturing in Cincinnati and he will not be back until Wednesday and I can send him a letter and tell him that I have to go to Europe now but I will see him later perhaps. So anyway I will be spared listening to any more of his depressing conversation. So Mr. Eisman gave me quite a nice string of pearls and he gave Dorothy a diamond pin and we all went to the Colony for dinner and we all went to a show and supper at the Trocadero and we all spent quite a pleasant evening.

Glory In The Daytime

Dorothy Parker

Mr. Murdock was one who carried no enthusiasm whatever for plays and their players, and that was too bad, for they meant so much to little Mrs. Murdock. Always she had been in a state of devout excitement over the luminous, free, passionate elect who serve the theater. And always she had done her wistful worshiping, along with the multitudes, at the great public altars. It is true that once, when she was a particularly little girl, love had impelled her to write Miss Maude Adams a letter beginning "Dearest Peter," and she had received from Miss Adams a miniature thimble inscribed "A kiss from Peter Pan." (That was a day!) And once, when her mother had taken her holiday shopping, a limousine door was held open and there had passed her, as close as *that*, a wonder of sable and violets and round red curls that seemed to tinkle on the air; so, forever after, she was as good as certain that she had been not a foot away from Miss Billie Burke. But until some three years after her marriage, these had remained her only personal experiences with the people of the lights and the glory.

Then it turned out that Miss Noyes, new-come to little Mrs. Murdock's own bridge club, knew an actress. She actually knew an actress; the way you and I know collectors of recipes and members of garden clubs and amateurs of needlepoint.

The name of the actress was Lily Wynton, and it was famous. She was tall and slow and silvery; often she appeared in the rôle of a duchess, or of a Lady Pam or an Honorable Moira. Critics recurrently referred to her as "that great lady of our stage." Mrs. Murdock had attended, over years, matinée performances of the Wynton successes. And she had no more thought that she would one day have opportunity to meet Lily Wynton face to face than she had thought — well, than she had thought of flying!

Yet it was not astounding that Miss Noyes should walk at ease among the glamorous. Miss Noyes was full of depths and mystery, and she could talk with a cigarette still between her lips. She was always doing something difficult, like designing her own pajamas, or reading Proust, or modeling torsos in plasticine. She played excellent bridge. She liked little Mrs. Murdock. "Tiny one," she called her.

"How's for coming to tea tomorrow, tiny one?" she said, at a therefore memorable meeting of the bridge club. "Lily Wynton's going to drop up. You might like to meet her."

The words fell so easily that she could not have realized their weight. Lily Wynton was coming to tea. Mrs. Murdock might like to meet her. Little Mrs. Murdock walked home through the early dark, and stars sang in the sky above her.

Mr. Murdock was already at home when she arrived. It required but a glance to tell that for him there had been no singing stars that evening in the heavens. He sat with his newspaper opened at the financial page, and bitterness had its way with his soul. It was not the time to cry happily to him of the impending hospitalities of Miss Noyes; not the time, that is, if one anticipated exclamatory sympathy. Mr. Murdock did not like Miss Noyes. When pressed for a reason, he replied that he just plain didn't like her. Occasionally he added, with a sweep that might have commanded a certain admiration, that all those women made him sick. Usually when she told him of the temperate activities of the bridge club meetings, Mrs. Murdock kept any mention of Miss Noyes's name from the accounts. She had found that this omission made for a more agreeable evening. But now she was caught in such a sparkling swirl of excitement that she had scarcely kissed him before she was off on her story.

"Oh, Jim," she cried. "Oh, what do you think! Hallie Noyes asked me to tea tomorrow to meet Lily Wynton!"

"Who's Lily Wynton?" he said.

"Ah, Jim," she said. "Ah, really, Jim. Who's Lily Wynton! Who's Greta Garbo, I suppose!"

"She some actress or something?" he said.

Mrs. Murdock's shoulders sagged. "Yes, Jim," she said. "Yes. Lily Wynton's an actress."

She picked up her purse and started slowly toward the door. But before she had taken three steps, she was again caught up in her sparkling swirl. She turned to him, and her eyes were shining.

"Honestly," she said, "it was the funniest thing you ever heard in you life. We'd just finished the last rubber — oh, I forgot to tell you, I won three dollars, isn't that pretty good for me? — and Hallie Noyes said to me, 'Come on in to tea tomorrow. Lily Wynton's going to drop up,' she said. Just like that, she said it. Just as if it was anybody."

"Drop up?" he said. "How can you drop *up*?"

"Honestly, I don't know what I said when she asked me," Mrs. Murdock said. "I suppose I said I'd love to — I guess I must have. But I was so simply — Well, you know how I've always felt about Lily Wynton. Why, when I was a little girl, I used to collect her pictures. And I've seen her in, oh, everything she's ever been in, I should think, and I've read every word about her, and interviews and all. Really and truly, when I think of *meeting* her — Oh,

I'll simply die. What on earth shall I say to her?"

"You might ask her how she'd like to try dropping down, for a change," Mr. Murdock said.

"All right, Jim," Mrs. Murdock said. "If that's the way you want to be."

Wearily she went toward the door, and this time she reached it before she turned to him. There were no lights in her eyes.

"It — it isn't so awfully nice," she said, "to spoil somebody's pleasure in something. I was so thrilled about this. You don't see what it is to me, to meet Lily Wynton. To meet somebody like that, and see what they're like, and hear what they say, and maybe get to know them. People like that mean — well, they mean something different to me. They're not like this. They're not like me. Who do I ever see? What do I ever hear? All my whole life, I've wanted to know — I've almost prayed that some day I could meet — Well. All right, Jim."

She went out, and on to her bedroom.

Mr. Murdock was left with only his newspaper and his bitterness for company. But he spoke aloud.

" 'Drop up!' " he said. " 'Drop *up*,' for God's sake!"

The Murdocks dined, not in silence, but in pronounced quiet. There was something straitened about Mr. Murdock's stillness; but little Mrs. Murdock's was the sweet, far quiet of one given over to dreams. She had forgotten her weary words to her husband, she had passed through her excitement and her disappointment. Luxuriously she floated on innocent visions of days after the morrow. She heard her own voice in future conversations . . . .

I saw Lily Wynton at Hallie's the other day, and she was telling me all about her new play — no, I'm terribly sorry, but it's a secret, I promised her I wouldn't tell anyone the name of it . . . . Lily Wynton dropped up to tea yesterday, and we just got to talking, and she told me the most interesting things about her life; she said she'd never dreamed of telling them to anyone else . . . . Why, I'd love to come, but I promised to have lunch with Lily Wynton . . . . I had a long, long letter from Lily Wynton . . . . Lily Wynton called me up this morning . . . . Whenever I feel blue, I just go and have a talk with Lily Wynton, and then I'm all right again . . . . Lily Wynton told me . . . . Lily Wynton and I . . . "Lily," I said to her. . .

The next morning, Mr. Murdock had left for his office before Mrs. Murdock rose. This had happened several times before, but not often. Mrs. Murdock felt a little queer about it. Then she told herself that it was probably just as well. Then she forgot all about it, and gave her mind to the selection of a costume suitable to the afternoon's event. Deeply she felt that her small wardrobe included no dress adequate to the occasion; for, of course, such an occasion had never before arisen. She finally decided upon a frock of dark blue serge with fluted white muslin about the neck and wrists. It was her style, that was the most she could say for it. And that was all she could say for herself. Blue serge and little white ruffles — that was she.

The very becomingness of the dress lowered her spirits. A nobody's frock, worn by a nobody. She blushed and went hot when she recalled the dreams she had woven the night before, the mad visions of intimacy of equality with Lily Wynton. Timidity turned her heart liquid, and she thought of telephoning Miss Noyes and saying she had a bad cold and could not come. She steadied, when she planned a course of conduct to pursue at teatime. She would not try to say anything; if she stayed silent, she could not sound foolish. She would listen and watch and worship and then come home, stronger, braver, better for an hour she would remember proudly all her life.

Miss Noyes's living-room was done in the early modern period. There were a great many oblique lines and acute angles, zigzags of aluminum and horizontal stretches of mirror. The color scheme was sawdust and steel. No seat was more than twelve inches above the floor, no table was made of wood. It was, as has been said of larger places, all right for a visit.

Little Mrs. Murdock was the first arrival. She was glad of that; no, maybe it would have been better to have come after Lily Wynton; no, maybe this was right. The maid motioned her toward the living-room, and Miss Noyes greeted her in the cool voice and the warm words that were her special combination. She wore black velvet trousers, a red cummerbund, and a white silk shirt, opened at the throat. A cigarette clung to her lower lip, and her eyes, as was her habit, were held narrow against its near smoke.

"Come in, come in, tiny one," she said. "Bless its little heart. Take off its little coat. Good Lord, you look easily eleven years old in that dress. Sit ye doon, here beside of me. There'll be a spot of tea in a jiff."

Mrs. Murdock sat down on the vast, perilously low divan, and, because she was never good at reclining among cushions, held her back straight. There was room for six like her, between herself and her hostess. Miss Noyes lay back, with one ankle flung upon the other knee, and looked at her.

"I'm a wreck," Miss Noyes announced. "I was modeling like a mad thing, all night long. It's taken everything out of me. I was like a thing bewitched."

"Oh, what were you making?" cried Mrs. Murdock.

"Oh, Eve," Miss Noyes said. "I always do Eve. What else is there to do? You must come pose for me some time, tiny one. You'd be nice to do. Ye-es, you'd be very nice to do. My tiny one."

"Why, I —" Mrs. Murdock said, and stopped. "Thank you very much, though," she said.

"I wonder where Lily is," Miss Noyes said. "She said she'd be here early — well, she always says that. You'll adore her, tiny one. She's really rare. She's a real person. And she's been through perfect hell. God, what a time she's had!"

"Ah, what's been the matter?" said Mrs. Murdock.

"Men," Miss Noyes said. "Men. She never had a man that wasn't a louse." Gloomily she stared at the toe of her flat-heeled patent leather pump. "A pack of lice, always. All of them. Leave her for the first little floozie that comes along."

"But —" Mrs. Murdock began. No, she couldn't have heard right. How could it be right? Lily Wynton was a great actress. A great actress meant romance. Romance meant Grand Dukes and Crown Princes and diplomats touched with gray at the temples and lean, bronzed, reckless Younger Sons. It meant pearls and emeralds and chinchilla and rubies red as the blood that was shed for them. It meant a grim-faced boy sitting in the fearful Indian midnight, beneath the dreary whirring of the *punkahs*, writing a letter to the lady he had seen but

329

once; writing his poor heart out, before he turned to the service revolver that lay beside him on the table. It meant a golden-locked poet, floating face downward in the sea, and in his pocket his last great sonnet to the lady of ivory. It meant brave, beautiful men, living and dying for the lady who was the pale bride of art, whose eyes and heart were soft with only compassion for them.

A pack of lice. Crawling after little floozies; whom Mrs. Murdock swiftly and hazily pictured as rather like ants.

"But —" said little Mrs. Murdock.

"She gave them all her money," Miss Noyes said. "She always did. Or if she didn't, they took it anyway. Took every cent she had, and then spat in her face. Well, maybe she's beginning to learn a little sense now. Oh, there's the bell — that'll be Lily. No, sit ye doon, tiny one. You belong there."

Miss Noyes rose and made for the archway that separated the living-room from the hall. As she passed Mrs. Murdock, she stooped suddenly, cupped her guest's round chin, and quickly, lightly kissed her mouth.

"Don't tell Lily," she murmured, very low.

Mrs. Murdock puzzled. Don't tell Lily what? Could Hallie Noyes think that she might babble to the Lily Wynton of these strange confidences about the actress's life? Or did she mean — But she had no more time for puzzling. Lily Wynton stood in the archway. There she stood, one hand resting on the wooden molding and her body swayed toward it, exactly as she stood for her third-act entrance of her latest play, and for a like half-minute.

You would have known her anywhere, Mrs. Murdock thought. Oh, yes, anywhere. Or at least you would have exclaimed, "That woman looks something like Lily Wynton." For she was somehow different in the daylight. Her figure looked heavier, thicker, and her face — there was so much of her face that the surplus sagged from the strong, fine bones. And her eyes, those famous dark, liquid eyes. They were dark, yes, and certainly liquid, but they were set in little hammocks of folded flesh, and seemed to be set but loosely, so readily did they roll. Their whites, that were visible all around the irises, were threaded with tiny scarlet veins.

"I suppose footlights are an awful strain on their eyes," thought little Mrs. Murdock.

Lily Wynton wore, just as she should have, black satin and sables, and long white gloves were wrinkled luxuriously about her wrists. But there were delicate streaks of grime in the folds of her gloves, and down the shining length of her gown there were small, irregularly shaped dull patches; bits of food or drops of drink, or perhaps both, sometime must have slipped their carriers and found brief sanctuary there. Her hat — oh, her hat. It was romance, it was mystery, it was strange, sweet sorrow; it was

Lily Wynton's hat, of all the world, and no other could dare it. Black it was, and tilted, and a great, soft plume drooped from it to follow her cheek and curl across her throat. Beneath it, her hair had the various hues of neglected brass. But oh, her hat.

"Darling!" cried Miss Noyes.

"Angel," said Lily Wynton. "My sweet."

It was that voice. It was that deep, soft, glowing voice. "Like purple velvet," someone had written. Mrs. Murdock's heart beat visibly.

Lily Wynton cast herself upon the steep bosom of her hostess, and murmured there. Across Miss Noyes's shoulder she caught sight of little Mrs. Murdock.

"And who is this?" she said. She disengaged herself.

"That's my tiny one," Miss Noyes said. "Mrs. Murdock."

"What a clever little face," said Lily Wynton. "Clever, clever little face. What does she do, sweet Hallie? I'm sure she writes, doesn't she? Yes, I can feel it. She writes beautiful, beautiful words. Don't you, child?"

"Oh, no, really I —" Mrs. Murdock said.

"And you must write me a play," said Lily Wynton. "A beautiful, beautiful play. And I will play in it, over and over the world, until I am a very, very old lady. And then I will die. But I will never be forgotten, because of the years I played in your beautiful, beautiful play."

She moved across the room. There was a slight hesitancy, a seeming insecurity, in her step, and when she would have sunk into a chair, she began to sink two inches, perhaps, to its right. But she swayed just in time in her descent, and was safe.

"To write," she said, smiling sadly at Mrs. Murdock, "to write. And such a little thing, for such a big gift. Oh, the privilege of it. But the anguish of it, too. The agony."

"But, you see, I —" said little Mrs. Murdock.

"Tiny one doesn't write, Lily," Miss Noyes said. She threw herself back upon the divan. "She's a museum piece. She's a devoted wife."

"A wife!" Lily Wynton said. "A wife. Your first marriage, child?"

"Oh, yes," said Mrs. Murdock.

"How sweet," Lily Wynton said. "How sweet, sweet, sweet. Tell me, child, do you love him very, very much?"

"Why, I —" said little Mrs. Murdock, and blushed. "I've known him for ages," she said.

"You love him," Lily Wynton said. "You love him. And is it sweet to go to bed with him?"

"Oh —" said Mrs. Murdock, and blushed till it hurt.

"The first marriage," Lily Wynton said. "Youth, youth. Yes, when I was your age I used to marry, too. Oh, treasure your love, child, guard it, live in it. Laugh and dance in the love of your man. Until you find out what

333

he's really like."

There came a sudden visitation upon her. Her shoulders jerked upward, her cheeks puffed, her eyes sought to start from their hammocks. For a moment she sat thus, then slowly all subsided into place. She lay back in her chair, tenderly patting her chest. She shook her head sadly, and there was grieved wonder in the look with which she held Mrs. Murdock.

"Gas," said Lily Wynton, in the famous voice. "Gas. Nobody knows what I suffer from it."

"Oh, I'm so sorry," Mrs. Murdock said. "Is there anything —"

"Nothing," Lily Wynton said. "There is nothing. There is nothing that can be done for it. I've been everywhere."

"How's for a spot of tea, perhaps?" Miss Noyes said. "It might help." She turned her face toward the archway and lifted up her voice. "Mary! Where the hell's the tea?"

"You don't know," Lily Wynton said, with her grieved eyes fixed on Mrs. Murdock, "you don't know what stomach distress is. You can never, never know, unless you're a stomach sufferer yourself. I've been one for years. Years and years and years."

"I'm terribly sorry," Mrs. Murdock said.

"Nobody knows the anguish," Lily Wynton said. "The agony."

The maid appeared, bearing a triangular tray upon which was set an heroic-sized tea service of bright white china, each piece a hectagon. She set it down on a table within the long reach of Miss Noyes and retired, as she had come, bashfully.

"Sweet Hallie," Lily Wynton said, "my sweet. Tea — I adore it. I worship it. But my distress turns it to gall and wormwood in me. Gall and wormwood. For hours, I should have no peace. Let me have a little, tiny bit of your beautiful, beautiful brandy, instead."

"You really think you should, darling?" Miss Noyes said. "You know —"

"My angel," said Lily Wynton, "it's the only thing for acidity."

"Well," Miss Noyes said. "But do remember you've got a performance tonight." Again she hurled her voice at the archway. "Mary! Bring the brandy and a lot of soda and ice and things."

"Oh, no, my saint," Lily Wynton said. "No, no, sweet Hallie. Soda and ice are rank poison to me. Do you want to freeze my poor, weak stomach? Do you want to kill poor, poor Lily?"

"Mary!" roared Miss Noyes. "Just bring the brandy and a glass." She turned to little Mrs. Murdock. "How's for your tea, tiny one? Cream? Lemon?"

"Cream, if I may, please," Mrs. Murdock said. "And two lumps of sugar, please, if I may."

"Oh, youth, youth," Lily Wynton said. "Youth and love."

335

The maid returned with an octagonal tray supporting a decanter of brandy and a wide, squat, heavy glass. Her head twisted on her neck in a spasm of diffidence.

"Just pour it for me, will you, my dear?" said Lily Wynton. "Thank you. And leave the pretty, pretty decanter here, on this enchanting little table. Thank you. You're so good to me."

The maid vanished, fluttering. Lily Wynton lay back in her chair, holding in her gloved hand the wide, squat glass, colored brown to the brim. Little Mrs. Murdock lowered her eyes to her teacup, carefully carried it to her lips, sipped, and replaced it on its saucer. When she raised her eyes, Lily Wynton lay back in her chair, holding in her gloved hand the wide, squat, colorless glass.

"My life," Lily Wynton said, slowly, "is a mess. A stinking mess. It always has been, and it always will be. Until I am a very, very old lady. Ah, little Clever-Face, you writers don't know what struggle is."

"But really I'm not — " said Mrs. Murdock.

"To write," Lily Wynton said. "To write. To set one word beautifully beside another word. The privilege of it. The blessed, blessed peace of it. Oh, for quiet, for rest. But do you think those Jew bastards would close that play while it's doing a nickel's worth of business? Oh, no. Tired as I am, sick as I am, I must drag along. Oh, child, child, guard your precious gift. Give thanks for it. It is the

336

greatest thing of all. It is the only thing. To write."

"Darling, I told you tiny one doesn't write," said Miss Noyes. "How's for making more sense? She's a wife."

"Ah, yes, she told me. She told me she had perfect, passionate love," Lily Wynton said. "Young love. It is the greatest thing. It is the only thing." She grasped the decanter; and again the squat glass was brown to the brim.

"What time did you start today, darling?" said Miss Noyes.

"Oh, don't scold me, sweet love," Lily Wynton said. "Lily hasn't been naughty. Her wuzzunt naughty dirl 't all. I didn't get up until late, late, late. And though I parched, though I burned, I didn't have a drink until after my breakfast. 'It is for Hallie,' I said." She raised the glass to her mouth, tilted it, and brought it away, colorless.

"Good Lord, Lily," Miss Noyes said. "Watch yourself. You've got to walk on that stage tonight, my girl."

"All the world's a stage," said Lily Wynton. "And all the men and women merely players. They have their entrance and their exitses, and each man in his time plays many parts, his act being seven ages. At first, the infant, mewling and puking —"

"How's the play doing?" Miss Noyes said.

"Oh, lousily," Lily Wynton said. "Lousily, lousily, lousily. But what isn't? What isn't, in

this terrible, terrible world? Answer me that."
She reached for the decanter.

"Lily, listen," said Miss Noyes. "Stop that.
Do you hear?"

"Please, sweet Hallie," Lily Wynton said.
"Pretty please. Poor, poor Lily."

"Do you want me to do what I had to do last
time?" Miss Noyes said. "Do you want me to
strike you, in front of tiny one, here?"

Lily Wynton drew herself high. "You do not
realize," she said, icily, "what acidity is." She
filled the glass and held it, regarding it as
though through a lorgnon. Suddenly her manner
changed, and she looked up and smiled at little
Mrs. Murdock.

"You must let me read it," she said. "You
mustn't be so modest."

"Read — " said little Mrs. Murdock.

"Your play," Lily Wynton said. "Your
beautiful, beautiful play. Don't think I am too
busy. I always have time. I have time for
everything. Oh, my God, I have to go to the
dentist tomorrow. Oh, the suffering I have
gone through with my teeth. Look!" She set
down her glass, inserted a gloved forefinger in
the corner of her mouth, and dragged it to the
side. "Oogh!" she insisted. "Oogh!"

Mrs. Murdock craned her neck shyly, and
caught a glimpse of shining gold.

"Oh, I'm so sorry," she said.

"As wah ee id a me ass ime," Lily Wynton
said. She took away her forefinger and let her

mouth resume its shape. "That's what he did to me last time," she repeated. "The anguish of it. The agony. Do you suffer with your teeth, little Clever-Face?"

"Why, I'm afraid I've been awfully lucky," Mrs. Murdock said. "I —"

"You don't know," Lily Wynton said. "Nobody knows what it is. You writers — you don't know." She took up her glass, sighed over it, and drained it.

"Well," Miss Noyes said. "Go ahead and pass out, then, darling. You'll have time for a sleep before the theater."

"To sleep," Lily Wynton said. "To sleep, perchance to dream. The privilege of it. Oh, Hallie, sweet, sweet Hallie, poor Lily feels so terrible. Rub my head for me, angel. Help me."

"I'll go get the eau de Cologne," Miss Noyes said. She left the room, lightly patting Mrs. Murdock's knee as she passed her. Lily Wynton lay in her chair and closed her famous eyes.

"To sleep," she said. "To sleep, perchance to dream."

"I'm afraid," little Mrs. Murdock began. "I'm afraid," she said, "I really must be going home. I'm afraid I didn't realize how awfully late it was."

"Yes, go, child," Lily Wynton said. She did not open her eyes. "Go to him. Go to him, live in him, love him. Stay with him always. But when he starts bringing them into the

339

house — get out."

"I'm afraid — I'm afraid I didn't quite understand," Mrs. Murdock said.

"When he starts bringing his fancy women into the house," Lily Wynton said. "You must have pride, then. You must go. I always did. But it was always too late then. They'd got all my money. That's all they want, marry them or not. They say it's love, but it isn't. Love is the only thing. Treasure your love, child. Go back to him. Go to bed with him. It's the only thing. And your beautiful, beautiful play."

"Oh, dear," said little Mrs. Murdock. "I — I'm afraid it's really terribly late."

There was only the sound of rhythmic breathing from the chair where Lily Wynton lay. The purple voice rolled along the air no longer.

Little Mrs. Murdock stole to the chair upon which she had left her coat. Carefully she smoothed her white muslin frills, so that they would be fresh beneath the jacket. She felt a tenderness for her frock; she wanted to protect it. Blue serge and little ruffles — they were her own.

When she reached the outer door of Miss Noyes's apartment, she stopped a moment and her manners conquered her. Bravely she called in the direction of Miss Noyes's bedroom.

"Good-by, Miss Noyes," she said. "I've simply got to run. I didn't realize it was so late. I had a lovely time — thank you ever so much."

"Oh, good-by, tiny one," Miss Noyes called. "Sorry Lily went by-by. Don't mind her — she's really a real person. I'll call you up, tiny one. I want to see you. Now where's that damned cologne?"

"Thank you ever so much," Mrs. Murdock said. She let herself out of the apartment.

Little Mrs. Murdock walked homeward, through the clustering dark. Her mind was busy, but not with memories of Lily Wynton. She thought of Jim; Jim, who had left for his office before she had arisen that morning, Jim, whom she had not kissed good-by. Darling Jim. There were no others born like him. Funny Jim, stiff and cross and silent; but only because he knew so much. Only because he knew the silliness of seeking afar for the glamour and beauty and romance of living. When they were right at home all the time, she thought. Like the Blue Bird, thought little Mrs. Murdock.

Darling Jim. Mrs. Murdock turned in her course, and entered an enormous shop where the most delicate and esoteric of foods were sold for heavy sums. Jim liked red caviar. Mrs. Murdock bought a jar of the shiny, glutinous eggs. They would have cocktails that night, though they had no guests, and the red caviar would be served with them for a surprise, and it would be a little, secret party to celebrate her return to contentment with her Jim, a party to mark her happy renunciation of all the glory

341

of the world. She bought, too, a large, foreign cheese. It would give a needed touch to dinner. Mrs. Murdock had not given much attention to ordering dinner, that morning. "Oh, anything you want, Signe," she had said to the maid. She did not want to think of that. She went on home with her packages.

Mr. Murdock was already there when she arrived. He was sitting with his newspaper opened to the financial page. Little Mrs. Murdock ran in to him with her eyes a-light. It is too bad that the light in a person's eyes is only the light in a person's eyes, and you cannot tell at a look what causes it. You do not know if it is excitement about you, or about something else. The evening before, Mrs. Murdock had run in to Mr. Murdock with her eyes a-light.

"Oh, hello," he said to her. He looked back at his paper, and kept his eyes there. "What did you do? Did you drop up to Hank Noyes's?"

Little Mrs. Murdock stopped right where she was.

"You know perfectly well, Jim," she said, "that Hallie Noyes's first name is Hallie."

"It's Hank to me," he said. "Hank or Bill. Did what's-her-name show up? I mean drop up. Pardon me."

"To whom are you referring?" said Mrs. Murdock, perfectly.

"What's-her-name," Mr. Murdock said. "The movie star."

"If you mean Lily Wynton," Mrs. Murdock

said, "she is not a movie star. She is an actress. She is a great actress."

"Well, did she drop up?" he said.

Mrs. Murdock's shoulders sagged. "Yes," she said. "Yes, she was there, Jim."

"I suppose you're going on the stage now," he said.

"Ah, Jim," Mrs. Murdock said. "Ah, Jim, please. I'm not sorry at all I went to Hallie Noyes's today. It was — it was a real experience to meet Lily Wynton. Something I'll remember all my life."

"What did she do?" Mr. Murdock said. "Hang by her feet?"

"She did no such thing!" Mrs. Murdock said. "She recited Shakespeare, if you want to know."

"Oh, my God," Mr. Murdock said. "That must have been great."

"All right, Jim," Mrs. Murdock said. "If that's the way you want to be."

Wearily she left the room and went down the hall. She stopped at the pantry door, pushed it open, and spoke to the pleasant little maid.

"Oh, Signe," she said. "Oh, good evening, Signe. Put these things somewhere, will you? I got them on the way home. I thought we might have them some time."

Wearily little Mrs. Murdock went on down the hall to her bedroom.

The Night The Bed Fell

James Thurber

I suppose that the high-water mark of my youth in Columbus, Ohio, was the night the bed fell on my father. It makes a better recitation (unless, as some friends of mine have said, one has heard it five or six times) than it does a piece of writing, for it is almost necessary to throw furniture around, shake doors, and bark like a dog, to lend the proper atmosphere and verisimilitude to what is admittedly a somewhat incredible tale. Still, it did take place.

It happened, then, that my father had decided to sleep in the attic one night, to be away where he could think. My mother opposed the notion strongly because, she said, the old wooden bed up there was unsafe: it was wobbly and the heavy headboard would crash down on father's head in case the bed fell, and kill him. There was no dissuading him, however, and at a quarter past ten he closed the attic door behind him and went up the narrow twisting stairs. We later heard ominous creakings as he crawled

344

into bed. Grandfather, who usually slept in the attic bed when he was with us, had disappeared some days before. (On these occasions he was usually gone six or eight days and returned growling and out of temper, with the news that the federal Union was run by a passel of blockheads and that the Army of the Potomac didn't have any more chance than a fiddler's bitch.)

We had visiting us at this time a nervous first cousin of mine named Briggs Beall, who believed that he was likely to cease breathing when he was asleep. It was his feeling that if he were not awakened every hour during the night, he might die of suffocation. He had been accustomed to setting an alarm clock to ring at intervals until morning, but I persuaded him to abandon this. He slept in my room and I told him that I was such a light sleeper that if anybody quit breathing in the same room with me, I would wake instantly. He tested me the first night — which I suspected he would — by holding his breath after my regular breathing had convinced him I was asleep. I was not asleep, however, and called to him. This seemed to allay his fears a little, but he took the precaution of putting a glass of spirits of camphor on a little table at the head of his bed. In case I didn't arouse him until he was almost gone, he said, he would sniff the camphor, a powerful reviver. Briggs was not the only member of his family who had his crotchets.

Old Aunt Melissa Beall (who could whistle like a man, with two fingers in her mouth) suffered under the premonition that she was destined to die on South High Street, because she had been born on South High Street and married on South High Street. Then there was Aunt Sarah Shoaf, who never went to bed at night without the fear that a burglar was going to get in and blow chloroform under her door through a tube. To avert this calamity — for she was in greater dread of anesthetics than of losing her household goods — she always piled her money, silverware, and other valuables in a neat stack just outside her bedroom, with a note reading: "This is all I have. Please take it and do not use your chloroform, as this is all I have." Aunt Gracie Shoaf also had a burglar phobia, but she met it with more fortitude. She was confident that burglars had been getting into her house every night for forty years. The fact that she never missed anything was to her no proof to the contrary. She always claimed that she scared them off before they could take anything, by throwing shoes down the hallway. When she went to bed she piled, where she could get at them handily, all the shoes there were about her house. Five minutes after she had turned off the light, she would sit up in bed and say "Hark!" Her husband, who had learned to ignore the whole situation as long ago as 1903, would either be sound asleep or pretend to be sound asleep. In either case he would not respond to her tugging and pulling, so that presently she would arise, tiptoe to the door, open it slightly and heave a shoe down the hall in one direction and its mate down the hall in the other direction. Some nights she threw them all, some nights only a couple of pair.

But I am straying from the remarkable incidents that took place during the night that the bed fell on father. By midnight we were all in bed. The layout of the rooms and the disposition of their occupants is important to an understanding of what later occurred. In the front room upstairs (just under father's attic bedroom) were my mother and my brother Herman, who sometimes sang in his sleep, usually "Marching Through Georgia" or "Onward, Christian Soldiers." Briggs Beall and myself were in a room adjoining this one. My brother Roy was in a room across the hall from ours. Our bull terrier, Rex, slept in the hall.

My bed was an army cot, one of those affairs which are made wide enough to sleep on comfortably only by putting up, flat with the middle section, the two sides which ordinarily hang down like the sideboards of a drop-leaf table. When these sides are up, it is perilous to roll too far toward the edge, for then the cot is likely to tip completely over, bringing the whole bed down on top of one with a tremendous banging crash. This, in fact, is precisely what happened, about two o'clock in the morning. (It was my mother who, in recalling the scene later, first referred to it as "the night the bed fell on your father.")

Always a deep sleeper, slow to arouse (I had lied to Briggs), I was at first unconscious of what had happened when the iron cot rolled me onto the floor and toppled over on me. It left me still warmly bundled up and unhurt, for the bed rested above me like a canopy. Hence I did not wake up, only reached the edge of consciousness and went back. The racket, however, instantly awakened my mother, in the next room, who came to the immediate conclusion that her worst dread was realized: the big wooden bed upstairs had fallen on father. She therefore screamed, "Let's go to your poor father!" It was this shout, rather than the noise of my cot falling, that awakened my brother Herman, in the same room with her. He thought that mother had become, for no apparent reason, hysterical. "You're all right, mamma!" he shouted, trying to calm her. They exchanged shout for shout for perhaps ten seconds: "Let's go to your poor father!" and "You're all right!" That woke up Briggs. By this time I was conscious of what was going on, in a vague way, but did not yet realize that I was under my bed instead of on it. Briggs, awakening in the midst of loud shouts of fear and apprehension, came to the quick conclusion that he was suffocating and that we were all trying to "bring him out." With a low moan, he grasped the glass of camphor at the head of his bed and instead of sniffing it poured it over himself. The room reeked of camphor. "Ugf, ahfg!" choked Briggs, like a drowning man, for he had almost succeeded in stopping his breath under the deluge of pungent spirits. He leaped out of bed and groped toward the open window, but he came up against one that was closed. With his hand, he beat out the glass, and I could hear it crash and tinkle in the alley-way below. It was at this juncture that I, in trying to get up, had the uncanny sensation of feeling my bed above me! Foggy with sleep, I now suspected, in my turn, that the whole uproar was being made in a frantic endeavor to extricate me from what must be an unheard-of and perilous situation. "Get me out of this!" I bawled. "Get me out!" I think I had the nightmarish belief that I was entombed in a mine. "Gugh!" gasped Briggs, floundering in his camphor.

By this time my mother, still shouting, pursued by Herman, still shouting, was trying to open the door to the attic, in order to go up and get my father's body out of the wreckage. The door was stuck, however, and wouldn't yield. Her frantic pulls on it only added to the general banging and confusion. Roy and the dog were now up, the one shouting questions, the other barking.

Father, farthest away and soundest sleeper of all, had by this time been awakened by the battering on the attic door. He decided that the house was on fire. "I'm coming, I'm coming!" he wailed in a slow, sleepy voice — it took him many minutes to regain full consciousness. My mother, still believing he was caught under the bed, detected in his "I'm coming!" the mournful, resigned note of one who is preparing to meet his Maker. "He's dying!" she shouted.

"I'm all right!" Briggs yelled, to reassure her. "I'm all right!" He still believed that it was his own closeness to death that was worrying mother. I found at last the light switch in my room, unlocked the door, and Briggs and I joined the others at the attic door. The dog, who never did like Briggs, jumped for him — assuming that he was the culprit in whatever was going on — and Roy had to throw Rex and hold him. We could hear father crawling out of bed upstairs. Roy pulled the attic door open, with a mighty jerk, and father came down the stairs, sleepy and irritable but safe and sound. My mother began to weep when she saw him. Rex began to howl. "What in the name of God is going on here?" asked father.

The situation was finally put together like a gigantic jigsaw puzzle. Father caught a cold from prowling around in his bare feet but there were no other bad results. "I'm glad," said mother, who always looked on the bright side of things, "that your grandfather wasn't here."

The Private Life of Mr. Bidwell

James Thurber

From where she was sitting, Mrs. Bidwell could not see her husband, but she had a curious feeling of tension: she knew he was up to something.

"What are you doing, George?" she demanded, her eyes still on her book.

"Mm?"

"What's the matter with you?"

"Pahhhhh-h-h," said Mr. Bidwell, in a long, pleasurable exhale. "I was holding my breath."

Mrs. Bidwell twisted creakingly in her chair and looked at him; he was sitting behind her in his favorite place under the parchment lamp with the street scene of old New York on it. "I was just holding my breath," he said again.

"Well, please don't do it," said Mrs. Bidwell, and went back to her book. There was silence for five minutes.

"George!" said Mrs. Bidwell.

"Bwaaaaaa," said Mr. Bidwell. "What?"

"Will you please stop that?" she said. "It

makes me nervous."

"I don't see how that bothers you," he said. "Can't I breathe?"

"You can breathe without holding your breath like a goop," said Mrs. Bidwell. "Goop" was a word that she was fond of using; she rather lazily applied it to everything. It annoyed Mr. Bidwell.

"Deep breathing," said Mr. Bidwell, in the impatient tone he used when explaining anything to his wife, "is good exercise. You ought to take more exercise."

"Well, please don't do it around me," said Mrs. Bidwell turning again to the pages of Mr. Galsworthy.

At the Cowans' party, a week later, the room was full of chattering people when Mrs. Bidwell, who was talking to Lida Carroll, suddenly turned around as if she had been summoned. In a chair in a far corner of the room, Mr. Bidwell was holding his breath. His chest was expanded, his chin drawn in; there was a strange stare in his eyes, and his face was slightly empurpled. Mrs. Bidwell moved into the line of his vision and gave him a sharp, penetrating look. He deflated slowly and looked away.

Later, in the car, after they had driven in silence a mile or more on the way home, Mrs. Bidwell said, "It seems to me you might at least have the kindness not to hold your breath in other people's houses."

"I wasn't hurting anybody," said Mr.

352

Bidwell.

"You looked silly!" said his wife. "You looked perfectly crazy!" She was driving and she began to speed up, as she always did when excited or angry. "What do you suppose people thought — you sitting there all swelled up, with your eyes popping out?"

"I wasn't all swelled up," he said, angrily.

"You looked like a goop," she said. The car slowed down, sighed, and came to a complete, despondent stop.

"We're out of gas," said Mrs. Bidwell. It was bitterly cold and nastily sleeting. Mr. Bidwell took a long, deep breath.

The breathing situation in the Bidwell family reached a critical point when Mr. Bidwell began to inhale in his sleep, slowly, and exhale with a protracted, growling "woooooooo." Mrs. Bidwell, ordinarily a sound sleeper (except on nights when she was sure burglars were getting in), would wake up and reach over and shake her husband. "George!" she would say.

"Hawwwwww," Mr. Bidwell would say, thickly. "Wahs maa nah, hm?"

After he had turned over and gone back to sleep, Mrs. Bidwell would lie awake, thinking.

One morning at breakfast she said, "George, I'm not going to put up with this another day. If you can't stop blowing up like a grampus, I'm going to leave you." There was a slight, quick lift in Mr. Bidwell's heart, but he tried to look surprised and hurt.

"All right," he said. "Let's not talk about it."

Mrs. Bidwell buttered another piece of toast. She described to him the ways he sounded in his sleep. He read the paper.

With considerable effort, Mr. Bidwell kept from inflating his chest for about a week, but one night at the McNallys' he hit on the idea of seeing how many seconds he could hold his breath. He was rather bored by the McNallys' party, anyway. He began timing himself with his wristwatch in a remote corner of the living-room. Mrs. Bidwell, who was in the kitchen talking children and clothes with Bea McNally, left her abruptly and slipped back into the living-room. She stood quietly behind her husband's chair. He knew she was there, and tried to let out his breath imperceptibly.

"I see you," she said, in a low, cold tone. Mr. Bidwell jumped up.

"Why don't you let me alone?" he demanded.

"Will you please lower your voice?" she said, smiling so that if anyone were looking he wouldn't think the Bidwells were arguing.

"I'm getting pretty damned tired of this," said Mr. Bidwell in a low voice.

"You've ruined my evening!" she whispered.

"You've ruined mine, too!" he whispered back. They knifed each other, from head to stomach, with their eyes.

"Sitting here like a goop, holding your breath," said Mrs. Bidwell. "People will think you are an idiot." She laughed, turning to greet a lady who was approaching them.

Mr. Bidwell sat in his office the next afternoon, a black, moist afternoon, tapping a pencil on his desk, and scowling. "All right, then, get out, get out!" he muttered. "What do I care?" He was visualizing the scene when Mrs. Bidwell would walk out on him. After going through it several times, he returned to his work, feeling vaguely contented. He made up his mind to breathe any way he wanted to, no matter what she did. And, having come to this decision, he oddly enough, and quite without effort, lost interest in holding his breath.

Everything went rather smoothly at the Bidwells' for a month or so. Mr. Bidwell didn't do anything to annoy his wife beyond leaving his razor on her dressing-table and forgetting to turn out the hall light when he went to bed. Then there came the night of the Bentons' party.

Mr. Bidwell, bored as usual, was sitting in a far corner of the room, breathing normally. His wife was talking animatedly with Beth Williamson about negligees. Suddenly her voice slowed and an uneasy look came into her eyes: George was up to something. She turned around and sought him out. To anyone but Mrs. Bidwell he must have seemed like any husband sitting

355

in a chair. But his wife's lips set tightly. She walked casually over to him.

"What are you doing?" she demanded.

"Hm?" he said, looking at her vacantly.

"What are you *doing?*" she demanded again. He gave her a harsh, venomous look, which she returned.

"I'm multiplying numbers in my head," he said, slowly and evenly, "if you must know." In the prolonged, probing examination that they silently, without moving any muscles save those of their eyes, gave each other, it became solidly, frozenly apparent to both of them that the end of their endurance had arrived. The curious bond that held them together snapped — rather more easily than either had supposed was possible. That night, while undressing for bed, Mr. Bidwell calmly multiplied numbers in his head. Mrs. Bidwell stared coldly at him for a few moments, holding a stocking in her hand; she didn't bother to berate him. He paid no attention to her. The thing was simply over.

George Bidwell lives alone now (his wife remarried). He never goes to parties any more, and his old circle of friends rarely sees him. The last time that any of them did see him, he was walking along a country road with the halting, uncertain gait of a blind man: he was trying to see how many steps he could take without opening his eyes.

The Ballet Visits the Splendide's Magician

Ludwig Bemelmans

The management of the Hotel Splendide, the luxurious establishment where I once worked as a busboy, a waiter, and eventually as an assistant maître d'hôtel in the banquet department, kept on file the addresses of a number of men who were magicians, fortune-tellers, or experts with cards. One of these entertainers frequently appeared at the end of the small dinner parties which were given in the private suites of the Splendide in the boom days, before the depression put an end to such pastimes and at last brought about the demise of the Splendide itself. Our entertainers had acclimated their acts to the elegance of the hotel, and the magicians, for example, instead of conjuring a simple white rabbit from their hats, cooked therein a soufflé Alaska or brought out a prize puppy with a rhinestone collar. When young girls were present, the magician pulled from their noses and out of corsages Cartier clips, bracelets, and brooches, which were presented

357

to them with the compliments of the host.

Among the best and most talented of our performers was Professor Maurice Gorylescu, a magician who did some palmistry on the side. He came to the hotel as often as two or three times a week. After coffee had been served, he would enter the private dining room, get people to write any number they wanted to on small bits of paper, and hold the paper to their foreheads. Then he would guess the numbers they had written down and add them up. The total would correspond to a sum he found on a dollar bill in the host's pocket. He did tricks with cards and coins, and he told people about the characteristics and the habits of dress and speech of friends long dead. He even delivered messages from them to the living.

At the end of his séances he would go into some vacant room nearby, sink into a chair, and sit for a while with his hand over his eyes. He always looked very tired. After about half an hour he would shake himself, drink a glass of water slowly, then eat something and go home.

Professor Gorylescu earned a good deal of money. His fee for a single performance was a flat hundred dollars, and he sometimes received that much again as a tip from a grateful host. But although he worked all during the season he spent everything he made and often asked for and received his fee in advance. All he earned went to women — to the support of a

Rumanian wife in Bucharest, to an American one who lived somewhere in New Jersey, and to what must have been a considerable number of New York girls of all nationalities to whom he sent little gifts and flowers.

When he came to the hotel during the day, he would hang his cane on the doorknob outside the ballroom office, ask me for a cigarette, and after a while steal a look at the book in which the reservations for small dinners were recorded. Very casually, and while talking of other things, he would turn the leaves and say something like "Looks very nice for the next two months," and put the book back. It took only a few seconds, but in this time his trick mind had stored away all the names, addresses, dates, and telephone numbers in the book. He went home with this information, called up the prospective party-givers, and offered his services.

There was a strict rule that no one should be permitted to look at these reservations, certainly not Professor Gorylescu, but I liked him, and when I was on duty in the ballroom office I would pretend not to see him when he peeked in the book. I also gave him left-over *petits fours*, candies, and after-dinner mints, of which he was very fond. He stuffed them into his pockets without bothering to wrap them up. He would wave goodbye with his immense hands, ask me to visit him soon at his home, and suggest that I bring along some *marrons glacés,* pastry, nuts — anything like that — and then he would leave, a stooping, uncouth figure, bigger than our tallest doorman.

Maurice Gorylescu lived on one of the mediocre streets that run between Riverside Drive and West End Avenue. He had a room in one of the small marble mansions that are common in that neighborhood. The rooming house in which Gorylescu lived was outstanding even among the ornate buildings of that district. It was a sort of junior Frankenstein castle, bedecked with small turrets, loggias, and balconies. It faced the sidewalk across a kind of moat — an air shaft for the basement windows — traversed by a granite bridge. The door was hung on heavy iron hinges that reached all the way across.

The character of this house was, moreover, complemented by the woman who rented its rooms, a Mrs. Houlberg. She stood guard much of the time at the window next to the moat, looking out over a sign that read "Vacancies." She always covered three-quarters of her face with her right hand, a long hand that lay diagonally across her face, the palm over her mouth, the nails of the fingers stopping under the right eye. It looked like a mask, and as if she always had a toothache.

Gorylescu lived on the top-floor front and answered to four short rings and one long one of a shrill bell that was in Mrs. Houlberg's entrance hall. Badly worn banisters led up four flights of stairs. From the balcony of his room one could see the time flash on and off in Jersey and the searchlights of a battleship in the Hudson. The room was large and newly painted in a wet, loud red, the shade of the inside of a watermelon. A spotty chartreuse velvet coverlet decorated a studio couch. Facing this was a chair, a piece of furniture such as you see in hotel lobbies or club cars, covered with striped muslin and padded with down. There was also a Sheraton highboy, which stood near a door that led into an adjoining room which was not his. From the ceiling hung a cheap bazaar lamp with carmine glass panes behind filigree panels. On shelves and on a table were the photographs of many women; in a box, tied together with ribbons in various colors, he kept packets of letters, in a particular drawer of the highboy was a woman's garter, an old girdle, and various other disorderly trophies.

Gorylescu reclined on the studio bed most of the time when he was at home. He wore a Russian blouse that buttoned under the left ear, and he smoked through a cigarette holder a foot long. One of his eyes was smaller and lower down in his face than the other, and between them rose a retroussé nose, a trumpet of a nose, with cavernous nostrils. Frequently and with great ceremony he sounded it into an immense handkerchief. His cigar-colored skin was spotted as if with a bluish kind of buckshot, and when he was happy he hummed through his nose, mostly the melody of a song whose title was "Tu Sais."

At home he was almost constantly in the company of women. He made the acquaintance of some of them at parties where he had entertained. They brought him gifts, and if they were fat and old, he read their minds and told them things of the past and future. At other times he went looking for girls along Riverside Drive, humming through his nose, and dragging after him a heavy cane whose handle was hooked into his coat pocket.

He went to various other places to find girls. He picked them up at dance halls in Harlem, on the subway, on roller coasters. He easily became acquainted with them anywhere, and they came to his room willingly and took their chances with him. I always thought I might find one of them, dead and naked, behind the Japanese screen, where he kept a rowing machine on which he built himself up. For the space of time that I knew him, love, murder, and that man seemed to be close together and that room the inevitable theatre for it.

The Professor gave me a series of lectures during my visits to his room in which he detailed for me the routines and the mechanisms of his untidy passions. He insisted during these long *études* that the most important piece of strategy was to get the subject to remove her shoes. "Once the shoes are off, the battle is already half won," he would say. "Get a woman to walk around without shoes, without heels — she looks a fool, she feels a fool, she is a fool. Without her shoes, she is lost. Take the soft instep in your hand, caress her ankles, her calf, her knee — the rest is child's play. But remember, first off with the shoes." While he talked, he would scratch his cat, which was part Siamese. The lecture was followed by a display of the collection of photographs he himself had taken, as evidence of the soundness of his theories.

When the Russian Ballet came to town, Professor Gorylescu was not to be had for any parties at the hotel. He went to all the performances, matinées and evenings alike, and he hummed then the music of "*Puppenfee, L'Après-Midi d'un Faune*, and the various *divertissements*, and was completely broke. One day he was in a state of the highest elation because he had invited a ballet dancer to tea. He wanted me to come too because she had a friend, who would be an extra girl for me; both of them were exquisite creatures, he assured me, and I was to bring some tea, *marrons glacés*, *petits fours*, and ladyfingers.

I came early and I brought everything. He darkened the room, lit a brass samovar, laid out some cigarettes, sliced some lemons, hid the rowing machine under the studio couch, and with the Japanese silk screen divided the room into two separate camps. On one side was the couch, on the other the great chair. He buttoned his Russian blouse, blew his nose frequently, and hummed as he walked up and down. He brushed the cat and put away a Spanish costume doll that might have made his couch crowded. He arranged the *petits fours* in saucers, and when the bell rang four times short and one long, he put a Chopin record on his victrola. "Remember about the shoes," he told me over his shoulder, "and always play Chopin for ballet dancers." He quickly surveyed the room once more, turned on the bazaar lamp, and, humming, opened the door — and then stopped humming suddenly. He had invited two of the dancers, but up the stairs came a bouquet of girls, more than a dozen of them.

All at once it was the month of May in the dimmed room. The lovely guests complimented the samovar, the cat, the music, and the view from the balcony, to which they had opened the door, letting much fresh air come in, which intensified the new mood. Gorylescu's voice became metallic with introductions; he ran downstairs to get more glasses for tea and came back breathing heavily. All the girls, without being asked, took their shoes off immediately, explaining that their feet hurt from dancing. They arranged the shoes in an orderly row, as one does on entering a Japanese house or a mosque, then sat down on the floor in a circle.

364

One of them even removed her stockings and put some slices of lemon between her toes. "Ah-h-h," she said.

There started after this a bewildering and alien conversation, a remote, foggy ritual, like a Shinto ceremonial. It consisted of the telling of ballet stories, and seemed to me a high, wild flight into a world closed to the outsider. The stories were told over and over until every detail was correct. In all of these stories appeared Anna Pavlova, who was referred to as "Madame" — what Madame had said, what Madame had done, what she had thought, what she had worn, how she had danced. There was an atmosphere of furious backstage patriotism. The teller of each story swayed and danced with hands, shoulders, and face. Every word was illustrated; for anything mentioned — color, light, time, and person — there was surprisingly expressive and fitting gesture. The talker was rewarded with applause, with requests for repetition of this or that part again and again, and there swept over the group of girls waves of intimate, fervent emotion.

The Professor served tea on his hands and knees and retired to the shadows of his room. He sat for a while in the great chair like a bird with a wounded wing, and then, with his sagging and cumbersome gait, he wandered around the group of innocents, who sat straight as so many candles, all with their shoes off. The room was alive with young heads and throats and flanks.

The Professor succeeded finally in putting his head into the lap of the tallest, the most racy of the nymphs. She quickly kissed him, said "Sh-h-h-h, daaaahrling," and then caressed his features, the terrible nose, the eyebrows, the corrugated temples, and the great hands, with the professional detachment of a masseuse, while she related an episode in Cairo during a performance of *Giselle* when the apparatus that carried Pavlova up out of her grave to her lover got stuck halfway, and how Madame had cursed and what she had said after the performance and to whom she had said it. An indignant fire burned in all the narrowed eyes of the disciples as she talked.

Suddenly one of them looked at her watch, remembered a rehearsal, and the girls got up and remembered us. They all had Russian names, but all of them were English, as most ballet dancers are; in their best accents, they said their adieus. With individual graces, they arranged their hair, slipped into their shoes, and thanked Maurice. Each one of them said "Daaaahrling" to us and to each other. It was Madame Pavlova's form of address and her pronunciation.

All the girls kissed us, and it was as if we all had grown up in the same garden, as if they were all our sisters. The Professor said a few mouthfuls of gallant compliments, and when they were gone he fished the rowing machine out from under the couch, without a word, and carried it in back of the Japanese screen. Together, we rearranged the room. The *marrons glacés* and the ladyfingers were all gone, but the cigarettes were still there.

Dusk In Fierce Pajamas

E. B. White

Ravaged by pink eye, I lay for a week scarce caring whether I lived or died. Only Wamba, my toothless old black nurse, bothered to bring me food and quinine. Then one day my strength began to return, and with it came Wamba to my bedside with a copy of *Harper's Bazaar* and a copy of *Vogue*. "Ah brought you couple magazines," she said proudly, her red gums clashing.

In the days that followed (happy days of renewed vigor and reawakened interest), I studied the magazines and lived, in their pages, the gracious lives of the characters in the ever-moving drama of society and fashion. In them I found surcease from the world's ugliness, from disarray, from all unattractive things. Through them I escaped into a world in which there was no awkwardness of gesture, no unsuitability of line, no people of no importance. It was an enriching experience. I realize now that my own life is by contrast an unlovely thing, with its disease, its banalities, its uncertainties, its toil, its single-breasted suits, and its wine from lesser years. I am aware of a life all around me of graciousness and beauty, in which every moment is a tiny pearl of good taste, and in which every acquaintance has the common decency to possess a good background.

Lying here in these fierce pajamas, I dream of the *Harper's Bazaar* world, the *Vogue* life; dream of being a part of it. In fancy I am in Mrs. Cecil Baker's pine-panelled drawing-room. It is dusk. (It is almost always dusk in the fashion magazines.) I have on a Gantner & Mattern knit jersey bathing suit with a flat-striped bow and an all-white buck shoe with a floppy tongue. No, that's wrong. I am in chiffon, for it is the magic hour after bridge. Suddenly a Chippendale mahogany hors-d'oeuvre table is brought in. In its original old blue-and-white Spode compartments there sparkle olives, celery, hard-boiled eggs, radishes — evidently put there by somebody in the employ of Mrs. Baker. Or perhaps my fancy wanders away from the drawing-room: I am in Mrs. Baker's dining-room, mingling unostentatiously with the other guests, my elbows resting lightly on the dark polished oak of the Jacobean table, my fingers twiddling with the early Georgian silver. Or perhaps I am not at Mrs. Baker's oak table in chiffon at all — perhaps instead I am at Mrs. Jay Gould's teakwood table in a hand-knitted Anny Blatt ensemble in diluted tricolors and an off-the-face hat.

It is dusk. I am dining with Rose Hobart at the Waldorf. We have lifted our champagne glasses. "To sentiment!" I say. And the haunting dusk is shattered by the clean glint of jewels by Cartier.

It is dusk. I am seated on a Bruce Buttfield pouf, for it is dusk.

Ah, magazine dreams! How dear to me now are the four evenings in the life of Mrs. Allan Ryan, Junior. I have studied them one by one, and I feel that I know them. They are perfect little crystals of being — static, precious. There is the evening when she stands, motionless, in a magnificent sable cape, her left arm hanging gracefully at her side. She is ready to go out to dinner. What will this, her first of four evenings, bring of romance, or even of food? Then there is the evening when she just sits on the edge of a settee from the Modernage Galleries, the hard bright gleam of gold lamé topping a slim, straight, almost Empire skirt. I see her there (the smoke from a cigarette rising), sitting, sitting, waiting. Or the third evening — the evening with books. Mrs. Ryan is in chiffon; the books are in morocco. Or the fourth evening, standing with her dachshund, herself in profile, the dog in full face.

So I live the lives of other people in my fancy: the life of the daughter of Lord Curzon of Kedleston, who has been visiting the Harold Talbotts on Long Island. All I know of her is that she appeared one night at dinner, her beauty set off by the lustre of artificial satin and the watery fire of aquamarine. It is all I know, yet it is enough; for it is her one perfect moment in time and space, and I know about it, and it is mine.

It is dusk. I am with Owen Johnson over his chafing dish. It is dusk. I am with Prince Matchabelli over his vodka. Or I am with the Countess de Forceville over her bridge tables. She and I have just pushed the tables against the wall and taken a big bite of gaspacho. Or I am with the Marquis de Polignac over his Pommery.

How barren my actual life seems, when fancy fails me, here with Wamba over my quinine. Why am I not to be found at dusk, slicing black bread very thin, as William Powell does, to toast it and sprinkle it with salt? Why does not twilight find me (as it finds Mrs. Chester Burden) covering a table with salmon-pink linens on which I place only white objects, even to a white salt shaker? Why don't I learn to simplify my entertaining, like the young pinch-penny in *Vogue*, who has all his friends in before the theatre and simply gives them champagne cocktails, caviar, and one hot dish, then takes them to the show? Why do I never give parties after the opera, as Mr. Paul Cravath does, at which I have the prettiest women in New York? Come to think of it, why don't the prettiest women in New York ever come down to my place, other than that pretty little Mrs. Fazaenzi, whom Wamba won't let in? Why haven't I a butler named Fish, who makes a cocktail of three parts gin to one part lime juice, honey, vermouth, and apricot brandy in equal portions — a cocktail so delicious that people like Mrs. Harrison Williams and Mrs. Goodhue Livingston seek him out to get the formula? And if I *did* have a butler named Fish, wouldn't I kid the pants off him?

All over the world it is dusk! It is dusk at Armando's on East Fifty-fifth Street. Armando has taken up his accordion; he is dreaming over the keys. A girl comes in, attracted by the accordion, which she mistakes for Cecil Beaton's camera. She is in stiff green satin, and over it she wears a silver fox cape which she can pull around her shoulders later in the evening if she gets feeling like pulling a cape around her shoulders. It is dusk on the Harold Castles' ranch in Hawaii. I have risen early to shoot a goat, which is the smart thing to do in Hawaii. And now I am walking silently through hedges of gardenias, past the flaming ginger flowers, for I have just shot a goat. I have on nothing but red sandals and a Martex bath towel. It is dusk in the Laurentians. I am in ski togs. I feel warm and safe, knowing that the most dangerous pitfall for skiers is *color*, knowing that although a touch of brilliance against the snow is effective, too much of it is the sure sign of the amateur. It is the magic hour before cocktails. I am in the modern penthouse of Monsieur Charles de Beistegui. The staircase is entirely of cement, spreading at the hemline and trimmed with padded satin tubing caught at the neck with a bar of milk chocolate. It is dusk in Chicago. I am standing beside Mrs. Howard Linn, formerly Consuelo Vanderbilt, formerly Sophie M. Gay, formerly Ellen Glendinning, formerly Saks-Fifth Avenue. It is dusk! A pheasant has Julian Street down and is pouring a magnificent old red Burgundy down his neck. Dreams, I'm afraid. It is really dusk in my own apartment. I am down on my knees in front of an airbound radiator, trying to fix it by sticking pins in the vent. Dusk in these fierce pajamas. Kneeling here, I can't help wondering where Nancy Yuille is, in her blue wool pants and reefer and her bright red mittens. For it is dusk. I said *dusk*, Wamba! Bring the quinine!

A Funny Thing Happened on the Way to the Theatre

Billy Rose

I was born the night President McKinley was shot, and a lot of fellows around Broadway will tell you they shot the wrong man.

The coming-out party took place on a kitchen table in a tenement on the lower East Side. When my mother first saw me, she prophesied, "Some day he'll be President." My father looked at me and said, "He's all right, I guess, but what we really needed was an icebox."

My Pop was what you might call a non-persuasive salesman. When fringe was the fashion, his sample-case would only contain passementerie. When people were crying for passementerie, he would only handle fringe. Consequently, money was a sometime thing around our house, and for years we changed residence every few months. It was cheaper to move than pay rent.

When I went to the High School of Commerce in 1915, the family stock was still empty. It was imperative that I learn something I could merchandise quickly, and so I concentrated on shorthand and typewriting. By working like an Igorot, I got to be something of a shorthand expert, and in 1917 I left school, went to Washington and got myself a job as stenographer with the War Industries Board. There I met its chairman, Bernard M. Baruch. He took a shine to me.

I was several hundred dollars ahead when the war ended and for reasons I can't remember, I decided to take a trip around the world. But my money lasted only as far as New Orleans. On the way back to New York, the boat I was on rammed and sank a freighter in a fog off Cape Hatteras. One of the survivors we picked up was a pretty girl named Edna Harris. When I handed her one of the five life-preservers I was wearing, it started a beautiful friendship. Before we docked, I made a date to see her in New York.

The first night I took her out, we walked up Broadway. Though I was crowding twenty at the time, I had never been on the Big Street at night. But Edna knew her way around. She steered me to Wolpin's, one of those under-ground delicatessens where celebrities gathered to eat the life-giving pastrami and quaff great beakers of celery tonic.

"That's Fred Fischer," she said, pointing to a man with an outsized head. "He wrote 'Dardanella.' And that's Walter Donaldson, the writer of 'Mammy.' "

"What kind of money do they make?" I asked.

"No telling," said Edna. "Couple of thousand a week, maybe."

"How long has this been going on?" I said to myself.

From then on, I did most of my eating at Wolpin's, and after a while got to know most of the songwriters. In those days I was a simple-hearted little bloke. My ambitions were to make a million dollars and marry Mary Pickford. I believed what everybody believed in 1922 — that U.S. Steel would hit 500, that nice girls didn't kiss the first time you took them out, and that Heaven was not for Democrats.

One night at Wolpin's I asked Harry Ruby, the composer, "Has anybody ever thought of rhyming 'June' with 'macaroon'?"

The entire delicatessen applauded and Harry shook my hand. A waiter handed me a pencil and a clean menu and said, "Mr. Rose, you're in business."

Six cups of coffee later, I dotted the last "i" on my first masterpiece.

Does the Spearmint lose its flavor on the bedpost overnight?
If you paste it on the left side will you find it on the right?
When you chew it in the morning will it be too hard to bite?
Does the Spearmint lose its flavor on the bedpost overnight?

It was published by Watterson, Berlin and Snyder, and the early ten-watt radio transmitters smallpoxed the air with it. I got an appointment with a Wrigley executive and told him I thought I was entitled to some money for my efforts on behalf of his product. He booted me out of his office without so much as a pack of gum for my trouble.

But I got my revenge. The time bomb I lit in 1922 exploded in 1939 with the Pepsi-Cola jingle. The rest, God help us, is history.

I wrote the first singing commercial.

There, I've said it! And I'm glad. For years I've been walking around with this secret, fraternizing with people who are kind to small animals and bathe every day. Now I've come clean.

Chop me up in little pieces and feed me to the lions. You won't hear a peep out of me.

Besides the Spearmint classic, I was responsible for "You Tell Her, I Stutter," and "You Gotta See Mama Every Night." These songs made quite a bit of money, and the following year I invested some of this loot in the nightclub business — principally, I think, because I wanted to wear a black hat and meet some girls. My first waterhole was hidden over a garage on 56th Street near Sixth Avenue. The iron-stomached citizens who survived the Noble Experiment may remember it as the Backstage Club — the place where Helen Morgan first climbed up on a piano to avoid the tables which were advancing upon her across the dance floor.

The Backstage Club represented an outlay of $4,000. It amortized itself the opening night.

A few months later I opened a second trap on Fifth Avenue — I wanted to meet a better class of girls. It was called the Fifth Avenue Club, and it exhaled so much fake swank that on opening night my French headwaiter suggested I stay out of sight in the office. The show was written by a couple of kids fresh out of Columbia — Rodgers and Hart. I had really arrived socially. My new neighbors included Samuel Untermyer, the Union League Club, and John D. Rockefeller, Sr.

Eyebrows shot up all over the neighborhood the night we opened. John D. was at the age when he needed his sleep something fierce, and when my bug-eyed musicians erupted with "Somebody Stole My Gal" at four in the morning he hollered copper at the top of his ancient lungs. A dozen of New York's Finest roared up on motorcycles, but when they found I wasn't selling whiskey, they compromised on making me mute half my trumpets.

To keep the club exclusive, I slapped on a $5 cover charge. Well, that did it. Pretty soon it was so exclusive the waiters were playing penny casino with each other. In a couple of months I was feeling through the pockets of old suits for lunch money.

One night I got an idea. I would sell my club

to a blonde who was running a speakeasy in Greenwich Village. Her boy friend was one of our leading bathtub chemists.

I went down to the Village to see her. "Queenie," I said, "this speak is no showcase for a woman of your talents. You belong on Fifth Avenue."

"You can say that again, dearie," said Queenie, "but what would I do up there? I can't sing and my gentleman friend made me give up hoofin'."

"All great women of the world have had salons," I said airily. "Du Barry, Pompadour, Marie Antoinette. Princes and statesmen flocked around just to hear these women talk."

I moved in for the kill. "Get your boy friend to buy my club for you. Advertise yourself as 'Mistress of Conversation.' Wear a stylish gown — something transparent and expensive. And when the customers arrive, talk to them — just talk to them. It'll be tremendous!"

Queenie bought the dream, and next morning the bathtub chemist bought my sick little nightclub. He ran big ads, billing her as "Mistress of Conversation." But the place folded in a few weeks.

Poor Queenie! Though she was willing to talk to anybody, nobody wanted to talk to *her*.

After the Fifth Avenue Club, I went back to songwriting. You may remember one of the ditties I wrote around that time — "Barney Google with the Goo-Goo-Googly Eyes." Deems

Taylor said it was probably the worst song in the history of the music business — but Deems always was a jealous fellow.

In 1926 I wrote a vaudeville act for Fanny Brice. During its out-of-town tryouts, I found that Fanny and I liked the same jokes and disliked the same people. In 1928 I persuaded the great comedienne to become Mrs. Rose. The day she did, I automatically became known as Mr. Brice. You see, in those days, Fanny's house was a hangout for the Whitneys and Wanamakers, and outside of Irving Berlin, a pop songwriter was considered small spuds.

One night C. B. Dillingham attended one of Fanny's at-homes. I noticed that everybody made a fuss over the producer. A few nights later a similar fuss was made over Ziegfeld. "If you want your name back," I said to myself, "you'll have to become a producer."

And so, in 1931 I made my bow on Broadway with a musical revue called *Sweet and Low*. Though I had worked on it for a year and put every penny I had in it, it wasn't much of a show. An angry critic dismissed it with the line, "The Rose that does not smell so sweet."

The day after it closed a press agent named Ned Alvord came into my office. He was sporting a seersucker cutaway, a derby hat and a turned-around collar like a minister. In a train-whistle voice he announced I could get my dough back if I had the guts to juice up the show, take it to the hinterlands, and sell it like Barnum used to sell his circus. He gave off sparks and I caught fire.

I went out and hocked my ASCAP royalties, revamped *Sweet and Low*, and changed the title to *Crazy Quilt*. And I'll never forget how Ned advertised this pale little revue — "A Saturnalia of Wanton Rhythm" — "Voluptuous Houris" — "Dashing Demoiselles" — every sentence ending with "Since the Dawn of Time!"

When I pointed out that we were carrying only a few curtains and eighteen bandy-legged chorus girls, Ned fog-horned, "Take the money and run for the train." And for a screamingly successful year that's just what we did!

It was Ned who taught me that the short cut to the customer's poke is by way of the roadside fence — that "bill it like a circus" sells more tickets than "to be or not to be."

My first lesson in paper-and-paste came when I commissioned a lad with a lavender tie to design a twenty-four-sheet for our traveling show. He delivered a layout in delicate blues and pinks. I showed it to Alvord. "It stinks, sir," he said.

"But it's pretty," I protested.

"Then hang it in your bedroom," he snapped. "It's a foggy night in Kansas and our poster is on an outhouse. I want to see it, sir."

We settled on something in black and yellow — you couldn't look at it without smoked glasses. And the only switch I've made in twenty years was when I ordered the posters for *Carmen Jones*. Instead of yellow and black, I changed the color scheme to black and yellow.

Shortly after *Crazy Quilt* closed, I produced a play called *The Great Magoo* by Ben Hecht and Gene Fowler. It lasted a week. The following year, I opened a theatre restaurant called the Casino de Paree. It was bankrolled by a group of gentlemen whose pictures have appeared in some of our finest post offices.

A few months later, I ripped the insides out of Arthur Hammerstein's pretty theatre on 53rd and Broadway and opened another cabaret called the The Billy Rose Music Hall. Its feature number was a potpouri of oldtime vaudevillians — fire-eaters, acrobats and Swiss bell-ringers — who did an abbreviated version of their turns. This was my first meeting with the pretty lady called "Nostalgia" and we've been buddies ever since.

The electric sign on this music hall was a seven-day wonder on Broadway. It was eighteen stories high and the mazdas spelled out just two words — "BILLY ROSE." The first night it was burning, I went outside to admire it. As I stood on the corner, I heard someone ask, "Billy Rose? Who dat?"

"That's Fanny Brice's husband," someone answered. I finally took care of this Mr. Brice situation a few months later when I gave birth to a theatrical dream child called *Jumbo*. No year in my life has been wackier than the one devoted to producing this musical circus at the

New York Hippodrome. The author, director, and player credits read like a Burke's Peerage of the theatre — Hecht and MacArthur, Rodgers and Hart, John Murray Anderson, George Abbott, Jimmy Durante, Paul Whiteman and his orchestra.

This country-sized candy box was largely financed by Jock Whitney and his sister, Joan, a couple of amiable tots whose Pop had left them $175,000,000. As production costs mounted, the standard gag around Broadway was, "This will make Rose or break Whitney."

Carried away by the notion of marrying a circus to a musical comedy, we showed no more respect for the law of gravity than do the characters in a Silly Symphony. The opening number was climaxed by shooting an adagio dancer out of a cannon into the arms of her partner fifty feet away. Dohoes, an educated white horse from Copenhagen, did everything but play first base. In one sequence a troupe of daredevils indulged in fingertip balancing over an open cage of lions.

But *Jumbo* was too big for its cash registers. Though it received superb notices and played to over a million customers, it lost money. A few years ago the Whitneys got some of it back when Metro bought the movie rights. I don't know when the studio is going to get around to making this picture, but before it does, I would suggest that it send the director to New York and instruct him to stand still some night near the parking space at 43rd Street and Sixth Avenue where the old Hippodrome stood. If he listens closely, he'll still hear them yocking it up at what drama critics agree was the biggest laugh in the history of show business. It came near the end of the first act when a sheriff caught Jimmy Durante trying to steal an elephant.

"Where are ya going with that elephant?" yelled the copper.

"What elephant?" asked Jimmy.

Finding the elephant for the title role in *Jumbo* was quite a chore. A fellow who had sold me some monkeys said I might be able to rent one from Mr. Charles W. Beall in Oceanside, Long Island.

According to the monkey man, this Mr. Beall was quite a fellow. From Monday to Friday, he was vice-president of the Chase National Bank; Saturdays and Sundays he devoted to training wild animals.

The following Saturday I drove out to Oceanside. The monkey man hadn't overstated the case. On his beautiful ten-acre estate, Mr. Beall, a fine figure of a tycoon, maintained one of the most complete private zoos in America. In addition to lions, tigers, leopards, and black panthers, his cages contained at least one each of the animals on exhibit at the Bronx Zoo.

At the house, a butler told me Mr. Beall was working out with the animals in a cage back of the garage. I walked around and watched the amateur Clyde Beatty. He handled the whip and chair like a pro, and the big cats were slinking around as though they had guilt complexes.

"What can I do for you, young man?" he said when the beasts were all up on their inverted tubs.

"Want to sell, lease or rent an elephant?" I called through the bars.

Mr. Beall clicked the cage door open. "Come in," he said. "They won't hurt you."

You can judge how badly I needed an elephant when I tell you I walked into that cage.

"Afraid I can't do anything for you," said the banker after I had explained my problem. "I'm down to six elephants, and I like to have at least that many around. They relax me."

After lunch he showed me around his place. I didn't see any women on the estate and I got the impression he was a bachelor.

On the way back to town, I got to wondering about his private life. What sort of women, for instance, would appeal to a millionaire who hobnobbed with lions and panthers?

A few years later, the tabloids told me. It appeared that Mr. Beall had hired a vaudeville performer named Nana Bates as secretary. He had seen this lady do a tiger dance in a local theatre and had been impressed by her qualifications.

According to the tabloids, Mr. Beall had gotten along fine with his secretary until he sent her to Hollywood on business. During her absence, he had made the mistake of hiring another actress-stenographer. When the Tiger Woman returned unexpectedly and found her pretty successor on the porch, she reached for a hatpin.

The two shorthand experts indulged in some fancy scratching and floor-rolling. A neighbor phoned the Oceanside police. The old financier was caught in the middle — something which hadn't happened to him either on Wall Street or in the lions' cage.

Most of the later rounds were staged in court, where the judge finally told the banker to make up his mind which secretary he wanted. Mr. Beall chose the Tiger Woman.

While these legal shenanigans were going on, I happened to be driving through Oceanside. I found Mr. Beall sitting on a stool in the lions' cage. The big cats were on their tubs, unusually quiet. The amateur trainer's face was all scratched up and there were bits of court plaster on his neck and hands.

"Did a cat take a poke at you?" I asked.

The financier nodded. "Yes," he said. "One of the two-legged ones."

"What's the idea of sitting out here?" I said.

Mr. Beall got up, walked over to one of the lions and scratched it behind the ears. "Frankly," he sighed, "this is the only place on the estate where I feel perfectly safe."

On the strength of the *Jumbo* press notices,

Amon Carter and the other city farmers of Fort Worth asked me to stage the Texas Centennial Exposition of 1936–37. Dallas, thirty-two miles away, was preparing a $25,000,000 industrial fair, and "Little Old Cowtown" wanted a show that would steal the spotlight from its rival.

Carter told me the job had to be done in a hundred days and asked what I wanted for my services. Taking a deep breath, I said, "A hundred thousand dollars." The city fathers conferred for all of three minutes and agreed. And if I may be pardoned a brag, I think I earned my fee the next day when I coined the slogan, "Dallas for Education, Fort Worth for Entertainment."

I arrived in Fort Worth with a small boy's notions of the Wild West. As a kid, I had read Zane Grey with a flashlight under the blankets after my old man had chased me off to bed. In the nickelodeons I had whooped "Look out" when the bad guy snuck up behind William S. Hart.

Naturally, when I planned the shows for the Exposition, I included one with cowboys and Indians. I labeled it "The Last Frontier," and you'll get some idea of the dimensions of this hootnanny when I tell you we used a quarter of a million dollars' worth of livestock in it.

I started out by hiring the cowboy stars who had won important prize money at every rodeo from Pendleton to Madison Square Garden. These lads were wonderful at riding, roping, and bulldogging the wild steer. But they were not so good when it came to Deadeye Dick stuff with a pistol.

The cowboys could draw quick and shoot straight, provided the target was man-sized and close-up. But when I wanted somebody to pop a clay pipe out of a girl's mouth at fifty feet, I had to import the national pistol champion, a slicker from Brooklyn who had studied marksmanship in a Coney Island shooting gallery. The cowboys oohed and aahed when they saw this kind of shooting, and my kid dreams got their first kick in the chaps.

But that was nothing compared with what the Indians did to my illusions. One day I called Carter and told him I needed some redskins for a big war-dance number. "How many?" he said, as if I had asked for desk blotters.

"Oh, a hundred and fifty," I said.

A couple of weeks later, a gent walked into the air-conditioned blockhouse in which I was officing. "I got your Indians," he said. "Where shall I put them?" I went outside and looked. There they were, blankets, feathers, papooses and goats. It looked like an explosion in a paint factory.

"They're all yours," said the agent. "Sign here."

"Have your people down at the Last Frontier arena at five this afternoon," I told the boss Indian. "I want to see them dance."

When I got to the arena a couple of braves were half-heartedly knuckling tomtoms. The Indians had already been dancing for half an hour, but their movements had as much abandon as those of a man standing in a moving bus.

"Tell 'em to cut loose," I said to the agent.

"They've cut," he replied. "Takes 'em a little time to warm up. They ought to git goin' good along about midnight. By tomorrow afternoon they should be jumpin'."

The Last Frontier opened with a parade of covered wagons instead of a war dance. . . .

I would have written off the whole Wild West legend as Gene Autry publicity except for one incident. One night there was a riot on the Midway. Somebody claimed he'd been cheated and the first thing I knew a hundred people were swinging at each other.

I phoned for the Rangers. A few minutes later one of them showed up. He walked into where they were fighting. Word spread like wild-fire through the melee that a Ranger was there, and the brawl was over in a minute.

As I watched him walk away, it was with the same eyes that used to read Zane Grey under the blanket.

One number in The Last Frontier was built around a song called "Memories of Buffalo Bill." I thought it would be a nice touch to close this scene with a herd of buffalo coming down the hills and exiting stage right to eight bars of music.

I phoned Carter. "Three dozen buffalo?" said Amon. "Will do!"

My good right arm in staging the Exposition was John Murray Anderson, the soft-spoken Englishman who has fashioned a score of musical successes on Broadway and Piccadilly. The night before the Exposition opened, I was scooting around on a motorcycle, putting Big Genius touches to this and that.

I dragged Murray away from the platoons of girls he was directing at the Casa Manana cabaret and took him in my sidecar to the dress rehearsal of The Last Frontier. Anderson had no zest for this Wild West show, but he went to work setting the light-cues in his best Nelson Monument manner.

Around four in the morning, we got to the Buffalo Bill sequence. I went over the number with Murray. It started with half a dozen cowboys around a campfire on one of the prop hills. To the plunking of a guitar, one of them would sing about his memories of Cody's famous Wild West show. As he finished the first chorus, the thirty-six buffalo would enter and come down the hills while the orchestra went heavy on the fiddles. Behind the smelly monsters would come a man on horseback, togged out like the Buffalo Bill of the posters.

I told Murray I wanted a soulful shade of blue to light my herd of buffalo. There are many blues a director can choose from, ranging from the sky-blue of gelatin No. 29 to the purplish-blue of gelatin No. 37. At his seat in the grandstand, Anderson picked up a portable phone and called the stage-manager behind the hills two blocks away. "Turn on the 29 blues," he said.

A moment later the giant sun-arcs flooded the field. Then Murray said in a bored voice, "Now the buffalo, please."

Zowie! They stormed out of the chutes and charged down the hills hellbent for the Gulf of Mexico. When they were halfway down my man-made cliffs, Murray raised a well-manicured hand as if he were addressing a line of Shubert chorus boys.

"Hold it please," he said. "Change that gelatin to a 31."

The hit of the Exposition was the Casa Manana cabaret, featuring Sally Rand. Her fan-is-quicker-than-the-eye routine went over big with the art-conscious customers that summer.

One night, Governor Dave Sholtz of Florida was in the house. I stopped by his table to ask if he'd mind being introduced from the stage before the show. Sholtz said he'd be honored.

As I started to walk away he asked if Miss Sally Rand were around. Said he had met her some years back when she played the Citrus Circuit in his state. I told him Sally was in her dressing room and offered to take him backstage.

When the Governor and I entered Sally's room, she was flat on the floor, wrapped in something pink, her chin propped up on her hands. And she was reading the Bible!

Scoffers will please leave quietly. Sally is always reading something or other. That summer it was the Bible straight through from Genesis to Revelation.

After Sally and the Governor had swapped hellos, he picked up the Good Book and said, "Let me read you a short passage which has always been a source of comfort to me." He turned to the Book of Psalms and began reading quietly.

It was almost show time. I heard Whiteman's orchestra tuning up and slipped out of the dressing room. A few minutes later I was at the center microphone on the big stage. As I introduced the first couple of celebrities, I kept looking off-stage towards Sally's room.

Someone in Sholtz's party hollered, "Introduce the Governor of Florida!"

"I'm sorry," I lied. "The Governor's talking long-distance to Tallahassee."

I wasn't going to stand there with my bare face hanging out and tell four thousand people that the Governor of Florida couldn't appear because he was reading the Bible in Sally Rand's dressing room!

Ring Out, Wild Bells

Wolcott Gibbs

When I finally got around to seeing Max
Reinhardt's cinema version of "A Midsummer-
Night's Dream," and saw a child called Mickey
Rooney playing Puck, I remembered suddenly
that long ago I had taken the same part.

Our production was given on the open-air
stage at the Riverdale Country School, shortly
before the war. The scenery was only the natural
scenery of that suburban dell, and the cast was
exclusively male, ranging in age from eleven to
perhaps seventeen. While we had thus preserved
the pure, Elizabethan note of the original, it
must be admitted that our version had its
drawbacks. The costumes were probably the
worst things we had to bear, and even Penrod,
tragically arrayed as Launcelot in his sister's
stockings and his father's drawers, might have
been embarrassed for us. Like Penrod, we were
costumed by our parents, and like the Schofields, they seemed on the whole a little weak
historically. Half of the ladies were inclined to

favor the Elizabethan, and they had constructed rather bunchy ruffs and farthingales for their offspring; others, who had read as far as the stage directions and learned that the action took place in an Athenian wood, had produced something vaguely Athenian, usually beginning with a sheet. Only the fairies had a certain uniformity. For some reason their parents had all decided on cheesecloth, with here and there a little ill-advised trimming with tinsel.

My own costume was mysterious, but spectacular. As nearly as I have ever been able to figure things out, my mother found her inspiration for it in a Maxfield Parrish picture of a court jester. Beginning at the top, there was a cap with three stuffed horns; then, for the main part, a pair of tights that covered me to my wrists and ankles; and finally slippers with stuffed toes that curled up at the ends. The whole thing was made out of silk in alternate green and red stripes, and (unquestionably my poor mother's most demented stroke) it was covered from head to foot with a thousand tiny bells. Because all our costumes were obviously perishable, we never wore them in rehearsal, and naturally nobody knew that I was invested with these peculiar sound effects until I made my entrance at the beginning of the second act.

Our director was a man who had strong opinions about how Shakespeare should be played, and Puck was one of his favorite characters. It was his theory that Puck, being "the incarnation of mischief," never ought to be still a minute, so I had been coached to bound onto the stage, and once there to dance up and down, cocking my head and waving my arms.

"I want you to be a little whirlwind," this man said.

Even as I prepared to bound onto the stage, I had my own misgivings about those dangerously abundant gestures, and their probable effect on my bells. It was too late, however, to invent another technique for playing Puck, even if there had been room for anything but horror in my mind. I bounded onto the stage.

The effect, in its way, must have been superb. With every leap I rang like a thousand children's sleighs, my melodies foretelling God knows what worlds of merriment to the enchanted spectators. It was even worse when I came to the middle of the stage and went into my gestures. The other ringing had been loud but sporadic. This was persistent, varying only slightly in volume and pitch with the vehemence of my gestures. To a blind man, it must have sounded as though I had recklessly decided to accompany myself on a xylophone. A maturer actor would probably have made up his mind that an emergency existed, and abandoned his gestures as impracticable under the circumstances. I was thirteen, and incapable of innovations. I had been told by responsible authorities that gestures went with this part, and I continued to make them. I also continued to ring — a silvery music, festive and horrible.

If the bells were hard on my nerves, they were even worse for the rest of the cast, who were totally unprepared for my new interpretation. Puck's first remark is addressed to one of the fairies, and it is mercifully brief.

I said, "How now, spirit! Whither wander you?"

This unhappy child, already embarrassed by a public appearance in cheesecloth and tinsel, was also burdened with an opening speech of sixteen lines in verse. He began bravely:

"Over hill, over dale,
  Thorough bush, thorough brier,
Over park, over pale,
  Thorough flood, thorough fire . . ."

At the word "fire," my instructions were to bring my hands up from the ground in a long, wavery sweep, intended to represent fire. The bells pealed. To my startled ears, it sounded more as if they exploded. The fairy stopped in his lines and looked at me sharply. The jingling, however, had diminished; it was no more than as if a faint wind stirred my bells, and he went on:

"I do wander every where,
  Swifter than the moone's sphere . . ."

Here again I had another cue, for a sort of swoop and dip indicating the swiftness of the moone's sphere. Again the bells rang out, and again the performance stopped in its tracks. The fairy was clearly troubled by these interruptions. He had, however, a child's strange acceptance of the inscrutable, and was even able to regard my bells as a last-minute adult addition to the program, nerve-racking but not to be questioned. I'm sure it was only this that got him through that first speech.

My turn, when it came, was even worse. By this time the audience had succumbed to a helpless gaiety. Every time my bells rang, laughter swept the spectators, and this mounted and mingled with the bells until everything else was practically inaudible. I began my speech, another long one, and full of incomprehensible references to Titania's changeling.

"Louder!" said somebody in the wings. "You'll have to talk louder."

It was the director, and he seemed to be in a dangerous state.

"And for heaven's sake, stop that jingling!" he said.

I talked louder, and I tried to stop the jingling, but it was no use. By the time I got to the end of my speech, I was shouting and so was the audience. It appeared that I had very little control over the bells, which continued to jingle in spite of my passionate efforts to keep them quiet.

All this had a very bad effect on the fairy, who by this time had many symptoms of a complete nervous collapse. However, he began his next speech:

> "Either I mistake your shape and making
> quite,
> Or else you are that shrewd and knavish
> sprite
> Call'd Robin Goodfellow: are you not he
> That . . ."

At this point I forgot that the rules had been changed and I was supposed to leave out the gestures. There was a furious jingling, and the fairy gulped.

"Are you not he that, that . . ."

He looked miserably at the wings, and the director supplied the next line, but the tumult was too much for him. The unhappy child simply shook his head.

"Say anything!" shouted the director desperately. "Anything at all!"

The fairy only shut his eyes and shuddered.

"All right!" shouted the director. "All right, Puck. *You* begin *your* next speech."

By some miracle, I actually did remember my next lines, and had opened my mouth to begin on them when suddenly the fairy spoke. His voice was a high, thin monotone, and there seemed to be madness in it, but it was perfectly clear.

"Fourscore and seven years ago," he began, "our fathers brought forth on this continent a new nation, conceived . . ."

He said it right through to the end, and it was certainly the most successful speech ever made on that stage, and probably one of the most successful speeches ever made on any stage. I don't remember, if I ever knew, how the rest of us ever picked up the dull, normal thread of the play after that extraordinary performance, but we must have, because I know it went on. I only remember that in the next intermission the director cut off my bells with his penknife, and after that things quieted down and got dull.

Modern Humor

To A Small Boy Standing On My Shoes While I Am Wearing Them

Ogden Nash

Let's straighten this out, my little man,
And reach an agreement if we can.
I entered your door as an honored guest.
My shoes are shined and my trousers are
    pressed,
And I won't stretch out and read you the
    funnies
And I won't pretend that we're Easter
    bunnies.
If you must get somebody down on the
    floor,
What in the hell are your parents for?
I do not like the things that you say
And I hate the games that you want to play.
No matter how frightfully hard you try,
We've little in common, you and I.
The interest I take in my neighbor's
    nursery
Would have to grow, to be even cursory,
And I would that performing sons and
    nephews

Were carted away with the daily refuse,
And I hold that frolicsome daughters and
  nieces
Are ample excuse for breaking leases.
You may take a sock at your daddy's
  tummy
Or climb all over your doting mummy,
But keep your attentions to me in check
Or, sonny boy, I will wring your neck.
A happier man today I'd be
Had someone wrung it ahead of me.

Insert Flap "A" and Throw Away

S. J. Perelman

One stifling summer afternoon last August, in the attic of a tiny stone house in Pennsylvania, I made a most interesting discovery: the shortest, cheapest method of inducing a nervous breakdown ever perfected. In this technique (eventually adopted by the psychology department of Duke University, which will adopt anything), the subject is placed in a sharply sloping attic heated to 340°F. and given a mothproof closet known as the Jiffy-Cloz to assemble. The Jiffy-Cloz, procurable at any department store or neighborhood insane asylum, consists of half a dozen gigantic sheets of red cardboard, two plywood doors, a clothes rack, and a packet of staples. With these is included a set of instructions mimeographed in pale-violet ink, fruity with phrases like "Pass Section F through Slot AA, taking care not to fold tabs behind washers (see Fig. 9)." The cardboard is so processed that as the subject struggles convulsively to force the staple

405

through, it suddenly buckles, plunging the staple deep into his thumb. He thereupon springs up with a dolorous cry and smites his knob (Section K) on the rafters (RR). As a final demonic touch, the Jiffy-Cloz people cunningly omit four of the staples necessary to finish the job, so that after indescribable purgatory, the best the subject can possibly achieve is a sleazy, capricious structure which would reduce any self-respecting moth to helpless laughter. The cumulative frustration, the tropical heat, and the soft, ghostly chuckling of the moths are calculated to unseat the strongest mentality.

In a period of rapid technological change, however, it was inevitable that a method as cumbersome as the Jiffy-Cloz would be superseded. It was superseded at exactly nine-thirty Christmas morning by a device called the Self-Running 10-Inch Scale-Model Delivery-Truck Kit Powered by Magic Motor, costing twenty-nine cents. About nine on that particular morning, I was spread-eagled on my bed, indulging in my favorite sport of mouth-breathing, when a cork fired from a child's air gun mysteriously lodged in my throat. The pellet proved awkward for a while, but I finally ejected it by flailing the little marksman (and his sister, for good measure) until their welkins rang, and sauntered in to breakfast. Before I could choke down a healing fruit juice, my consort, a tall, regal creature indistinguishable from Cornelia, the Mother of the Gracchi, except that her foot was entangled in a roller skate, swept in. She extended a large, unmistakable box covered with diagrams.

"Now don't start making excuses," she whined. "It's just a simple cardboard toy. The directions are on the back —"

"Look, dear," I interrupted, rising hurriedly and pulling on my overcoat, "it clean slipped my mind. I'm supposed to take a lesson in crosshatching at Zim's School of Cartooning today."

"On Christmas?" she asked suspiciously.

"Yes, it's the only time they could fit me in," I countered glibly. "This is the big week for crosshatching, you know, between Christmas and New Year's."

"Do you think you ought to go in your pajamas?" she asked.

"Oh, that's O.K.," I smiled. "We often work in our pajamas up at Zim's. Well, goodbye now. If I'm not home by Thursday, you'll find a cold snack in the safe-deposit box." My subterfuge, unluckily, went for naught, and in a trice I was sprawled on the nursery floor, surrounded by two lambkins and ninety-eight segments of the Self-Running 10-Inch Scale-Model Delivery-Truck Construction Kit.

The theory of the kit was simplicity itself, easily intelligible to Kettering of General Motors, Professor Millikan, or any first-rate physicist. Taking as my starting point the only sentence I could comprehend, "Fold down on all lines marked 'fold down'; fold up on all lines marked 'fold up,' " I set the children to work and myself folded up with an album of views of Chili Williams. In a few moments, my skin was suffused with a delightful tingling sensation and I was ready for the second phase, lightly referred to in the directions as "Preparing the Spring Motor Unit." As nearly as I could determine after twenty minutes of mumbling, the Magic Motor ("No Electricity — No Batteries — Nothing to Wind — Motor Never Wears Out") was an accordion-pleated affair operating by torsion, attached to the axles. "It is necessary," said the text, "to cut a slight notch in each of the axles with a knife (see Fig. C). To find the exact place to cut this notch, lay one of the axles over diagram at bottom of page."

"Well, *now* we're getting someplace!" I boomed, with a false gusto that deceived nobody. "Here, Buster, run in and get Daddy a knife."

"I dowanna," quavered the boy, backing away. "You always cut yourself at this stage." I gave the wee fellow an indulgent pat on the head that flattened it slightly, to teach him civility, and commandeered a long, serrated bread knife from the kitchen. "Now watch me closely, children," I ordered. "We place the axle on the diagram as in Fig. C, applying a strong downward pressure on the knife handle at all times." The axle must have been a factory second, because an instant later I was in the bathroom grinding my teeth in agony and attempting to stanch the flow of blood. Ultimately, I succeeded in contriving a rough bandage and slipped back into the nursery without awaking the children's suspicions. An agreeable surprise awaited me. Displaying a mechanical aptitude clearly inherited from their sire, the rascals had put together the chassis of the delivery truck.

"Very good indeed," I complimented (naturally, one has to exaggerate praise to develop a child's self-confidence). "Let's see — what's the next step? Ah, yes. 'Lock into box shape by inserting tabs C, D, E, F, G, H, J, K, and L into slots C, D, E, F, G, H, J, K, and L. Ends of front axle should be pushed through holes A and B.' " While marshaling the indicated parts in their proper order, I emphasized to my rapt listeners the necessity of patience and perseverance. "Haste makes waste, you know," I reminded them. "Rome wasn't built in a day. Remember, your daddy isn't always going to be here to show you."

"Where *are* you going to be?" they demanded.

"In the movies, if I can arrange it," I snarled. Poising tabs C, D, E, F, G, H, J, K, and L in one hand and the corresponding slots in the other, I essayed a union of the two, but in vain. The moment I made one set fast and tackled another, tab and slot would part company, thumbing their noses at me. Although the children were too immature to understand, I saw in a flash where the trouble lay. Some idiotic employee at the factory had punched out the wrong design, probably out of sheer spite. So that was his game, eh? I set my lips in a grim line and, throwing one hundred and fifty-seven pounds of fighting fat into the effort, pounded the component parts into a homogeneous mass.

"There," I said with a gasp, "that's close enough. Now then, who wants candy? One, two, three — everybody off to the candy store!"

"We wanna finish the delivery truck!" they wailed. "Mummy, he won't let us finish the delivery truck!" Threats, cajolery, bribes were of no avail. In their jungle code, a twenty-cent gewgaw bulked larger than a parent's love. Realizing that I was dealing with a pair of monomaniacs, I determined to show them who was master and wildly began locking the cardboard units helter-skelter, without any regard for the directions. When sections refused to fit, I gouged them with my nails and forced them together, cackling shrilly. The side panels collapsed; with a bestial oath, I drove a safety pin through them and lashed them to the roof. I used paper clips, bobby pins, anything I could lay my hands on. My fingers fairly flew and my breath whistled in my throat. "You want a delivery truck, do you?" I panted. "All right, I'll show you!" As merciful blackness closed in, I was on my hands and knees, bunting the infernal thing along with my nose and whinnying, "Roll, confound you, roll!"

"Absolute quiet," a carefully modulated voice was saying, "and fifteen of the white tablets every four hours." I opened my eyes carefully in the darkened room. Dimly I picked out a knifelike character actor in pince-nez lenses and a morning coat folding a stethoscope into his bag. "Yes," he added thoughtfully, "if we play our cards right, this ought to be a long, expensive recovery." From far away, I could hear my wife's voice bravely trying to control her anxiety.

"What if he becomes restless, Doctor?"

"Get him a detective story," returned the leech. "Or better still, a nice, soothing picture puzzle — something he can do with his hands."

Down with the Restoration!

S. J. Perelman

Does anybody here mind if I make a prediction? I haven't made a prediction since the opening night of *The Women* some years ago, when I rose at the end of the third act and announced to my escort, a Miss Chicken-Licken, "The public will never take this to its bosom." Since the public has practically worn its bosom to a nubbin niggling up to *The Women,* I feel that my predictions may be a straw to show the direction the wind is blowing away from. I may very well open up a cave and do business as a sort of Cumaean Sibyl in reverse. You can't tell me people would rather climb up that Aventine Hill and have a man mess around with the entrails of a lot of sacred chickens when they can come down into my nice cool cave and get a good hygienic prediction for a few cents. So just to stimulate trade and start the ball rolling, here goes my first prediction: One of these days two young people are going to stumble across a ruined farmhouse and leave it alone . . . .

Well, what are you sitting there gaping at? You heard what I said. That's my prediction.

Honest Injun, I hate to sound crotchety, and the last thing in the world I want to do is throw the editors of all those home-making magazines like *Nook and Garden* and *The American Home-Owner* into an uproar, but the plain fact is that I've got a bellyful. For over two years now, every time I start leafing through one of those excellent periodicals, I fall afoul of another article about a couple of young people who stumble across a ruined farmhouse and remodel it on what is inelegantly termed spit and coupons. Or maybe it's the same article. I couldn't be reading the same issue over and over, could I?

All these remodelling articles are written by the remodellers themselves and never by the ruined farmer or the man who didn't get paid for the plastering, which accounts for their rather smug tone. They invariably follow the same pattern. A young couple named Mibs and Evan have decided to return to the land. I see Mibs as one of those girls on the short side, with stocky legs, a low-slung posterior, and an untidy bun of straw-colored hair continually unwinding on the nape of her neck. Before anyone ever heard of Salzburg, she wore a high-bodiced dress with full skirts, a sort of horrid super-dirndl with home-cooked hems that have a tendency to hang down in back. She is usually engaged in reading a book written by two unfrocked chemists which tells women how to make their own cold cream by mixing a little potash with a dram of glycerine and a few cloves. Evan is a full-haunched young man in a fuzzy woollen suit (I don't suppose there's any such thing as a fuzzy cotton suit, but you know what I mean) who is forever rubbing a briar pipe along his nose to show you the beauty of the grain. He smokes his own mixture of perique, Latakia, and Imperial Cube Cut, for the very good reason that nobody else will smoke it, and he has probably read more of Arthur Machen than any man alive.

Well, as I say, your average remodelling yarn begins with Mibs and Evan stumbling across the most adorable ruin of an eighteenth-century farmhouse. It doesn't *have* to be a farmhouse; it can be a gristmill, or a tobacco barn, or a Mennonite schoolhouse. It can even be an early Colonial hen house, with delightful hand-hewn beams and perfectly sweet old tar paper scaling off the sides. Apparently nobody previous to Mibs and Evan has realized its possibilities, but Evan takes one look at it and says in a guarded tone, "Two hundred dollars would restore that beautifully if you didn't go crazy putting in a lot of bathrooms you didn't need." "Oh, Evan!" breathes Mibs, her eyes shining above her adenoids and her brain reeling with visions of Cape Cod spatter floors. "Dare we . . . ?" That night, at dinner in the Jumble Shop, they put their heads together — Evan removes the pipe from alongside his nose, of course — and decide to jump at the chance. It involves giving up that trip to Europe, a choice the characters in these stories always have to make, but Mibs has always dreamed of a sunny garden filled with old-fashioned flowers of the type her mother used to read about in Max Schling's catalogue. So they bravely draw two hundred dollars out of their little hoard, leaving a hundred in case they ever want to take a really long trip to some place like Bali, and lay it on the line.

After considerable excitement, in which everybody searches the title like mad and Mibs discovers the quaintest old parchment deed describing their land in terms of rods, chains, and poods, they are ready to take the "Before" snapshots. Evan digs up one of the cameras used by Brady at the battle of Antietam, waits for a good cloudy day, and focuses across a mound of guano at the most ramshackle corner of the "manse," as Mibs calls it with irreverent mischief. The article generally carries several gray smudges captioned "Southwest corner of the house before work began," and you can't help wondering where those giant oaks came from in the "After" photographs. Maybe they sprang up from acorns dropped by the workmen while they were having lunch.

The first thing the high-hearted pair decide on is a new roof. This fortunately costs only eight dollars, as they use second-hand wattles and hire a twelve-year-old scab — all right, maybe he only mislaid his union card — to tack them on. The outside walls are a problem, but an amazing stroke of good fortune comes to their rescue. Opening a trap door they hadn't investigated, Mibs and Evan stumble across countless bundles of lovely old hand-split shingles which have been overlooked by previous tenants, like the hens. Two superb Adam fireplaces, hitherto concealed by some matchboarding, now make their appearance, in one of them a box of dusty but otherwise well-preserved pieces of Sandwich and Stiegel glass. "The attic!" shout Mibs and Evan simultaneously, suddenly remembering their resolution to look through it some rainy day, and sure enough, there they find a veritable treasure trove of pewter ware, cherry escritoires, Chippendale wing chairs, sawbuck tables, and Field beds, hidden away by survivors of the Deerfield massacre. "It just didn't seem *possible*," recalls Mib candidly, up to her old trick of taking the words out of your mouth.

And now, suddenly, the place becomes a hive of activity. A salty old character named Lafe (who is really Paul Bunyan, no matter what *Nook and Garden* says) appears and does the work of ten men at the price of one. He pulls down trees with his bare hands, lays new floors, puts up partitions, installs electricity, diverts streams, forges the ironware, bakes porcelain sinks, and all but spins silk for the draperies.

How this djinn ever escaped from his bottle, and where he is now, the article neglects to mention. The upshot is that in a little over two weeks, the last hooked rug — picked up by Mibs at an auction for ten cents after spirited bidding — is in place and the early Salem kettle is singing merrily on the hob. A fat orange tabby blinks before the fire and Evan, one arm around Mibs, is adding up a column of figures. "Think of it, lover," whispers Mibs with dancing eyes. "We did the whole thing for only *fifty-one dollars and eighteen cents!*" "Less than we'll get for that article in *The American Home-Owner,*" murmurs Evan exultantly, reaming the cake from his pipe. "Tell me, does oo love its 'ittle —" . . . . And now would you hate me if I stole out very quietly? I'm afraid there's going to be just a wee bit of baby talk.

Inflexible Logic

Russell Maloney

When the six chimpanzees came into his life, Mr. Bainbridge was thirty-eight years old. He was a bachelor and lived comfortably in a remote part of Connecticut, in a large old house with a carriage drive, a conservatory, a tennis court, and a well-selected library. His income was derived from impeccably situated real estate in New York City, and he spent it soberly, in a manner which could give offence to nobody. Once a year, late in April, his tennis court was resurfaced, and after that anybody in the neighborhood was welcome to use it; his monthly statement from Brentano's seldom ran below seventy-five dollars; every third year, in November, he turned in his old Cadillac coupé for a new one; he ordered his cigars, which were mild and rather moderately priced, in shipments of one thousand from a tobacconist in Havana; because of the international situation he had cancelled arrangements to travel abroad, and after due thought had decided to spend his travelling allowance on wines, which seemed likely to get scarcer and more expensive if the war lasted. On the whole, Mr. Bainbridge's life was deliberately, and not too unsuccessfully, modelled after that of an English country gentleman of the late eighteenth century, a gentleman interested in the arts and in the expansion of science, and so sure of himself that he didn't care if some people thought him eccentric.

Mr. Bainbridge had many friends in New York, and he spent several days of the month in the city, staying at his club and looking around. Sometimes he called up a girl and took her out to a theatre and a night club. Sometimes he and a couple of classmates got a little tight and went to a prizefight. Mr. Bainbridge also looked in now and then at some of the conservative art galleries, and liked occasionally to go to a concert. And he liked cocktail parties, too, because of the fine footling conversation and the extraordinary number of pretty girls who had nothing else to do with the rest of their evening. It was at a New York cocktail party, however, that Mr. Bainbridge kept his preliminary appointment with doom. At one of the parties given by Hobie Packard, the stockbroker, he learned about the theory of the six chimpanzees.

It was almost six-forty. The people who had intended to have one drink and go had already gone, and the people who intended to stay were fortifying themselves with slightly dried canapés and talking animatedly. A group of stage and radio people had coagulated in one corner, near Packard's Capehart, and were wrangling about various methods of cheating the Collector of Internal Revenue. In another corner was a group of stockbrokers, talking about the greatest stockbroker of them all, Gauguin. Little Marcia Lupton was sitting with a young man, saying earnestly, "Do you really want to know what my greatest ambition is? I want to be myself," and Mr. Bainbridge smiled gently, thinking of the time Marcia had said that to him. Then he heard the voice of Bernard Weiss, the critic, saying, "Of course he wrote one good novel. It's not surprising. After all, we know that if six chimpanzees were set to work pounding six typewriters at random, they would, in a million years, write all the books in the British Museum."

Mr. Bainbridge drifted over to Weiss and was introduced to Weiss's companion, a Mr. Noble. "What's this about a million chimpanzees, Weiss?" he asked.

"Six chimpanzees," Mr. Weiss said. "It's an old cliché of the mathematicians. I thought everybody was told about it in school. Law of averages, you know, or maybe it's permutation and combination. The six chimps, just pounding away at the typewriter keys, would be bound to copy out all the books ever written by man. There are only so many possible combinations of letters and numerals, and they'd produce all of them — see? Of course they'd also turn out a mountain of gibberish, but they'd work the books in, too. All the books in the British Museum."

Mr. Bainbridge was delighted; this was the sort of talk he liked to hear when he came to New York. "Well, but look here," he said, just to keep up his part in the foolish conversation, "what if one of the chimpanzees finally did duplicate a book, right down to the last period, but left that off? Would that count?"

"I suppose not. Probably the chimpanzee would get around to doing the book again, and put the period in."

"What nonsense!" Mr. Noble cried.

"It may be nonsense, but Sir James Jeans believes it," Mr. Weiss said, huffily. "Jeans or Lancelot Hogben. I know I ran across it quite recently."

Mr. Bainbridge was impressed. He read quite a bit of popular science, and both Jeans and Hogben were in his library. "Is that so?" he murmured, no longer feeling frivolous. "Wonder if it has ever actually been tried? I mean, has anybody ever put six chimpanzees in a room with six typewriters and a lot of paper?"

Mr. Weiss glanced at Mr. Bainbridge's empty cocktail glass and said drily, "Probably not."

Nine weeks later, on a winter evening, Mr. Bainbridge was sitting in his study with his friend James Mallard, an assistant professor of mathematics at New Haven. He was plainly nervous as he poured himself a drink and said, "Mallard, I've asked you to come here — Brandy? Cigar? — for a particular reason. You remember that I wrote you some time ago, asking your opinion of . . . a certain mathematical hypothesis or supposition."

"Yes," Professor Mallard said, briskly. "I remember perfectly. About the six chimpanzees and the British Museum. And I told you it was a perfectly sound popularization of a principle known to every schoolboy who had studied the science of probabilities."

"Precisely," Mr. Bainbridge said. "Well, Mallard, I made up my mind. . . . It was not difficult for me, because I have, in spite of that fellow in the White House, been able to give something every year to the Museum of Natural History, and they were naturally glad to oblige me. . . . And after all, the only contribution a layman can make to the progress of science is to assist with the drudgery of experiment. . . . In short, I —"

"I suppose you're trying to tell me that you have procured six chimpanzees and set them to work at typewriters in order to see whether they will eventually write all the books in the British Museum. Is that it?"

"Yes, that's it," Mr. Bainbridge said. "What a mind you have, Mallard. Six fine young males, in perfect condition. I had a — I suppose you'd call it a dormitory — built out in back of the stable. The typewriters are in the conservatory. It's light and airy in there, and I moved most of the plants out. Mr. North, the man who owns the circus, very obligingly let me engage one of his best animal men. Really, it was no trouble at all."

Professor Mallard smiled indulgently. "After all, such a thing is not unheard of," he said. "I seem to remember that a man at some university put his graduate students to work flipping coins, to see if heads and tails came up an equal number of times. Of course they did."

Mr. Bainbridge looked at his friend very queerly. "Then you believe that any such principle of the science of probabilities will stand up under an actual test?"

"Certainly."

"You had better see for yourself." Mr. Bainbridge led Professor Mallard downstairs, along a corridor, through a disused music room, and into a large conservatory. The middle of the floor had been cleared of plants and was occupied by a row of six typewriter tables, each one supporting a hooded machine. At the left of each typewriter was a neat stack of yellow copy paper. Empty wastebaskets were under each table. The chairs were the unpadded, spring-backed kind favored by experienced stenographers. A large bunch of ripe bananas was hanging in one corner, and in another stood a Great Bear water-cooler and a rack of Lily cups. Six piles of typescript, each about a foot high, were ranged along the wall on an improvised shelf. Mr. Bainbridge picked up one of the piles, which he could just conveniently lift, and set it on a table before Professor Mallard. "The output to date of Chimpanzee A, known as Bill," he said simply.

" ' "Oliver Twist," by Charles Dickens,' " Professor Mallard read out. He read the first and second pages of the manuscript, then feverishly leafed through to the end. "You mean to tell me," he said, "that this chimpanzee has written —"

"Word for word and comma for comma," said Mr. Bainbridge. "Young, my butler, and I took turns comparing it with the edition I own. Having finished 'Oliver Twist,' Bill is, as you see, starting the sociological works of Vilfredo Pareto, in Italian. At the rate he has been going, it should keep him busy for the rest of the month."

"And all the chimpanzees" — Professor Mallard was pale, and enunciated with difficulty — "they aren't all —"

"Oh, yes, all writing books which I have every reason to believe are in the British Museum. The prose of John Donne, some Anatole France, Conan Doyle, Galen, the collected plays of Somerset Maugham, Marcel Proust, the memoirs of the late Marie of Rumania, and a monograph by a Dr. Wiley on

424

the marsh grasses of Maine and Massachusetts. I can sum it up for you, Mallard, by telling you that since I started this experiment, four weeks and some days ago, none of the chimpanzees has spoiled a single sheet of paper.''

Professor Mallard straightened up, passed his handkerchief across his brow, and took a deep breath. "I apologize for my weakness," he said. "It was simply the sudden shock. No, looking at the thing scientifically — and I hope I am at least as capable of that as the next man — there is nothing marvellous about the situation. These chimpanzees, or a succession of similar teams of chimpanzees, would in a million years write all the books in the British Museum. I told you some time ago that I believed that statement. Why should my belief be altered by the fact that they produced some of the books at the very outset? After all, I should not be very much surprised if I tossed a coin a hundred times and it came up heads every time. I know that if I kept at it long enough, the ratio would reduce itself to an exact fifty per cent. Rest assured, these chimpanzees will begin to compose gibberish quite soon. It is bound to happen. Science tells us so. Meanwhile, I advise you to keep this experiment secret. Uninformed people might create a sensation if they knew."

"I will, indeed," Mr. Bainbridge said. "And I'm very grateful for your rational analysis. It reassures me. And now, before you go, you must hear the new Schnabel records that arrived today."

During the succeeding three months, Professor Mallard got into the habit of telephoning Mr. Bainbridge every Friday afternoon at five-thirty, immediately after leaving his seminar room. The Professor would say, "Well?" and Mr. Bainbridge would reply, "They're still at it, Mallard. Haven't spoiled a sheet of paper yet." If Mr. Bainbridge had to go out on Friday afternoon, he would leave a written message with his butler, who would read it to Professor Mallard: "Mr. Bainbridge says we now have Trevelyan's 'Life of Macaulay,' the Confessions of St. Augustine, 'Vanity Fair,' part of Irving's 'Life of George Washington,' the Book of the Dead, and some speeches delivered in Parliament in opposition to the Corn Laws, sir." Professor Mallard would reply, with a hint of a snarl in his voice, "Tell him to remember what I predicted," and hang up with a clash.

The eleventh Friday that Professor Mallard telephoned, Mr. Bainbridge said, "No change. I have had to store the bulk of the manuscript in the cellar. I would have burned it, except that it probably has some scientific value."

"How dare you talk of scientific value?" The voice from New Haven roared faintly in the receiver. "Scientific value! You — you — chimpanzee!" There were further inarticulate sputterings, and Mr. Bainbridge hung up with a disturbed expression. "I am afraid Mallard is overtaxing himself," he murmured.

Next day, however, he was pleasantly surprised. He was leafing through a manuscript that had been completed the previous day by Chimpanzee D, Corky. It was the complete diary of Samuel Pepys, and Mr. Bainbridge was chuckling over the naughty passages, which were omitted in his own edition, when Professor Mallard was shown into the room. "I have come to apologize for my outrageous conduct on the telephone yesterday," the Professor said.

"Please don't think of it any more. I know you have many things on your mind," Mr. Bainbridge said. "Would you like a drink?"

"A large whiskey, straight, please," Professor Mallard said. "I got rather cold driving down. No change, I presume?"

"No, none. Chimpanzee F, Dinty, is just finishing John Florio's translation of Montaigne's essays, but there is no other news of interest."

Professor Mallard squared his shoulders and tossed off his drink in one astonishing gulp. "I should like to see them at work," he said. "Would I disturb them, do you think?"

"Not at all. As a matter of fact, I usually look in on them around this time of day. Dinty may have finished his Montaigne by now, and it is always interesting to see them start a new work. I would have thought that they would continue on the same sheet of paper, but they don't, you know. Always a fresh sheet, and the title in capitals."

Professor Mallard, without apology, poured another drink and slugged it down. "Lead on," he said.

It was dusk in the conservatory, and the chimpanzees were typing by the light of student lamps clamped to their desks. The keeper lounged in a corner, eating a banana and reading *Billboard*. "You might as well take an hour or so off," Mr. Bainbridge said. The man left.

Professor Mallard, who had not taken off his overcoat, stood with his hands in his pockets, looking at the busy chimpanzees. "I wonder if you know, Bainbridge, that the science of probabilities takes everything into account," he said, in a queer, tight voice. "It is certainly almost beyond the bounds of credibility that these chimpanzees should write books without a single error, but that abnormality may be corrected by — *these!*" He took his hands from his pockets, and each one held a .38 revolver. "Stand back out of harm's way!" he shouted.

"Mallard! Stop it!" The revolvers barked, first the right hand, then the left, then the right. Two chimpanzees fell, and a third reeled into a corner. Mr. Bainbridge seized his friend's arm and wrested one of the weapons from him.

"Now I am armed, too, Mallard, and I advise you to stop!" he cried. Professor Mallard's answer was to draw a bead on Chimpanzee E and shoot him dead. Mr. Bainbridge made a rush, and Professor Mallard fired at him. Mr. Bainbridge, in his quick death agony, tightened his finger on the trigger of his revolver. It went off, and Professor Mallard went down. On his hands and knees he fired at the two chimpanzees which were still unhurt, and then collapsed.

There was nobody to hear his last words. "The human equation . . . always the enemy of science . . ." he panted. "This time . . . vice versa . . . I, a mere mortal . . . savior of science . . . deserve a Nobel . . ."

When the old butler came running into the conservatory to investigate the noises, his eyes were met by a truly appalling sight. The student lamps were shattered, but a newly risen moon shone in through the conservatory windows on the corpses of the two gentlemen, each clutching a smoking revolver. Five of the chimpanzees were dead. The sixth was Chimpanzee F. His right arm disabled, obviously bleeding to death, he was slumped before his typewriter. Painfully, with his left hand, he took from the machine the completed last page of Florio's Montaigne. Groping for a fresh sheet, he inserted it, and typed with one finger, "UNCLE TOM'S CABIN, by Harriet Beecher Stowe. Chapte . . ." Then he, too, was dead.

Shaggy-Dog Stories

Bennett Cerf

Shaggy-dog stories, as almost everybody must know by this time, are the kind of tales in which animals talk, humans do inexplicable things, and the punch lines make no sense at all. They are generally anathema to literal-minded females. There is nothing like a string of shaggy-dog stories to make your wife's Aunt Minnie cut short a visit and go back where she came from. They receive their name from the following legend.

A Kansas City barfly picked up a year-old copy of the London *Times* one day — don't ask me how it got there — and found therein a personal ad offering a ten-pound reward for the return of a very shaggy dog to its bereft owner in Bishop's Bowes, Essex. Ten minutes later he stumbled over the shaggiest darn pup you ever saw. Being a man of decision, he promptly bundled the canine under his arm, took the Twentieth Century to New York, the *Queen Mary* to Southampton, and a limousine to

Bishop's Bowes. In keen anticipation, he sought out the lady who had advertised, and rang her bell. She answered herself. "You lost a shaggy dog, madam," he reminded her, holding up the pooch. "Would this be it?" "Good heavens, no," she snapped. "It wasn't *that* shaggy" — and slammed the door in his face.

Well, now that we've settled that, we propose to give you thirty-two examples of the species. We figure that fewer than that would not do the subject full justice; more might set the most avid addicts to baying at the moon. Note that we have numbered the entries. You can't tell the bayers without a number.

1. Two race horses fretted impatiently in adjoining stalls the night before a Kentucky Derby. "You might as well save yourself the effort of competing tomorrow," spoke one, "I've got the Derby sewed up." "Says you," scoffed the other. "What makes you so sure of yourself?" "Didn't you see my owner whispering in my ear just now?" said the first horse. "He was telling me that if I won tomorrow, he'd give me two extra bales of hay. And, brother, that ain't money!"

2. "A quarter's worth of rat poison," ordered the man at the delicatessen store. "Yes, sir," the clerk answered. "Shall I wrap it up for you?" "Oh, you needn't bother," the man said pleasantly. "I'll eat it here."

3. A bat family was flying home from a picnic

— Papa Bat, Mama Bat, and Sonny Bat. "Thank heaven that picnic's over," said Sonny Bat. "Now the four of us can have some peace." "Four?" queried Papa. "I only see three." Sonny Bat flared up. "You know very well I can't count," he grumbled.

4. "This dog," Mr. Weber once said to Mr. Fields, "is worth five hundred dollars." To which Mr. Fields replied, "How could a dog save that much money?"

5. A customer entered a saloon and ordered a dozen martinis. He poured the liquor onto the floor, and began munching contentedly on the glasses themselves. The stems, however, he would have no traffic with. A barfly watched the performance with absorbed interest, but pointed to the twelve stems. "You darn fool," he said. "You're leaving the best part."

6. The oysters found a fine new bed several miles up the Sound, and were happily packing their belongings — all except little Mary Oyster, who sat sobbing bitterly in a corner. "What's the matter?" asked her father anxiously. "We'll have a wonderful new home. There's nothing to cry about." "Oh, yes, there is," wailed Mary. "Johnny Bass will never be able to find me now, and I love him with all my heart." "But does Johnny Bass reciprocate your devotion?" inquired the parent. "Indeed he does," Mary assured him. "Last night he took me in his arms at the end of the pier out there. First he kissed me here on the forehead. Then he

kissed me here on the lips. And then — my God, my *pearl!*"

7. A very shy young man sat next to a glamorous debutante at a dinner party. In the middle of the main course he seized a bowl of succotash and poured it over the debutante's chic coiffure. The young lady rose indignantly. "How dare you?" she blazed, plucking corn and peas out of her hair. "How dare you throw succotash at me?" The young man blanched. "Good heavens," he stammered. "Was that succotash? I thought it was spinach!"

8. A man's ear was bleeding like a stuck pig. "I bit myself," he explained. "That's impossible," said the doctor. "How can a man bite himself in the ear?" The man said, "I was standing on a chair."

9. Two herrings stopped at a neighborhood café for a couple of snifters. One of them disappeared for a moment, and a puzzled onlooker accosted the one who was left alone at the bar. "Where is your brother?" he challenged. "How in heck should I know," replied the indignant herring. "Am I my brother's kipper?"

10. A man staggered from a railroad car, his complexion a sickly green. "Riding backwards for six hours," he explained. "I never *could* stand that." "Why," his wife inquired, "didn't you ask the party sitting opposite to change seats with you?" "I couldn't do that," said the man. "There wasn't anybody there."

11. A crotchety old bachelor saw a gaily plumed parrot go under the hammer at a country auction, and suddenly decided that the bird might be good company for him on lonely evenings. The bidding grew unexpectedly stiff, but the bachelor was carried away by the spirit of the occasion and before he quite realized what he had done, he bought the Poll for forty-nine dollars. He carried it home, and stood it on the table before him. "Now," he commanded, "talk to me!" The parrot simply drew in its head and glared at him. "I said talk to me," repeated the man. "After all, I bought you to keep me company." Again the parrot glared but said nothing. "Good heavens," cried the exasperated gentleman. "Do you mean to say that after what I paid for you, you can't even *talk?*" "Can't even talk?" echoed the parrot. "Who in hell do you think it was that bid you up to forty-nine dollars?"

12. A cotton-tail rabbit, nibbling thoughtfully at his evening carrot, noticed that his son was in a particularly jovial mood. "What makes Junior so happy?" he asked. Mamma rabbit explained, "He had a wonderful time in school today. He learned how to multiply."

13. At a gala ship concert aboard a liner, a trained parrot did his act, and then teetered excitedly on his perch in the wings while an extraordinary magician performed feats of legerdemain. First he made a goldfish disappear, then a buxom blonde assistant, finally a chest

containing three husky sailors. At that moment the liner was struck by a torpedo. The parrot found himself all alone on the Atlantic Ocean, bobbing up and down on a piece of driftwood, with nothing else in sight. "Amazing," marveled the Poll. "What will he think of next?"

14. (Very, very old.) "Give me a soda," commanded the young sprout, "without flavor." "Without what flavor?" asked the soda jerk. "Without vanilla." "Ain't got no vanilla." "All right, gimme one without strawberry."

15. Two brothers, identical twins, often went fishing together. One twin was always lucky. The other could never catch a thing. They could stand right next to each other and one brother would haul in fish after fish while the other's line dangled idly in the water. One day the unlucky twin decided on a desperate course. He woke in the middle of the night and put on his brother's clothes. He took his brother's rod and went to the very spot where his brother had caught thirty-four trout the day before. For three hours he stood there without getting a nibble. Finally his hopes rose when he saw a magnificent trout swimming his way. The fish ignored the bait and, leaping out of the water, called, "Hey, bud, where's your brother?"

16. Sitting opposite Miss Haas on a northbound subway train one evening sat a man calmly reading his paper with three pigeons resting on top of him — one on his head, the others on his shoulders. Miss Haas contemplated

the situation until she could stand it no longer. She tapped his paper, and said, "Pardon me, but what on earth are you doing with those pigeons in the subway?" "Them?" said the man. "I really don't know, lady. They musta got on at 59th Street."

17. A man dropped in to pay a friend an unexpected visit, and was amazed to find him playing chess with his dog. The man watched in silence for a few minutes, then burst out with "That's the most incredible dog I ever saw in my life!" "Oh, he isn't so smart," was the answer. "I've beaten him three games out of four!"

18. One day a man said to Billy Rose, "Would you like to see me dive into a barrel of water from a thousand feet?" Billy Rose said he certainly would, and next day he called his workmen and had them set up a thousand-foot ladder. Mr. Rose held his breath while the man climbed to the top, and stared fascinated as he took a flying leap and landed, splash, in the barrel of water.

"Magnificent," said Billy Rose. "I'll hire you for $100 a week."

"No," said the man.

"$250 a week," said Billy Rose.

"No," said the man.

"You drive a hard bargain," said Billy Rose, "but your act is worth it. Let's not count pennies. I'll hire you for a thousand a week."

"No," said the man.

"Say, fellow," said Billy Rose, "how much do you want to jump into that barrel?"

"Nothing," said the man. "This is the first time I ever did it, and I don't like it."

19. A worm met another worm coming up from the ground and declared, "You're very beautiful and I'd like to marry you." "Don't be a dope," was the reply. "I'm your other end."

20. (One of the very first.) An elephant looked down at a mouse and exclaimed, "You're about the puniest, most insignificant object I ever laid eyes on." "I'm not always this little," the mouse squeaked angrily. "I've been sick."

21. A dignified old clergyman owned a parrot of which he was exceedingly fond, but the bird had picked up an appalling vocabulary of cuss words from a previous owner and, after a series of embarrassing episodes, the clergyman decided he would have to kill his pet. A lady in his parish suggested a last-ditch remedy. "I have a female parrot," she said, "who is an absolute saint. She sits quietly on her perch and does nothing but pray from morning until night. Why don't you bring your parrot over and see if my own bird's good influence doesn't reform him?" The clergyman said it was worth a trial, and the next night arrived with his pet tucked under his arm. The bird took one look at the lady parrot and chirped, "Hi, toots. How about a little loving?" "Come to mama," cried the lady parrot gleefully. "What do you think

I've been praying for all these years?"

22. A doctor saved a baby elephant's life in the jungle, then returned to America. Years later he was down on his luck, and had to borrow a quarter to see the circus when it came to town. Out came the elephants. One of them saw the doctor, and trumpeted recognition. He wrapped his trunk around the doctor, lifted him out of the twenty-five-cent seat — and planked him down in a box seat worth three dollars.

23. A kangaroo yanked her young one out of her pouch and gave it a healthy smack on the backside. "I'll teach you," she declared, "to eat crackers in bed!"

24. When the manager of the Brooklyn ball club lost his star center fielder on the eve of a crucial swing through the West, he sent out a frantic call for a replacement. Almost a week went by and there were no applications. The manager sat dejectedly on the bench with his head in his hands. He heard an apologetic whinny behind him, and looking around, saw a horse standing there.

"Go away," he said to the horse. "Can't you see I've got a headache?"

"But I'm applying for that spot in center field," said the horse.

"That's ridiculous," snapped the manager. "Horses don't play baseball — not even in Brooklyn!"

The horse insisted, however, and finally the

manager allowed him to exhibit his wares. It developed that he could field like Tris Speaker and hit like Joe Di Maggio. The delighted manager promptly inserted him into the lineup.

In the ninth inning of that day's game, with the score 0–0, the horse strode to the plate and lashed a wicked liner against the right-field fence.

Then — to everyone's amazement — he stood stock still at the plate, twirling his bat.

"Run, you idiot, run!" — beseeched the frantic manager. "This means the game!"

"Don't be silly," said the horse. "Who ever heard of a horse running bases?"

25. A colony of ostriches — ninety-nine birds in all — had their heads buried neatly in the sand when ostrich number one hundred came galumping onto the scene. He looked about in a puzzled way and inquired, "Where on earth *is* everybody?"

26. A reporter was assigned, a long time ago, to interview Mr. Barnum's favorite midget, Tom Thumb. The hotel clerk directed the reporter to Room 308, but when he knocked on that door, it was opened by a giant fully nine feet tall. "I must have the wrong room," apologized the newsman. "Who were you looking for?" countered the giant. "Tom Thumb, the dwarf," laughed the reporter. "Well, come in," said the giant. "I'm Tom Thumb." "You Tom Thumb!" the reporter scoffed. "Why, you're nine feet tall!" "I know,"

said the giant. "But, you see, this is my day off."

27. Mr. Nussbaum was a regular patron of Finkelstein's Shangri-La Bar and Grille. One evening he declared, "I feel like some fried flounder tonight." The waiter brought a generous portion, but just as Nussbaum was about to dive in, the flounder shook his head and threw a warning glance. Nussbaum ran for the sidewalk. A month later he tried again. "We got fresh flounder for you," said the waiter. "Just came in today." But at the last moment it turned out to be the same old flounder, who shook his head even more vigorously than the first time. "This does it," cried Nussbaum. "Never do I come to this joint again!" Some weeks later his wife took him to a swanky Park Avenue hotel. "Here I will get flounder what is flounder," exulted Nussbaum. The waiter brought a steaming platter, beautifully garnished with parsley and lemon. Just as Nussbaum was reaching for his fork the flounder lifted his head from the plate. "Ah ha!" he sneered. "So Finkelstein's ain't good enough for you no more!"

28. "Do you realize," said a man in a cafeteria to a stranger across the table, "that you are reading your newspaper upside down?"

"Of course I realize it," snapped the stranger. "Do you think it's easy?"

29. A pigeon came home very late for dinner one evening, with his feathers bedraggled, and

his eyes bloodshot. "I was out minding my own business," he explained, "when bingo! I get caught in a badminton game!"

30. The bartender noticed that his customer had a big carrot behind his ear, but he decided not to mention it. "Probably just waiting for people to ask him what it's for. I'll fool him." For twenty-seven consecutive days the customer appeared, with a carrot always tucked behind his ear. Then, on the twenty-eighth day, the routine was varied: a banana had replaced the carrot! The bartender could stand it no longer. "What's the idea of that banana behind your ear, fellah?" he demanded, leaning over the counter. "Couldn't find no carrot today," explained the customer.

31. A couple of frogs were dining at the Ritz one evening. "You're angry at me," accused Abdul Amnal (he was a Turkish frog). "You haven't spoken to me all evening." "It isn't that at all," explained the other with some difficulty. "I just can't talk tonight. I've got a man in my throat."

32. A brown horse, hitched to a milk wagon, looked up one morning to see a poster staring her in the face. The Ringling Circus was in town! She calmly trotted over to the stage door of Madison Square Garden, and entered. "Hi, girls!" she neighed, to be greeted with noisy expressions of surprise and delight. "But, Beulah," protested one nag, "what are you doing with that cheesy milk wagon you're

hitched to? A year ago you were the star of the show here, with blue plumes over your ears, and beautiful performers somersaulting on your back!" "Aw," answered Beulah, "what can you expect from that darn Hollywood agent of mine?"

Laughter in the Basement

Peter De Vries

"She has no mind, merely a mind of her own" is something I recently said in open conversation, with less profit than I had anticipated. When I say anticipated, I mean over a fairly long stretch, for the remark is one of a repertory of retorts I carry about in my head, waiting for the chance to spring them. This is a form of wit I call prepartee — prepared repartee for use in contingencies that may or may not arise. For instance, I have been waiting for years for some woman to dismiss a dress she has on as "just something I slipped into," so that I can say, behind my hand, "Looks more like something she slipped and *fell* into."

There are two types of prepartee: the kind you can wangle an opening for, and the kind you can't. The sally about the woman who had no mind, merely a mind of her own, required no specific straight line but only a general one, in a context I was able to steer the conversation to after bringing the woman into it myself. But

443

my plan to retort dryly when next I hear somebody say that money doesn't matter, "No, provided one has it," is something else again. I can, of course, bring up the *subject* of money any time I choose, but though you can lead a stooge to water, you can't make him drink, and unless somebody says, "Money doesn't matter," in so many words, or virtually that, I will never get to use the riposte.

The chances of my getting a feeder for it are slimmer than you might think. Clichés are like cops, in that you can never find one when you want one. This applies to trite questions as well as trite statements. I have been waiting since 1948 for some poor devil to ask, "What does a woman want most in a man?," so that I can come back, quick as a flash, with "Fiscal attraction." And I have been lying in wait even longer to hear so much as the vaguest reference to current realistic fiction as a reflection of our time, so that I can murmur, "I had thought it rather a reflection *on* it."

I almost murmured that one in Cos Cob. I was at a buffet supper in the home of friends there, and found myself in the library with the hostess and a couple of other guests. It was a week after my quip about the woman with no mind, and I had been trying to analyze just why it had failed. I had finally diagnosed my waggeries as, texturally, the suave and under-played sort, requiring small groups and an intimate, offhand delivery, so I was happy to find myself in the snug library with just a handful of people, well away from the general commotion in the living room, so reminiscent of the previous week's mob. Coffee had been poured and brandy was passed. I began setting up the conversation for my little mot about realistic novels. Having lit my pipe, I squeezed from the packed shelves a volume of fiction suited to my design and casually asked the hostess, "Have you read this?"

She nodded briskly. "Yes, I thought it pretty good of its kind," she said.

"Ah, of its kind. But what good is its kind?" I asked.

By dint of such questions, by tirelessly jockeying the discussion this way and that, by nudging, cuing, and tinkering with her responses, I succeeded in maneuvering her to within striking distance of my aphorism. Pre-partee is very much like those games in which, over a course beset with delays, digressions, "penalties," and other pitfalls, one tries to move a disc to a goal marked "Home." After a quarter of an hour, I heard the hostess say, "Well, I mean realistic novels of this sort, whatever you may think of them artistically, do have some value for our time."

I sat on the edge of my chair. One more jump and I would be Home. Very carefully, very deliberately, I said, "How do you mean?"

At that moment, a hearty character in tweeds boomed into the room. "Just a minute," I snapped. "Ethel here is talking. Go on, Ethel. What was it you were saying? What are these novels in connection with our time?"

"They hold a mirror up to it," she said.

I sat back in my chair. "I see," I said, and reached for my cold cup of coffee.

With Home so hard to gain in manipulable contexts, the chances of scoring with rejoinders depending on straight lines you can't even *begin* to finagle are discouraging indeed. Thus the odds against my ever being told, by a newcomer to my community, "We'd like to meet some people who count," in order that I may answer, "Well, I can introduce you to a couple of bank tellers," are really astronomical. And I long ago decided not to hold my breath till I hear someone refer to a third party as "my cousin twice removed," so I can say, "I didn't know he was your cousin, but I knew he was twice removed — once as treasurer of his firm and later to the state prison at Ossining."

Recognizing all this, I eventually scaled my ambitions down to where I bluntly *asked* people to stooge for me, as you do in putting a riddle. This is a tawdry substitute for the real thing, but better than nothing when you're bent on making an impression, as I was recently at a party where I found myself *à deux* with a toothsome girl, a house guest of the host and hostess. We were sitting together on the floor, through which the sound of laughter from the basement game room occasionally seeped. We sat leaning against chairs, with our elbows hitched up on the seats, having a pleasant chat. I had spotted her from the first as a merry, responsive sort, a kid who could go along with a joke. In no connection, I turned to her and said, "Did I ever tell you about my cousin twice removed?"

She shook her head, tossing a wealth of black hair. "No. What about him?" she asked.

"Well, as I say, he was twice removed — once as treasurer of the bank he was connected with and later to the state prison at Ossining."

She laughed gaily, throwing her head back. "So you've got a banker in jail in your family?" she said. "Well, we've got a congressman at large in ours."

Having failed with large groups, then with small, and finally with a single companion (the less said about that brash chit the better), there seemed nothing left for me to do but talk to myself, a state to which frustration has brought stronger men than I. However, I rallied after making what you might call one more strategic retreat. I thought I would apply the technique I had evolved to the lowest common denominator — the practical joke.

We know a couple, living in one of the suburban towns near Westport, named Moses. They are of impressive Yankee extraction, and moved down from Vermont six years ago. One

447

of the nuisances of living in the country is, of course, power failures, and I got the notion of ringing them up sometime when the electricity was off, and asking, "Where was Moses when the lights went out?" This is admittedly a far cry from my early high ideals for prepartee — so far, indeed, as to be not true prepartee at all. Nevertheless, as some philosopher or other has said, a difference in quantity, if great enough, becomes a difference in quality, and this gag depended on such a number of factors going just right — that is to say, just wrong — that I felt it to be qualitatively unique. It required, to begin with, a meteorological mishap of such extent and duration as to plunge into darkness an area wide enough to embrace Westport, where I live, and the town where Moseses' place is, a good ten miles inland. It called for the most perfect timing, in that it would have to be pulled when falling limbs had broken the power lines, which are strung along the tops of the poles, but not yet the telephone connections underneath. It would depend on the Moseses and ourselves being brought simultaneously to the same pass. Having met these conditions, it would still require the phone's being answered by Mrs. Moses and not Moses himself. (I couldn't say, "Where were you when the lights went out?") So the sporting odds against my getting Home were actually greater than they had been across more cerebral courses.

It wasn't until the ice storm early last January, or three and a half years after the gag's conception, that the necessary factors coincided. I thought I saw my chance during the big blow of '51, when the winds attained hurricane force, but our power and phone lines were both reduced to spaghetti before I could get my wits about me. However, in this winter's glacéed adventure, our juice went at dusk, taking with it light, heat, and cooking power. The phone still worked, but, of course, it was being monopolized for the time being by housewives on the party line making unnecessary calls.

During dinner, which consisted of shredded wheat crouched over by candlelight, I mentally reviewed the situation. Everything was in order; it remained to be seen only whether the Moseses could be got through to by phone. (That they had no power was a fair certainty, for it had been knocked out or shut off for miles around.) I vibrated like a scientist for whom every long-awaited element is fortuitously aligning itself in his favor, hurrying him toward the exquisite moment of experiment. Dinner over, I slipped into our dark vestibule and sat down at the phone. I found it alive and free, and, what was more, the operator got me the number I wanted after only a few moments' delay. Hearing the ring at the other end, I sat erect, realizing I had forgotten there was still a final requisite beyond that of the other phone's working — a woman's voice would have to answer.

449

I heard the phone picked up. "Hello?" a voice said. It was a woman's.

"Where was Moses when the lights went out?" I asked.

"In bed," she said. "He hasn't been at all well."

"Aw, gosh, that's too bad. I'm sorry to hear that," I said. "What seems to be the trouble?"

"Oh, the usual — flu, grippe, or whatever you want to call it," Mrs. Moses said. "Who is this?"

I told her. Then I added, "I've had a cold myself, which is probably why you didn't recognize my voice. Well, we were just wondering how you two were making out over there. Is there anything we can . . ."

Thus prepartee, in either its pure or debased form, is no indolent hobby, no pastime for the weak-nerved. The life of a parlor desperado, with its long hours in ambush, is a hard and often wearing one. It has its midnight post-mortems just like its more familiar counterpart, departee — which is, I think, the proper term for remarks thought up on the way home. I don't know which is the more frustrating, moments to which one has proved unequal or stunners for which no occasion arose, but I have found both abrasive. My little tittup about Moses and the lights came to an end when I hung up to find my wife behind me with a flashlight, a child clinging to either leg. "Who

450

was that?" she asked, playing the beam on me. I told her. I also told her why I had phoned, and said that I wondered why Mrs. Moses hadn't been more on the ball. I asked my wife whether *she* didn't think the line was funny. *"Funny!"* she said. "Don't make me laugh."

Love Thy Neighbor

Andy Rooney

It seems to me that neighbors are going out of style in America. The friend next door from whom you borrowed four eggs or a ladder has moved, and the people in there now are strangers.

Some of the old folklore of neighborliness is impractical or silly, and it may be just as well that our relations with our neighbors are changing. The biblical commandment to "Love Thy Neighbor" was probably a poor translation of what must have originally been "Respect Thy Neighbor." Love can't be called up on order.

Fewer than half the people in the United States live in the same house they lived in five years ago, so there's no reason to love the people who live next door to you just because they happened to wander into a real estate office that listed the place next door to yours. The only thing neighbors have in common to begin with is proximity, and unless something more develops, that isn't reason enough to be best friends. It sometimes happens naturally, but the chances are very small that your neighbors will be your choice as buddies. Or that you will be theirs, either.

The best relationship with neighbors is one of friendly distance. You say hello, you small-talk if you see them in the yard, you discuss problems as they arise and you help each other in an emergency. It's the kind of arrangement where you see more of them in the summer than in the winter. The driveway or the hedge or the fence between you is not really a cold shoulder, but it is a clear boundary. We all like clearly defined boundaries for ourselves.

If neighbors have changed, neighborhoods have not. They still comprise the same elements. If you live in a real neighborhood you can be sure most of the following people will be found there:
— One family with more kids than they can take care of.
— A dog that gets into garbage cans.
— One grand home with a family so rich that they really aren't part of the neighborhood.
— A bad kid who steals or sets fire to things, although no one has ever been able to prove it.
— People who leave their Christmas decorations up until March.
— A grouchy woman who won't let the kids cut through her backyard.
— Someone who doesn't cut their grass more

than twice a summer.

— Someone who cuts their grass twice a week and one of the times always seems to be Sunday morning at 7:30.

— One driveway with a junky-looking pickup truck or trailer that's always sitting there.

— A family that never seems to turn off any lights in the house.

— A teenager who plays the radio too loud in summer with the windows open.

— Someone who leaves their barking dog out until 11:30 most nights.

— One mystery couple. They come and go but hardly anyone ever sees them and no one knows what they do.

— A couple that has loud parties all the time with guests that take an hour to leave once they get outside and start shouting good-bye at each other.

— Someone who doesn't pull the shades.

— A house with a big maple tree whose owners don't rake the leaves until most of them have blown into someone else's yard.

It is easier to produce nostalgia about a neighborhood than about a community, but a community is probably a better unit. A neighborhood is just a bunch of individuals who live in proximity, but a community is a group of people who rise above their individual limitations to get some things done in town.

The 55 MPH Speed Limit

Andy Rooney

You'll all be pleased to read that I'm not going to give you an opinion on (1) gun control, (2) abortion or (3) the Equal Rights Amendment. Just trust me that I'm in one hundred percent agreement with you on these issues. I can't imagine how any right-thinking person could possibly believe other than we do. I trust, in turn, that if you're for one, you're for them all. If you're against one, you're *against* them all.

The fourth most controversial issue is the matter of the fifty-five mph speed limit. I'm going to comment on that because, while it gets people yelling and hollering at each other a lot, it doesn't bring out quite the same dirty, bitter, low-down kind of viciousness in nice people that those other issues do.

I stand unequivocally equivocal about it. I'm firmly of two minds. It's a law I hate and break all the time, but if I had been in Congress when it passed into law, I'd have voted in favor of it. To be honest with you, I think everyone *but me* should be limited to driving fifty-five mph.

Even though I'd have voted for it, it seems to me the law is too general to cover every driving situation. It ought to be more flexible. I know people who are safer driving seventy-five than my sister is driving thirty-five. She's basically a good person, but she's a lousy driver. She could never roller skate, either. Does my sister get to drive as fast on the highway as Richard Petty or Mario Andretti?

If fifty-five is safe for a competent driver, we ought to have a lower limit for incompetent ones. It's ridiculous to suggest that all of us have equal skill at the wheel of a car. There's no reason to think there's any less difference between a great skier and a bad one than there is between a good driver and my sister. The two skiers shouldn't have to come down the mountain at the same speed.

Besides the difference in the competence of drivers, there's the difference in road conditions. The fifty-five mph speed limit is too fast on a narrow, winding macadam road with traffic, even if it's legal. It isn't fast enough on a six-lane highway that stretches for a hundred straight miles in Wyoming. Why should the speed limit be the same in both places?

There's some evidence that the speed limit has saved both lives and gas. The National Safety Council estimates eight thousand lives were saved last year. If it's true, that's a persuasive argument. The trouble with the statistic is that people are driving a lot less than they were five years ago because of the cost of gas. If people drive less, fewer of them die driving. If no one ever drove at all, of course, no one would ever die in an auto accident, but the government isn't prepared to go that far. Where it stops and starts protecting us from each other is a very difficult decision for the government to make. It would be safer if no one ever crossed a street, too. That would make some life-saving statistic if we all avoided crossing a street for one year.

I've always objected to any law making it compulsory for me to wear a seat belt for my own safety. Passing a law to keep me from going too fast in order to protect *other* people's lives is one thing, but when the government passes a law making something mandatory *for my own good*, the government has gone too far. My life is none of the government's damn business. I'll save it or spend it as I please.

If Congress was serious about the fifty-five mph speed limit, it would have taken one effective step years ago. It would have made it illegal for anyone to sell a car that can *go* faster than fifty-five. What sense does it make to be producing cars that will go a hundred thirty miles an hour when there isn't a road in the country you can legally drive them on that fast?

And that's where I stand on the speed limit, straddling the solid white line.

Types

Andy Rooney

There are only two types of people in the world, Type A and Type Z. It isn't hard to tell which type you are. How long before the plane leaves do you arrive at the airport?

Early plane catchers, Type A, pack their bags at least a day in advance, and they pack neatly. If they're booked on a flight that leaves at four in the afternoon, they get up at five-thirty that morning. If they haven't left the house by noon, they're worried about missing the plane.

Late plane catchers, Type Z, pack hastily at the last minute and arrive at the airport too late to buy a newspaper.

What do you do with a new book? Type A reads more carefully and finishes every book, even though it isn't any good.

Type Z skims through a lot of books and is more apt to write in the margins with a pencil.

Type A eats a good breakfast; Type Z grabs a cup of coffee.

Type A's turn off the lights when leaving a room and lock the doors when leaving a house. They go back to make sure they've locked it, and they worry later about whether they left the iron on or not. They didn't.

Type Z's leave the lights burning and, if they lock the door at all when they leave the house, they're apt to have forgotten their keys.

Type A sees the dentist twice a year, has an annual physical checkup and thinks he may have something.

Type Z has been meaning to see a doctor.

Type A squeezes a tube of toothpaste from the bottom and rolls it very carefully as he uses it, puts the top back on every time.

Type Z squeezes the tube from the middle, and he's lost the cap under the radiator.

Type Z's are more apt to have some Type A characteristics than Type A's are apt to have any Type Z characteristics.

Type A's always marry Type Z's.
Type Z's always marry Type A's.

Good News

Andy Rooney

All of us who work in television news are constantly being accused of emphasizing the negative side of everything. We get letters saying we never cover a story unless something terrible happens.

Tonight we've put together a little news broadcast to give you an idea of how it would look if you had it your way.

"I'm here by the Mississippi. It's raining but the river is not overflowing its banks.

"As a matter of fact, it doesn't look to me as though there's any danger of a flood whatsoever. People are not piling up sandbags. No one has been forced to evacuate his home and the Governor has not asked that this be declared a federal disaster area."

"O'Hare Airport in Chicago is one of the nation's busiest. At 11 A.M., a jet aircraft with 168 passengers and ten crew members on board started down the long runway. The plane, headed for London, took off without incident. It landed without incident too. Everyone on board is now in London.

"One passenger on board that plane was quoted as saying he didn't like the fake milk they served with the coffee."

"For a report from New York City we take you to our correspondent standing in front of the Plaza, one of New York City's most luxurious hotels.

"This is the Plaza, one of New York City's most luxurious hotels. CBS News has learned that last evening, after a night on the town, the Shah of Franakapan and his semi-beautiful wife returned to their hotel suite after depositing more than a million dollars' worth of jewelry in the hotel safe. The jewels included the famous Cooch Behar Diamond.

"This morning, when the safe was opened, all the jewelry including the famous Cooch Behar Diamond was right there where they'd left it."

"In Florida, the orange crop was hit by another night of average weather.

"The oranges just hung in there and grew."

"Oil industry officials announced today they were lowering prices because they just don't need the money. One reason for their affluence is their safety records.

"The oil tanks behind me are very close to a residential area. If they were on fire, smoke would be seen billowing up for miles around. They aren't on fire, though; they're just sitting there."

"In Detroit, a General Motors spokesman announced today that more than 174,000 Chevrolets made in the late fall of 1974 would not be recalled. They are all perfect.

"At eleven-thirty this evening, CBS News will present a special report listing the serial numbers of those cars."

And if that's what you want to hear, that's the way it was.

Good evening.

The *Tonight* Show

Steve Allen

At the end of our first season the *Tonight* program was, as I had expected, put on the full NBC network, after which it ran for two more years. The three seasons that our gang held down the time spot were wonderfully happy. A separate book could be written about the program, but for now I'll have to content myself with just reminiscing about its highspots and about some of the people who came into my life as a result of the show. Dwight Hemion, my TV director, was part of the team almost from the first, as was Bill Harbach, our producer. These two young men have never gotten the credit they deserve for the success of both the late-night show and the once-a-week program that followed it. Bill is a cheerful enthusiast with a wonderful, albeit whacky, manner of handling people and getting their best work out of them. Best of all, considering that he is producing comedy shows, he loves to laugh.

But without knowing it, Bill is funny himself. He does not mean to be. He is not a jokester or a cutup. But something about his ferretlike nervous system and a certain difficulty in expressing himself when he is excited combine to make him say some of the most outlandish things this side of Sam Goldwyn.

One day while involved in a heated debate with Jules Green, our executive producer, Bill hit the ceiling at one of Jules' suggestions. "There you go, Jules," he shouted. "For the first time you're wrong again!"

Another time, wanting to conclude our program with a religious number that was not too slow in tempo, he came running in to my office and said, "What's a good *up* hymn?"

And, under the same general heading, there was the day he attempted to enumerate the Holy Trinity. "You know," he explained, "the Holy Father, Your Son, and the Ghost."

I should perhaps remind the reader that he says things of this sort with a perfectly straight face, and in all seriousness.

Once, in Havana, Cuba, when Jules inquired as to what time the various members of our group were dispersing to return home, Bill replied, "I'm dispersing Wednesday."

Then there was the day he came into my office to discuss something about the program and I noticed he was wearing a heavy overcoat. "Do you have a chill?" I said.

"No," he said. "Why?"

"Well," I said, "you're walking around indoors with your coat on."

"Oh," he said, in surprise, "I forgot to take it off. No! I forgot to go home." And with that he dashed out of the room and ran for the elevator.

Another peculiarity of Bill's is that he has the world's worst memory for names. Not only does he forget them, but, tantalizingly enough, some shred of their memory remains in his mind, causing him to cry out strange variations upon names he is trying to call to mind. Instructing his secretary to call Charlton Heston for rehearsal one afternoon, he shouted, "Get me — uh — Charleston Huston. Er, uh — Carleton Hudson. You know, Chester Moses."

And another time, when we were talking about doing a show from a swimming pool, he said, "There's only one guest to book for a show like that . . . whatsername . . . Ethel Waters." Naturally he meant Esther Williams.

He has also been known to refer to the comedy iceskating team of Fric and Frac as Trick or Treat and he has called Shai K. Ophir, the brilliant mime, Ootie Shankar. Even stranger to relate, he has been heard to say, "When is Christmas?" while standing looking at the month of December on a calendar, and to ask, "How many feet in a foot?" while estimating the dimensions of a set.

But the strangest thing I ever heard him say was a brief phrase he mumbled one afternoon as he excused himself from a production meeting: "Let me be right back."

Jules Green was my agent for a good many years, since the old Hollywood days, and, like Bill, he is something of a character and frequently amusing without intending to be. Like Bill, too, he sometimes lets his emotion run away with his tongue. For example, in talking about an unpopular political figure who died and for whom someone in the room was expressing mild sympathy, Jules snapped, "To hell with him. There are dead men walking the streets tonight because of him!"

Two writers who have been with me since the old local New York days are Stan Burns and Herb Sargent. They, too, seem like a couple of characters out of fiction. Stan is a big, husky ex-Marine with the pleasantest personality in the world. In twelve years I have never known him to have a glum moment, and his wife and children seem as jovial as he. Oddly enough his speciality in comedy is what has come to be known as the Sick Joke. His subject matter is apt to include death, Hitler, accidents, national catastrophes, and the like. Needless to say, some of his most impressive jokes could never be used on the air. He was the originator, for example, of that much-quoted Sick classic, "Remember folks, _____ Airlines is the Airline of the Stars. Carole Lombard, Grace Moore, Will Rogers . . ." And I was not surprised one afternoon while on a plane with Stan to see him wandering up and down the aisle with a small box of sweets borrowed from a stewardess.

"After-crash mints, anyone?" he was saying.

His partner, Sargent, also a brilliant joke-smith (recently producer of *That Was the Week That Was*) is tall, dark, and quiet. Given to wearing tweed sports jackets, he has the short Connecticut haircut, the grizzled Ivy League look of the men in the cigarette ads. While lost in thought he may stand in the middle of the room shrugging his shoulders and quietly flapping his fingers, arms held slightly out from his sides. When I go into his office to talk to him I often do this gesture. He laughs and then we go on with the conversation. I say *go on* rather than *start*, for in our office conversations are never really begun or concluded. They all seem to begin in the middle, taking off from some point of earlier reference, and are invariably broken off in mid-sentence or interrupted by another party. This has been the case, oddly enough, from the very first days of the late-night TV show.

The show itself, seen in retrospect, brings up a great many memories. For example, there were the *regulars* of the studio audience, those hardy souls who seemed to have no purpose in life but to spend every waking moment — and some sleeping ones — at one or another radio or TV show. Most M.C.'s avoid them like the plague and issue stern instructions that they are to be cattle-penned off to the rear seats. Personally I like the regulars. They entertain and amuse me. They do the same, I think, for audiences watching at home. Given a choice between a regular and an unknown quantity represented, let's say, by a stranger in a gray suit sitting on the aisle, I'll head for the regular eight times out of ten. It isn't just that I get more mileage out of the steady customers; it's that I'm constantly on the lookout for the person who seems eccentric, extroverted, and willing to talk, and that's a good description of a regular.

One of our most dependable steadies on the *Tonight* show was an elderly lady of obviously small financial means known simply as Mrs. Sterling. I do not know her first name to this day. I do not know where she lives. I think perhaps she still lives in the fourth row of NBC's Hudson Theatre and goes home only about once a month to change clothes.

Like most of the regulars, she was present nightly partly because she liked the show and partly (and perhaps predominantly) because she liked to carry home loot and knew that I gave things away to the people I interviewed.

Mrs. Sterling had a simple act, but it seemed invariably to amuse audiences. First she complimented me lavishly, then she demanded a gift, usually a "Pomeroy" camera. The camera's name is actually Polaroid, but Mrs. Sterling wasn't particular. Our conversations, which rarely varied, went something like this:

I: Good evening, Mrs. Sterling. How are you this evening?

MRS. S: Mr. Allen, you're wonderful.

I: That may well be, Mrs. Sterling, but I didn't come over here to listen to your compliments again, flattering as they are.

MRS. S: But I just want everybody to know what an angel you are, Mr. Allen. I hope you're feeling well.

I: But Mrs. Sterling, I —

MRS. S: You're not working too hard, are you?

I: Up until this moment I wasn't, no.

MRS. S: That's fine. Say, I'd like to have one of those Pomeroy cameras.

I don't recall just now whether I ever actually gave Mrs. Sterling a camera, but we did lavish upon her a rich assortment of stockings, record albums, salamis, wrist watches, perfumes, furniture, and electric appliances. I don't know whether she used these articles, sold them, or stored them away on the Collier brothers plan.

Not content, by the way, with demanding these things for herself, Mrs. Sterling usually demanded seconds for "my daughter." Several people on our staff suspected there was no daughter, but we nevertheless from time to time gave Mrs. Sterling two of this and that so that her daughter, if any, might not be disappointed.

Our at-home viewers became so intrigued by

Mrs. Sterling's insistence that I supply gifts for her daughter that once when a fan sent us a gold cup inscribed "To Mrs. Sterling" it was followed two days later by a small cup from another watcher. The second one was engraved "For Mrs. Sterling's Daughter."

One thing that our millions of viewers never knew is that from time to time Mrs. Sterling used to lurk outside the theater waiting for me to appear. When I did she would rush up and hand me a small paper bag or package. It would contain a present, usually handkerchiefs or candy, from her to me.

Another regular who visited us two or three nights a week for almost a year was a tall, thin man named John Schafer. To say that John talked a lot doesn't remotely give you the idea. Schafer had a long-playing tongue. I stumbled over him one night in the audience and started a conversation with the usual "And what's your name, sir?"

"Well," he said, speaking extremely rapidly, "my name is Schafer. John Schafer. I work as a farmer upstate. That is, it's not *my* farm, you understand, but my uncle's farm, but I figure eventually it'll be my farm. I mean if everything turns out all right. We raise quite a few nice things on the farm. It's about a hundred acres and we've been up in that section for the last two, three generations. I just come down to town once in a while to see the sights and have a little fun. Watch your show once in a while and thought I'd drop in and see it. What was it you wanted to ask me?"

"To tell you the truth, Mr. Schafer," I said, "I had five or six questions in mind but you've already answered all of them."

John came in quite regularly and one night I happened to ask him where he'd been the night before.

"Well," he said, "I seen this movie, *Mogambo,* with Clark Gable and this Ava Gardner woman and it was a pretty good picture, but to tell you the truth I couldn't figure out what old Clark was so interested in this Gardner woman for when I figgered he would've been better off with this blond girl, whatsername, this Kelly girl. Her father's from Philadelphia. 'Course it sure was something when all those old gorillas came running around and old Clark had to step lively to keep things on an even keel."

John went on lickety-split in that vein for about five minutes, during which time I did not say a single word. When he finished I said, "So that's what you did last night, eh?"

But I realized there was more value to John's monologues than met the eye. Not only were they the longest straight lines in the history of comedy, but his synopses of motion pictures had a childlike charm. We signed him up for a series of movie reviews, which were well received by our audiences, if not by the motion picture companies.

Perhaps our most unusual regular was a

gentleman we discovered one summer when we originated the program in Hollywood. The customary query as to his identity he brushed aside with the immediate suggestion that he sing a song for us. He was a short, stocky man with a heavy and, to me, still unidentifiable accent. His name, I later learned, was Carmen Mastren.

"What song would you like to sing?" I asked.

" 'Allagazanada's Ragatima Band,' " he said.

"What key do you sing in?" I asked, hoping to pick up a cue for Skitch Henderson, who was at the time our conductor.

"A," Carmen said. He sang every song in the key of A, it developed, or at least he *said* he did. Actually we never could figure out what key he sang in because he did every song *on one note*.

Another fascinating visitor to our studios was a little old man named Ben Belefonte. He called himself a rhyming inventor. This does not mean that he invented rhymes, but rather that he was an inventor who incidentally happened to write rhymes. I shall never forget his weird inventions. One of them was a hanger bank. This was not a device for hanging banks and it did not bank hangers. It was simply a common-variety, transparent plastic hanger in which Mr. Belefonte had cut some holes large enough to permit the passage of small coins. You simply dropped pennies, nickels, and dimes into the hanger until it was full and then you had a hanger full of coins. Don't ask me who would need such a device.

Ben spoke in rhymed but not rhythmic verse and undoubtedly his most fantastic invention was a rhyme that had never fallen from the lips of man before and I'm sure never will again. He somehow managed to make the word *the* rhyme with the word *inventor* by saying:

"I'm Ben Belefonte, *the*
Rhyming inven*tuh!*"

Another wild character was a man known as Professor Voss, who years later was to pop up again on my Westinghouse show. The professor was a well-preserved man in his late sixties. He spoke with a slight Germanic accent, liked to walk around with a bare chest in the coldest weather, and had some very unusual ideas about diet and exercise. One night a dreadful thing he said made the audience laugh for such a long time that I am sorry somebody didn't time the laugh with a stopwatch.

"Tell me, professor," I said, as he sat in a large tub filled with ice floating in freezing cold water, "to what do you attribute your remarkable physical condition?"

"Well," he explained. "It's water that does it. You've got to start off each day by drinking plenty of water."

"Do you do that?" I said.

"Oh yes, indeed," he said. "The first thing

you must do when you get up in the morning is drink four quarts of water!"

"Wow," I said. "Four quarts. That's a lot of water. And what do you do then?"

"Well," he said, as matter-of-factly as if he were discussing the weather, "you stand about three feet from the toilet —"

Naturally I cut him off immediately, but there was no stopping the audience.

Another night there was no stopping them one of our staff had booked as a guest a woman who was an expert on the care and feeding of cats. She had brought about twelve cats to the studio and on my desk she had placed a sort of doll's house, in and around which five or six of the cats were crawling, playing, sleeping, and what-have-you. As soon as I walked into the theater and saw this setup the word "cathouse" flashed across my mind so I gathered Skitch Henderson, Gene Rayburn, Steve Lawrence, Eydie Gorme, and the rest of our crew around me.

"Be sure," I instructed, "that when we start talking to the lady about her cats and the little house that they are playing in . . . be sure that *no one* uses the word cathouse." They chuckled at the possibility and all, of course, at once agreed that the dread word would not fall from their lips.

A few minutes later we went on the air and shortly thereafter I began to interview the woman who had brought all the cats.

"What is this thing?" I said, pointing to the little house.

"Oh, that," she said amiably. "That's a cathouse."

Another *Tonight* regular that people still ask me about was Joe Interleggi, whom I dubbed The Human Termite because he ate wood. Well, he didn't actually digest it, I suppose, but Joe's claim to fame was that he had jaws and teeth of such prodigious strength that he could bite holes in any piece of wood in the house. And he could. He could also open beer bottles with his teeth and then grind the bottle caps into small, twisted wads by rolling them around in his mouth. A native of Italy, Joe became tremendously popular with our viewers.

And there are so many other familiar faces that I recall with pleasure. There was Mrs. Dorothy Miller, a plump and pleasant lady in her fifties who has been sitting in my audiences now for about sixteen years, having started in Hollywood. And there is a woman known only as "Lillian," who also has seen many years of faithful service in the audience. The fantastic thing about Lillian was that *wherever* we went, she showed up. When we did the *Tonight* show once at Niagara Falls there she was, smiling up from the front row. And she followed our circus to Havana, to Hollywood, to Texas. We never knew how she got her tickets, how she managed to get a front-row seat, or where she stayed in the various cities to which she followed us. But there she was. When I moved my program and staff to Hollywood in 1959 she made that trip with us, too, staying in town for several weeks, although she eventually had to return to her home in New York.

And what wild nights there were on the old *Tonight* show, what crazy ad-lib routines. One of my favorites, because it was true, extemporaneous, and unpredictable comedy, was that in which we used to open the back door of the theater and just point a TV camera out into the night. Passers-by, having no idea that they could be seen on television from coast to coast, would saunter by, do a double take, and then casually, oh so casually, drift back and look into the theater, which meant, of course, that they were looking right into the camera.

After a few minutes drunks would pile out of the neighborhood saloons and wave at the camera deliberately, and then it would be time to end the routine, but those first few minutes were always priceless. I would keep a microphone open and make off-the-cuff comments on the various faces that loomed up on the screen, like strange fish floating before a submerged camera. If you never saw this routine it will be difficult to explain just why it was funny. But take my word for it, it was.

Another routine of the old *Tonight* show that used to be a great favorite was that in which we would suddenly open the back door, point a camera outside, and then I would walk quickly out into the night dressed in some peculiar costume and try to engage passers-by in conversation. The wildest thing that ever happened on the show under this particular heading, I guess, occurred the night that I dressed in a policeman's uniform, ran out on the street, and began stopping automobiles. I had no idea what I was going to say to the drivers, but I figured that just the sheer, insane idea of stopping actual cars on live TV and saying *anything* would make for unusual fare.

Since I had lived in the west and had on several occasions been stopped by the state police guard on the Arizona-California border, it was perhaps not surprising that I now heard myself saying to the first driver who slowed down, "Sorry, sir, but this is the border patrol and we're making a spot check for contraband."

"What band?" he said. Since the bright lights from the theater prevented his seeing the TV cameras, or for that matter from even recognizing that the building to his left was a theater, he had no reason to doubt that I was an actual policeman.

"I just wanted to know," I said, "if you're smuggling any fruits or nuts."

"No," he said. "Absolutely not." From inside the theater came a great roar of laughter.

"Drive on," I said, "and remember, the life you save . . . may not be worth it."

When I raised my hand to stop the next car its driver suddenly stepped on the gas and sped by me, almost knocking me down. This, too, the audience found vastly amusing.

"Border patrol," I shouted to the driver of the third car. "Are you smuggling anything?"

"No, sir," he said, blinking at the lights.

"Well, then," I cried, signaling to an associate who brought me an oversized salami, "take this to the river!"

"To the what?" he said, accepting the salami.

"Never mind," I shouted. "Just get going. And don't stop till you hear from me!" He sped off as if possessed.

The next car to come along was a taxi. I grabbed another salami and flagged the driver down. "Where to, chief?" he said, amiably.

"Never mind," I said, opening his back door and flinging the salami in. "Just take this to Grand Central, and fast!" Oddly enough he sped off at once into the night. The audience laughed so loudly that it sounded like a cheer from a football stadium. We never heard from the driver after the show and I have often wondered why he shot off down Forty-fifth Street that way, following such an insane order.

END OF AN ERA

By 1955 NBC had Allen doing not only the *Tonight* program but also a full comedy hour Sunday nights at eight o'clock opposite Ed Sullivan. About this same time, he somehow also managed to star in the *Benny Goodman Story* for Universal-International. But the pace proved killing, even for the energetic Allen. Reluctantly he decided to give up the *Tonight* program. At first the network asked him to do at least three nights a week, giving up just two. He suggested either Jack Paar or Ernie Kovacs as his replacement and the NBC brass chose Kovacs. But after a few months Allen had to quit *Tonight* entirely. Rather than continue without him NBC canceled the program. The outpouring of grief at the passing of the show was nationwide, and genuine. Joe Reilly, columnist for the Brockton *Daily Enterprise*, of Brockton, Massachusetts, expressed the general sentiment well:

" 'Heigho-Stevo, and good night, Sweet Prince.' That telegram from Louis Nye just about wrapped it up on the occasion of Steve Allen's departure from TV's *Tonight*. It summed up succinctly our emotions as we sat watching Allen ring down his final curtain with the good taste and restraint that are hallmarks of his personality and humor. Sure, now and again tears filled our eyes. The good-byes packed an emotional wallop. But we were cheered that the young man was moving onward and upward.

"Allen's good-byes to his country-wide *Tonight* fans were touching—because they were from the heart, without the least sign

of self-dramatization. No touch of the maud-
lin was in evidence, although it would have
been so easy to have been swung in that
direction. Steve recognized, for instance, the
deprivation his departure meant to shut-ins
and the like. He said so. You could tell it
truly grieved him that that's the way the
cards fell. In all likelihood he valued those
fans beyond all others. That seems to be the
nature of the man. But he bade them goodbye, man-fashion, with a cushion of affection.
Tempering the blow was the fact he'll still
be around on Sunday nights.

"By this time you're aware that I hold
Steve Allen in considerable esteem. If you
don't happen to go for him, that's okay, too.
It takes all kinds to make a world, they say.
But his particular brand of comedy I like,
and I admire a man who can dish it out—
the trite and the tripe he steers away from in
favor of the novel and many times even the
bizarre. He knew what he liked to see and
hear over television.

"He grasped the opportunity to boost
talented newcomers. Even some not so talented. He was bound that they would have a
hearing. They did. It was interesting to watch
their development under Steve's banner.
Eydie Gorme and young Steve Lawrence, for
example. They came a long way. So did
others. They all have Allen to thank.

"For some time the word was around that

the Allen format of *Tonight* was doomed. If he was out, so was the program. There was no one to replace him. It just wasn't the same show without Allen."

Critic John Crosby also lamented the fact that Allen had given up the *Tonight* show.

"There will be a *Tonight* show next year, but it won't be the show as we know it. Or to be more specific, Steve Allen won't be on it, and I'll miss that special quality he brought to it.

"The Allen humor is an offhand, throwaway, irrelevant type of humor that is hard to imitate and even harder to explain. Once when he was explaining that the West Coast saw his show by kinescope, he said, 'The program is seen out there three hours later — due to carelessness.' I don't know why that amuses me, except that it seems to poke a hole in all our electronic wonders of today — kinescope, television, the whole works.

"There is no situation I've ever seen that Allen couldn't rise above — and there have been some pretty wild ones. Once, for example, a well-upholstered young lady who was demonstrating a mattress explained she was 'Miss Foam Bedding of 1957.'

"That title, I think, would have struck me speechless. I simply wouldn't know how to continue a conversation with a girl who announced she was Miss Foam Bedding of 1957. But Allen had the perfect gambit.

" 'What happened to Miss Foam Bedding of *1956?*' " he asked.

" 'She's not with us any more,' " said Miss Foam Bedding of 1957.

"As I say, I'll miss it.

"Louis Nye, one of Allen's greatest discoveries, was on hand for the final broadcast. 'Steve,' he said, 'this marks the end of an era in television.'

"He was right."

The New Airlines

Art Buchwald

As more and more major airlines eliminate cities and towns from their schedules, the slack is being taken up by tiny, struggling commuter lines.

What makes this exciting is that the new airlines are flying everything from World War II DC-3s to little planes that carry no more than six passengers at one time. The planes have none of the frills of a Boeing or a Lockheed jetliner, but there is a sense of adventure about flying one that makes you think you're in a time warp, and part of the early days of flight, before they had stewardesses and in-flight movies.

We have such an airline on Martha's Vineyard, which provides service between the Vineyard, Boston, and New York. Every trip on and off the island is an experience that none of the major airlines can give us.

My friend Peter Stone took me to the airport for a flight to Boston. Since we both had flown the route before, we discussed it as if he were Spencer Tracy and I were Clark Gable.

"I'll take the flight, and you marry Jane," he said.

"No," I told him. "I'll take the flight and you marry Jane. She really loves you."

"How do you know?" he asked.

"Because she begged me not to let you take the flight."

"Why didn't she say something to me?"

"Because she was afraid you'd do something stupid like knock me out, and then take the flight so we could get married."

"Okay, you take the flight and I'll marry Jane. If the marriage doesn't work out, I'll take the next flight and you marry her if I don't make it."

When we got to the airport, I checked in my luggage. The man behind the counter was wearing a sharp blue uniform with four strips on it.

"You counter people have snappy uniforms," I said.

"What do you mean 'counter people'?" he said. "I'm the pilot." He put my baggage on the scales, and then he asked me how much I weighed.

I lied and said 190. He wrote down 200.

"People always lie by ten pounds," he said. Then he gave me a boarding card. "Heavy people will sit up front — lighter ones in the back of the plane."

As flight time approached I stood outside with Stone. Suddenly Jane drove up. "I've changed my mind," she said, throwing her arms around me. "I want Peter to take the flight and I want to marry you."

We went back inside but the pilot said it was too late. He had to load the luggage on the plane. He picked up his microphone and said, "Cumulus Airlines' Flight one-seven-eight-six is now boarding for Boston with intermediate stops in Hyannisport, Provincetown, and Woods Hole."

"But," I protested, "There are eight of us already, and with two pilots that makes ten. Why do we have to stop?"

"Who said anything about two pilots?" he replied. "We have room for one more passenger in the copilot's seat, and we may get lucky and pick up one at an intermediate stop."

"Look," I said to Peter, "you take my place and I'll marry Jane."

"Are you crazy?" Peter said, "If you make it to Boston you can marry anybody you want."

The passengers walked towards the tiny plane and before climbing the two steps, the pilot took our boarding passes. Then he crawled in behind us, closed the door and crawled down to his seat.

"Welcome to Cumulus Airlines," he said. "On behalf of the entire crew we hope that you have an enjoyable flight. Government regulations require me to tell you that in the unlikely event of any trouble your seat is your flotation jacket, so please don't forget it when going out the emergency exit door, which is the same door you came in by."

The pilot got out of the plane, turned both propellers by hand, returned to the plane, and then we were barreling down the runway.

I looked out the tiny window of the plane and saw Peter and Jane waving. This didn't shake me. What shook me was that the pilot had taken his hands off the throttle and was waving back.

They've been trying to keep it a secret, but there is a serious paper shortage in Washington. A strike of Western paper workers, which is expected to be taken up by workers on the East Coast, has caused a paper deficit in Washington. The reason the government has been keeping it a secret is it fears that if the word gets out, panic will set in and different departments and agencies will start hoarding paper, while others might resort to some very dirty tricks to ensure that its memo flow is not turned off.

One department, which shall remain anonymous, got wind of the shortage and has already held 27 meetings on the crisis.

At the last meeting it was decided to alert all employees to the situation.

In a memo, which was sent to the agency's 27,500 workers, a deputy director wrote: "It has been brought to my attention that we can expect a serious paper shortage in the next few months, which could affect productivity and the morale of this agency. Therefore, I am asking everyone to conserve every sheet of paper possible, even if it involves such dire emergencies as using both sides of the paper. I am also requesting all employees to submit to me in writing how the agency can conserve paper. These suggestions should be made out in triplicate with one copy for me, one for your supervisors and one to keep for yourself in case any action is taken.

"Supervisors are requested to submit weekly reports to the Administrative Supply Office as to how many employees are following this directive, and if this memorandum has increased or decreased the use of present supplies. If an employee does not send in a suggestion, his or her supervisor must put in writing to the personnel director why he or she failed to do so. The personnel director will evaluate and report on Form 2-D to his superior whether or not the excuse is valid.

"What we plan to do with the suggestion is have the public affairs division compile a collection of the most interesting ones, which will then be distributed to all personnel — not only from this agency but from corresponding agencies, which find themselves in the same shortfall position.

"It is my hope that this compilation can be published by the General Printing Office and sold to the public. A steering committee has been appointed to study the best methods of distribution, as well as costs, and the report should be on my desk by the early part of next month. Each department head will receive a copy of the report comments as well as additional thoughts.

"To facilitate matters on the book project, it is suggested that all departmental correspondence concerning conservation be submitted on yellow 8 x 10 Memorandum sheets (G-234 forms), while those regarding distribution be written on the blue double carbon pads (K-677). If you do not have these colors in stock, you can obtain them from the supply room by filling out Form 2323.

"It goes without saying that this agency will be out of business if it is unable to supply the documentation to justify the written decisions it makes. Therefore, everyone from the top agency officials to the mailroom personnel must comply with all regulations regarding the conservation of our paper supply.

"The first of these regulations is now being distributed. If you do not receive it in a week, please notify this office on Green Form 1456, using the White No. 10 envelope.

"Anyone who does not have a Green Form 1456 may apply for a written waiver by using the Manila Folder 10-DC in which the memo is being distributed." — A. Clancy, Acting Chief Deputy Counsel, Paper Conservation Committee.

One Half of Two On the Aisle

Jean Kerr

In my short and merry life in the theater, I have discovered that there are two sharply contrasting opinions about the place of the drama critic. While in some quarters it is felt that the critic is just a necessary evil, most serious-minded, decent, talented theater people agree that the critic is an unnecessary evil. However, if there is some room for argument about the value of the critic, there is none whatever about the value of the critic's wife. To the producer, in particular, it is painful enough that the reviewer must bring his own glum presence to the theater, but the thought that he will also bring his wife and that she, too, will occupy a free seat is enough to cool the cockles of his heart and send him back on a soft diet. "What if a doctor had to bring his wife along when he performed an operation?" he will ask you. "Can't you see her sitting there murmuring, 'Here's a nice suture, dear, and why don't you try this clamp?' "

In their innermost souls, the producer and the press agent are convinced that the wife has a bad effect on the critic and consequently a bad effect on the notice. Of course, not all critics have wives; some of them habitually attend the theater in the company of pretty actresses, a practice which is thought to be not only suitable but even, on occasion, inspiring.

It isn't that anyone believes a wife's influence is direct or intentional. Presumably no one has suggested that it is her practice to tuck her spouse into a cab at eleven o'clock with the stern admonition, "Now you hurry right back to that little office and say what a bad play this was, hear?" No, the whole thing is much more intangible than that, and I'm afraid it boils down to the sobering fact that the producer feels that the mere physical presence of a wife depresses the critic, lowers his spirits, clogs his areas of good will, and leaves his head rattling with phrases like "witless," "tasteless," and "below the level of the professional theater."

On the other hand, just let some wife absent herself from the happy revelers at an opening and you will see consternation settle like a fine dew upon producer and press agent alike. Souls are searched. Old wounds are probed. Is the jig up? Have runners been coming in from Philadelphia with the bad word? Have those preview audiences been squealing? Clearly somebody talked. The lady has had fair warning and is at home with a good book.

It is my impression that my own attendance record is rather higher than the average. This can be explained by the fact that I have those children and naturally have to get out a lot. When my husband first went on a newspaper, and for several years thereafter, I brought my larklike disposition and gooey good will to every single solitary show that opened. Lately, however, I've begun to develop a small, cowardly instinct for self-preservation, and I find that there are two kinds of plays I can bear not to see: plays about troubled adolescents who can't find themselves, and plays about the Merchant of Venice.

During this past summer we paid a visit to Stratford, England, and saw a number of plays not including *The Merchant of Venice*. It seemed to make the whole trip worth while. I have friends, old-time theatergoers who have seen every Hamlet since Forbes-Robertson, and they love to sit around and reminisce about the way Leslie Howard played the ghost scene and how Gielgud read the speech to the players. Now, I hope to spend my twilight years reminiscing about the Shylocks I haven't seen. Donald Wolfit, Luther Adler, Clarence Derwent, Morris Carnovsky, Hume Cronyn — oh, it's a splendid gallery already and I expect to add to it before I'm through.

As everyone knows, one of the chief problems of going to the theater with a critic is getting out of there a split second after the curtain comes down or, if the show is a very long one, a split second before. Lately I've become very adept at judging the precise line of dialogue on which to start pulling the sleeves of my coat out from under the lady next to me. This might be when an actress says, "In future years, when you speak of me, be kind," or when an actor says, "Now that I've got you, darling, I'll never let you go," although I have known shows in which he let her go for another ten minutes after that.

Then follows a wild scramble down a dark and crowded aisle. I used to forge stolidly ahead, having developed a technique for this sort of thing in Ohrbach's basement, but one night, when I felt I had Walter firmly by the hand and was propelling him out into the traffic, I heard a plaintive voice muttering, "Hey, lady, gee, lady, please!" I looked up to discover that I had Farley Granger firmly by the hand. It's things like that that make one pause and reconsider.

After the show, most wives go out with their friends or go home to their peaceful apartments. I tag along to the office because we live in Larchmont and neither one of us wants to make the trip back alone. Obviously, if I were planning to influence my husband, my golden opportunity would come during the cab ride over to the office. The only trouble is that he immediately assumes the yogi-like silence and the glazed manner of a sandhog in a decompression chamber.

I used to think he was going into shock, but I have gradually gleaned that he is just trying to think of an opening sentence. I wouldn't dream of breaking the cathedral hush that surrounds us. However, if there is one thing a cab driver does not seem to recognize, it is a cathedral hush. All the cab drivers we get at ten forty-five in the evening are sports, bon vivants, and raconteurs. One man the other night had a really tantalizing story about how he had to drive a burro to Riverdale. My only question is, where are all these gay blades during the six-o'clock rush hour in front of the Biltmore?

Once my husband is at his desk, he sets to work immediately, furiously consulting the dozens of penciled notes he makes during the show on intricately folded yellow paper. I glanced at the notes one evening and the first one said, "Why he shedelepp so often, especially in the speckeldiff?" I only hope he doesn't lose them some night. They might be found, and how would he prove they're not atomic secrets?

Anyway, while he's working, I'm not idle. I sit at an empty desk and read back copies of *The Hollywood Reporter* and draw horses. Sometimes I chat with bright young copyboys, who, it would appear, are serious students of the theater. The only difficulty is that they want

494

to discuss Toller and Strindberg, whereas, at that hour of the night, I want to discuss Lindsay and Crouse. Occasionally someone wants to know why Kafka's *The Trial* is never done. Of course I have no figures here, but I have this feeling that it is done all the time. Maybe not.

Then, too, my husband sometimes consults me while he's writing a review. A hoarse shout will come over the partition, "Hey, how do you spell desiccate?" But this is patently ridiculous. If I could spell desiccate I would long since have assumed my rightful place in the world of letters.

An interesting aspect of dramatic criticism is that an actor can remember his briefest notice well into senescence and long after he has forgotten his phone number and where he lives. Thus it is quite a common occurrence for a critic to meet a nice young thing at a party and have her say, "Oh, don't you remember me? You saw me in *The Squared Circle* four years ago and you said I was 'earnest, effortful, and inane.' " Well, that's what makes cocktail parties so interesting.

On the other hand, most people who read more than one drama critic quickly forget who said what. We had an interesting demonstration of this one summer in London when we met a film actress who was chatting wisely and wittily about the theater until she reached the subject of a certain musical comedy. Then she declared with some heat, "I don't know what gets into

Brooks Atkinson sometimes. Do you know what he said about that show?"

Whereupon she proceeded to recite from memory two paragraphs, word for word, semicolon for semicolon, of Walter's review. After the brief hush that followed this recital, I murmured, "Did Brooks really say that? Well, there you are — even Homer nods," the while my husband made little clicking sounds indicating that he was too shocked even to comment.

In common with the wives of other critics, I am so anxious to indicate that I in no way influence or attempt to influence my husband's opinions that I rather overstate the case and perhaps give the impression that we never discuss the theater at all — that our conversation is exclusively concerned with stories about our adorable children and the cute way they spilled 3-in-1 oil all over the living-room rug, interspersed occasionally with highlights from the world of sport.

The fact is that we have many an intelligent discussion of the play coming home on the train, at which time I have a carbon copy of the review to read. A typical opening gambit in such a conversation would be: "Boy! If *that* was a magical, memorable performance . . . !"

Aunt Jean's Marshmallow Fudge Diet

Jean Kerr

Fred Allen used to talk about a man who was so thin he could be dropped through a piccolo without striking a single note. Well, I'm glad I never met *him;* I'd hate to have to hear about *his* diet.

I can remember when I was a girl — way back in Truman's Administration — and No-Cal was only a gleam in the eye of the Hirsch Bottling Company. In those days it was fun to go to parties. The conversation used to crackle with wit and intelligence because we talked about *ideas* — the aesthetic continuum in Western culture, Gary Cooper in Western movies, the superiority of beer over lotion as a wave-set, and the best way to use left-over veal.

Go to a party now and the couple next to you won't say a word about the rich, chocolate texture of their compost heap or how practical it's been to buy bunk-beds for the twins. They won't talk about anything except their diets — the one they've just come off, the one they're

497

on now, or the one they're going to have to start on Monday if they keep lapping it up like this.

I really blame science for the whole business. Years ago when a man began to notice that if he stood up on the subway he was immediately replaced by *two* people, he figured he was getting too fat. So he went to his doctor and the doctor said, "Quit stuffing yourself, Joe." And Joe either stopped or he didn't stop, but at least he kept his big mouth shut. What was there to talk about?

Today, with the science of nutrition advancing so rapidly, there is plenty of food for conversation, if for nothing else. We have the Rockefeller diet, the Mayo diet, high-protein diets, low-protein diets, "blitz" diets which feature cottage cheese and something that tastes like thin sandpaper, and — finally — a liquid diet that duplicates all the rich, nourishing goodness of mother's milk. I have no way of knowing which of these takes off the most weight, but there's no question that as a conversation-stopper the Mother's Milk Diet is way out ahead.

Where do people get all these diets, anyway? Obviously from the magazines; it's impossible to get a diet from a newspaper. For one thing, in a newspaper you can never catch the diet when it *starts*. It's always the fourth day of Ada May's Wonder Diet and, after a brief description of a simple slimming exercise that could be performed by anybody who has had five years' training with the ballet, Ada May gives you the menu for the day. One glass of skim milk, eight prunes, and three lamb's kidneys. This settles the matter for most people, who figure — quite reasonably — that if this is the *fourth* day, heaven deliver them from the first.

However, any stoics in the group who want to know just how far Ada May's sense of whimsy will take her can have the complete diet by sending twenty-five cents in stamps to the newspaper. But who has twenty-five cents in stamps? And if you're going to go out and get the stamps you might as well buy a twenty-five-cent magazine which will give you not only the same diet (now referred to as *Our Wonder Diet*) but will, in addition, show you a quick and easy way to turn your husband's old socks into gay pot holders.

In a truly democratic magazine that looks at all sides of the picture you will also find a recipe for George Washington's Favorite Spice Cake which will replace any weight you may have haphazardly lost on that wonder diet.

If you have formed the habit of checking on every *new* diet that comes along, you will find that, mercifully, they all blur together, leaving you with only one definite piece of information: French fried potatoes are out. But once in a great while a diet will stick in your mind. I'll never forget one I read about last summer. It urged the dieter to follow up his low-calorie meals by performing a series of calisthenics in the bathtub. No, not in the bath*room*. I read it twice, and it said in the bath*tub*. What a clever plan! Clearly, after you've broken both your arms you won't be able to eat as much (if at all) and the pounds will just melt away. In fact, if you don't have a cooperative husband who is willing to feed you like a two-year-old you may be limited to what you can consume through a straw, in which case let me suggest that Mother's Milk Formula.

The best diet I've heard about lately is the simplest. It was perfected by the actor Walter Slezak after years of careful experimentation. Under the Slezak plan, you eat as much as you want of everything you don't like. And if you should be in a hurry for any reason (let's say you're still wearing maternity clothes and the baby is eight months old) then you should confine yourself to food that you just plain hate.

Speaking about hateful food, the experts used to be content with merely making food pallid — by eliminating butter, oil, and salt. Not any more. Nowadays we are taught that, with a little imagination and a judicious use of herbs, anyone can turn out a no-calorie dish that's downright ghastly. Just yesterday I came across a dandy recipe for sprucing up good old boiled celery. You just simmer the chopped celery (with the tops) in a little skim milk. When it's tender, you add chopped onion, anise, chervil, marjoram, a dash of cinnamon, and you have a dish fit for the Dispose-All. And you'd better have a Dispose-All, because it's awfully messy if you have to dump it into a newspaper and carry it out to the garbage can.

And where is all this dieting getting us? No place at all. It's taken all the fun out of conversation and all the joy out of cooking. Furthermore, it leads to acts of irrational violence. A friend of mine keeps all candy and other luscious tidbits in the freezer, on the theory that by the time they thaw out enough to be eaten she will have recovered her will power. But the other night, having been driven berserk by a four-color advertisement for Instant Brownies, she rushed out to the freezer, started to gnaw on a frozen Milky Way, and broke a front tooth.

But let's get to the heart of the matter. All these diets that appear so monotonously in the flossy magazines — who are they for? Are they aimed at men? Certainly not; most men don't read these magazines. Are they intended for fat teen-agers? Probably not; teen-agers can't afford them. Do not ask for whom the bell tolls. It tolls for you — Married Woman, Mother of Three, lumpy, dumpy, and the source of concern to practically every publication in the United States. And why, why is the married woman being hounded into starvation in order to duplicate an ideal figure which is neither practical nor possible for a person her age? I'll tell you why.

First, it is presumed that when you're thinner you live longer. (In any case, when you live on a diet of yogurt and boiled grapefruit, it *seems* longer.) Second, it is felt that when you are skin and bones you have so much extra energy that you can climb up and shingle the roof. Third — and this is what they're really getting at — when you're thin you are so tasty and desirable that strange men will pinch you at the A & P and your husband will not only follow you around the kitchen breathing heavily but will stop and smother you with kisses as you try to put the butter back in the icebox. This — and I hope those in the back of the room are listening — is hogwash.

Think of the happy marriages you know about. How many of the ladies are still wearing size twelve? I've been giving this a lot of thought in the last twenty minutes, and I have been examining the marriages in my own troubled circle. What I have discovered is that the women who are being ditched are one and all willowy, wand-like, and slim as a blade. In fact, six of them require extensive padding even to look flat-chested.

That the fourteen divorcees, or about-to-be divorcees, whom I happen to know personally are all thin may be nothing more than a coincidence. Or it may just prove that men don't divorce fat wives because they feel sorry for them. Then again — and this is rather

502

sinister — men may not divorce fat wives because they imagine that the poor, plump dears will never locate *another* husband and they'll be paying alimony to the end of their days. (I mention this possibility, but my heart's not in it.)

The real reason, I believe, that men hang onto their well-endowed spouses is because they're comfy, and nice to have around the house. In a marriage there is nothing that stales so fast as physical beauty — as we readers of *Modern Screen* have observed. What actually holds a husband through thick and thick is a girl who is fun to be with. And any girl who has had nothing to eat since nine o'clock this morning but three hard-boiled eggs will be about as jolly and companionable as an income-tax inspector.

So I say, ladies, find out why women everywhere are switching from old-fashioned diets to the *modern* way: no exercise, no dangerous drugs, no weight loss. (And what do they mean "ugly fat"? It's *you*, isn't it?) For that tired, run-down feeling, try eating three full meals a day with a candy bar after dinner and pizza at eleven o'clock. Don't be intimidated by pictures of Audrey Hepburn. That girl is nothing but skin and bones. Just sit there smiling on that size twenty backside and say, "Guess what we're having for dinner, dear? Your favorite — stuffed breast of veal and corn fritters."

All your friends will say, "Oh, Blanche is a mess, the size of a house, but he's crazy about her, just *crazy* about her!"

On Conning Ed

Russell Baker

In New York they have the Consolidated Edison
electrical company. When I lived elsewhere,
New Yorkers would come and bore me with
tales of this berserk corporate monster, and I
would dismiss it as New York hysteria and
laugh a bored and torpid laugh.

Corporations are berserk all over America, I
would tell them. You cannot scare me with
what is after all only a small, localized nightmare. Me, I have gone up against the Columbia
Record Club and the Sears, Roebuck computer.
I have seen American Express run wild, have
struggled with the friendly skies of United
Airlines.

As one who had been buffeted by corporate
incompetence on the continental scale, how
could I be anything but bored by tales of a
local nuisance known as the Consolidated Edison
electrical company? It was to laugh. A cosmic
corporate monster might break my spirit some
day, and probably would, but a piffling Con-

solidated Edison electrical company? Never.

Insouciantly, I moved to New York for a stay. I arrived on a fourth of December. On the fifth, I received a letter from the Consolidated Edison electrical company. It announced that my electricity was going to be turned off for nonpayment of $325.

"Look here," I said on the telephone, in the voice which had crushed many a computer at the Chesapeake & Potomac Telephone Company, "since I have been in the house less than 24 hours, it is impossible that I can already have used $325 worth of Consolidated Edison electricity."

The uncrushed voice of the Consolidated Edison electrical company replied that the $325 was not for electricity used during the night previous, but was a deposit the company required of new customers.

But $325! That would have paid the bill for 18 months in my previous residence, which was three times as big, I explained. "That is our standard deposit charge for small-business establishments," the voice said.

"This is not a small business. Only a very small house."

"We will call you back," said the voice.

Sure enough, another voice called back. "We have made a mistake and will accept a smaller deposit."

"How much?"

"How much do you want to pay?" it replied.

I said I would think about it, proceeding on my theory that when dealing with idiot corporations nothing works like the stall.

A few hours later, I was rewarded. The Consolidated Edison electrical company telephoned again. "It is all a mistake," said the voice. "You needn't pay anything in advance. The deposit has been waived."

I called a number of New Yorkers and crowed about the ease with which a skilled guerrilla could defeat the local monster. It was the top of the world. New York was beautiful.

Eight days later came another letter from the Consolidated Edison electrical company. It was my final warning. The juice would stop flowing almost instantly unless I came across with the deposit. It was accompanied by a statement of my legal rights. If I could afford Louis Nizer's fee, I apparently had a fighting chance to avoid a percentage of the company gouge.

I went back to the stall. If I didn't call attention to myself, they might forget me in their own confusion. December gave way to January, and the electricity flowed. I had forgotten the matter entirely by the time the first snowstorm of the winter occurred when out of the gale in dead of night crept an ancient gnarled gentleman to ring the doorbell.

He was from the Consolidated Edison electrical company, he said. He had come to see about terminating the juice on my small-business establishment. I showed him that it was only a small house. He was delighted.

"Do not worry," he said, "for all is well. There is no need for a deposit payment." He vanished in the snow. I celebrated.

The following week, the Consolidated Edison electrical company wrote threatening to black me out in 10 days unless I forked over $110. I have just written the check and blotted it with tears, for I am certain that the Consolidated Edison electrical company will phone back soon and tell me the check is not required and, the week after that, will come to cut off the power on the ground that they haven't received my check.

I do not believe they are in the electrical business at all. I believe they are in the business of training corporate workers to be assigned to berserk corporations all over America to speed up the breaking of the human spirit.

Tell me, Consolidated Edison electrical company, how did a smart man like Edison ever get mixed up with you?

Marcel Proust Meets the New Jersey Tailgater, and Survives

Jean Shepherd

"Let's throw him in the crapper!"

" . . . a cow flop in his soup."

How's that *for Utopia, gang? Did you notice that the little buggers immediately began torturing the incoming rookies just as they had been harassed in their day?*

True, true, the minute one generation discovers the first wrinkle, it relentlessly attacks the upcoming generation as being callow, lacking in morals of any sort, hopelessly dumb. Going back to the days when men squatted in caves, eating clams, it has been so. I can just see a barrel-chested Neanderthal glaring across his flickering fire at a skulking teen-age Neanderthal and grunting:

"Get off your lazy ass. You never do anything around the cave. You kids don't know what it was like when I was your age. Why, we . . ."

The line in my lane of the tunnel began to move again, slowly, tentatively. I laughed out loud, picturing the scene in the cave. I could

509

almost smell the charred bones of elk, the same dampness of this god damned tunnel.

I stuck my head out of the window and yelled at the next generation, ahead in their Charger.

"Move it, you dumb boobs. Get your thumbs out!" I was carrying on an ancient tradition.

We ground to a halt. My mind searched for another idea to worry, to play with. Boredom was setting in. I examined the interior of my car minutely. The headliner, the sun visor, my little world of gauges and locked doors, sealed in a bathysphere under the mysterious waters. How many hours of my life had I spent alone in this metal cocoon, my only companion a fevered imagination?

MARCEL PROUST MEETS THE NEW JERSEY TAILGATER, AND SURVIVES

"Marcel Proust, the great French Impressionist writer, had a cork-lined room built so that he could write in absolute concentration. This cork-lined room cut out all sounds from the outside world so that he could concentrate and relive his past, which he put into his finely detailed works."

The pasty-faced TV professor cleared his throat nervously and blinked at the camera with a noticeably spasmodic ticlike wink. He cleared his throat again, and continued — his voice crackly like dry onionskin paper that's been left in the sun too long.

"On the other hand, Balzac found it necessary to have heavy curtains hung over the windows and doors of his study. He wrote late at night, by the light of a candle. He said he had to do this to concentrate, to get away from the world."

The Prof glanced frantically off to someone or something to his right, just out of camera range. Apparently, he was getting a cue. I leaned forward sleepily. It isn't often I see "Morning Classics," an educational college course-type program that comes on the screen either so late or so early — depending on your point of view — that hardly anybody ever sees it, except maybe the professor's wife and a few video freaks who see everything, including the test patterns.

"Er . . ." he stammered in confusion.

"Er . . ." that is, I'll be back tomorrow with . . ."

He was abruptly cut off the screen and replaced with a sixty-second plug for Girl Scout cookies. Poor Prof, I thought, he just ain't used to picking up his cues. So the whole point, if he had any, of his lecture went down the drain with the Girl Scout cookies and the morning news, which replaced him.

I fixed some instant coffee and as dawn was breaking somewhere out over the dark Atlantic I got to thinking of old Marcel Proust in his cork-lined room and Balzac scratching away with a quill pen with all those curtains hanging around him, at two in the morning. I sipped a bit of the lukewarm coffee and thought maybe I ought to build a cork-lined room, or hang black curtains over the window like those old-time writers did. I poured more coffee, and then it hit me —

Of course! I do have the equivalent of a cork-lined, black-curtain-draped concentration chamber, cut off from the rest of the world. My car!

I wonder how many guys there are in this world who actually find that the only time in the whole hectic day when they are away from phone calls, mysterious visitations, constant meetings, endless talks, are those few daily private times that they spend absolutely alone in their cars. A lone driver has no family, no job, no age — he is just an individual bit of human protoplasm humming through space. The mind drifts like some rudderless sailboat over the murky sea of consciousness. One part of you expertly, using some inbuilt secret mind-computer, steers the machine, calculating accurately all the changing vectors of speed, light, other traffic, road conditions, that go to make up fast driving. In fact, after you've put in enough hours behind the wheel under all kinds of conditions, you never even think about it any more. You just do it. All the while, that other part of your mind drifts around dreamily, dredging up wild thoughts, long-forgotten memories, and fragments of old disappointments. Proust had his cork-lined room; I have my vinyl-lined GT.

Take the other day. I'm battling it out with all the other sweating lonesome travelers on Jersey's Route 22, which like all the Route 22s of America has a surreal landscape which makes anything by Salvador Dali look like Norman Rockwell: Dairy Queens, McDonalds, instant seat cover palaces, a pizza joint that calls itself the Leaning Tower of Pizza that actually does lean, a gas station which for some reason has a forty-foot-high plastic North Woodsman swinging a motor-driven ax twenty-four hours a day, his face the color of an overripe watermelon, Gino's, Colonel Sanders, the works, all laced together with an unbelievable spiderweb of high tension wires, phone wires, wire wires, and miles of neon tubing. My mind is just idling away at maybe one-tenth throttle, thinking of nothing, when I glance up and see in my rear-view mirror that one of Jersey's folk artists has zeroed in on me.

Jersey natives have made a fine creative art form of tailgating. I could see in the mirror that I was in the clutches of a real master. I speeded up. He clung to my rear deck like a shadow. I dodged around a bus, figuring I'd scrape him off like a barnacle. No way. I shifted lanes. He moved with me like Earl Campbell following a blocker. He edged closer and closer to my rear bumper. We were hurtling along Route 22 at the usual cruise speed of that 55 mph limit artery — 75 plus. I slowed up, figuring that no true tailgater ever resists an opportunity to pass anything. There are guys who look upon all traffic as an endless obstacle to be passed. This is your average tailgater.

He wasn't buying it. I slowed up; he slowed up. I quickly switched lanes and made a fast feint toward the asphalt parking lot of a Carvel ice cream joint, figuring he'd get mouse-trapped into thinking I was stopping by for a quick Banana Boat. He clung to my rear deck like a Band-Aid. He was good, in fact, one of the best I'd ever seen. He was so close now that his face filled my entire rearview mirror. I couldn't even see the hood or the grille of his car. I noticed that he had nicked himself while shaving. There was a piece of toilet paper plastered on his steel-blue chin. He was also eating a Big Mac casually as we screamed along, locked in mortal combat.

Suddenly I became aware that something was blotting out the gray Jersey sky inches from my own grille. I had fallen for the oldest tailgater trick in the book. He had maneuvered me behind a giant flatbed truck, and there was no escape. I darted tentatively to my left, hoping to pass. The tailgater hemmed me in. I tried the right. No way. A Greyhound bus was in that lane. Inches separating us, we whistled along. My mind, operating fullbore, like Proust's or Balzac's, flashed visions of shattering glass, screaming metal, and I wondered briefly whether there was anything to this heaven and hell business.

The flatbed was now four or five feet ahead of my front bumper. Its load towered above me for what looked like two or three stories. I began to enjoy the scene. I could see the truck driver's face, pale and harassed, looking at me in his rearview mirror. He was muttering. A row of discount shoe stores flashed by us in a blur. I was so close to the flatbed that I began to examine its load minutely. My God, I thought, Proust never came up with a neater bit of irony in his life.

The load, stacked twenty-deep, consisted of a giant pile of flattened automobiles, each one maybe eight inches thick, crushed like so many sardine cans under a cosmic steam roller. I had a brief image of me and my car joining them and looking exactly like all the rest. The tailgater behind me was now impassively sucking at what looked like a sixty-four-ounce family-size bottle of Pepsi.

It was then that my mind really took off. Here we were, sealed in our own little noisy, smelly projectiles, hurtling over the landscape toward . . . what? I could see the crushed cars ahead of me creaking and groaning as if in mortal fear of the fiery fate that lay ahead for them in some distant foreign blast furnace. My God, I thought, they still have their paint on.

I began to recognize the makes. There was a seven-inch-high '57 Mercury, robin's egg blue. Above it, a '61 Plymouth Fury, thinner than a blueberry pancake at a cut-rate diner. It was sand beige. Then came a sad, peeling, forest green Nash Ambassador of indeterminate year. My mind flashed a brief headline on its beaded screen: Unknown Driver Killed By '51 Studebaker. Like a news story flashed in light bulbs that march around the tops of Times Square buildings, the story went on:

Driver annihilated when a '51 Studebaker that had been in a junk yard for twelve years and hadn't been driven since 1959 leaped off a flatbed truck to engage itself in its final fiery traffic crash.

The news item disappeared from my mind as the three of us howled through an overpass that echoed and boomed to the roar of the traffic. I peered ahead at the crushed cars. Tattered bumper stickers still clung to the hulks, a veritable cross section of ancient causes: LBJ — ALL THE WAY, I LIKE IKE, IMPEACH EARL WARREN, BAN THE BOMB, FREE THE PUEBLO.

My God, I thought, "Free The Pueblo." I could hardly even remember what that was all about, but that smashed Buick Skylark remembered.

Way up near the top was a twisted, battered

bumper from what looked like what was left of a moribund Dodge Charger. A torn sticker read WARNING — I BRAKE FOR ANIMALS. I thought dreamily, Poor bastard, after all that braking for chipmunks and box turtles somebody didn't brake for HIM. My mind thinks like that when I'm locked in my Proustian vinyl-lined GT, away from the cares and hubbub of everyday life with its phone calls and its feckless excursions and alarms.

I glanced in my rearview mirror. Blue Jowls, steady as a rock, was dogging me even closer. He seemed to have his front wheels up on my rear deck and was riding piggyback. He was also picking his teeth with what looked like a Boy Scout knife. I could clearly see the Scout insignia on its black bone handle. I continued reading the sad signs and pennants on the departed cars ahead of me.

Halfway up the pile, a canary-yellow Coronet had what looked like crude letters taped to its rusted bumper. They were made of faded red Day-Glo tape. I peered into the haze of blue diesel exhaust that was roaring over me from the truck. The letters spelled two names: WALT on the driver's side of the bumper, EMILY on the passenger side. Between them was a jagged, half-obliterated heart, pierced by a childish Day-Glo arrow.

Walt, I thought, poor Walt, where are you today? Somehow I felt a deep, sorrowful compassion for Walt, and Emily too. I saw that bright sunny day; that long-awaited day when they stood in the showroom taking the keys to their beautiful new Coronet. My mind conjured Walt up as being rather short, a bit beefy, but with a friendly sort of dumb face. His dark hair was cut in a bristly crew cut, the height of fashion for the day. His head looked a little like a furry bowling ball. Emily was thin and wore sagging blue shorts of the Montgomery Ward type, and she wore her hair in a Debbie Reynolds ponytail. I saw them together, polishing the Dodge on long summer weekends, Walt industriously working the Simoniz rag while Emily did the chrome. I had a brief vision of Walt making one of the endless payments on the Coronet at some sort of grilled window like they have in loan offices. He had lost a little hair and had gotten a little fatter, but you could tell it was still Walt all right. Through the window of the loan office I caught a glimpse of Emily waiting patiently in the car. There were now two kids jumping up and down on the back seat of the car. They both appeared to be boys, but it was hard to tell in all that diesel smoke coming back at me from the truck ahead. Emily looked even thinner, and her hair was put up in a pile of pink plastic curlers. The Coronet had lost two of its hubcaps, the chrome was rusting, and there wasn't much left of that bright canary-yellow paint.

I glanced again in my rearview mirror. My tailgater was now jogging up and down, his eyes glazed, his mouth hanging slackly in the manner of tailgating rock fiends.

Walt, I thought, where are you today, Walt? Are you and Emily still together? Has one of the kids been busted for Possession? Walt, do you know that your Coronet, after all these years, is still roaring along Route 22? It will be tonight in the hold of a tramp freighter sailing out of the port of Newark, Walt, a ship called, maybe, the *Funky Maru*, manned by a polyglot crew of cutthroats. Walt, your Coronet may come back to you someday in the form of a 105 mm shell.

My mind dreamily moved on. Suddenly my tailgater whistled off 22 onto the Garden State Parkway exit. He was still sucking at his Pepsi bottle. I saw him fasten himself to the back of a Mustang II.

I shifted to the left and passed the flatbed and its load of memory-laden carcasses. The mind does great things in our vinyl-lined GTs. Proust would have understood. Maybe even Balzac, for that matter.

The Sensuous Angler

Patrick F. McManus

There would be a lot less divorce in this country if more husbands and wives fished together. Spouses that fish together stay together.

My wife, Bun, for example, used to absolutely detest fishing. Whenever I dragged her out on the lake, she would sit there in the boat with her eyes fixed on me in an unblinking stare that I often imagined to be almost murderous. From time to time I'd even speak a few kind words to her in an effort to break the spell: "Row a bit faster along here, will you, Bun? I don't want my lure to get snagged in the weeds." Of course, there are some people who just don't respond to kind words, and Bun seemed to be one of them.

Besides my compulsive interest in fishing, what complicated our marital situation even more was that women find me extraordinarily attractive. "Irresistible" would not be too strong a word. I sometimes have to laugh to myself at the great show they put on to make me think they're totally unaware of my existence. Just recently I was sitting next to a beautiful woman on the uptown bus. I could tell she was flustered by the way she rummaged around in her purse, finally dug out a compact, and started fixing her face. It was absolutely hilarious, particularly when she wiped off some excess eye shadow with the tip of my tie. I mean, there are no lengths to which women will not go in their pretense of ignoring me!

Bun, quite forgivably, used to be terribly jealous. I'd try to kid her out of it. When we would come home from grocery shopping, I'd say, "Did you see how that cute blonde at the store was pretending to ignore me? I nearly laughed out loud!"

"There's only one can of tuna here," Bun would say. "I could have sworn I bought two cans of tuna."

That's how bad it was. Mad, uncontrollable jealousy was practically destroying our marriage.

The combination of my obsession with fishing and my irresistible appeal to women took a more extreme turn for the worse one day when Bun discovered a reddish smudge on the collar of one of my white dress shirts.

"Aha, I've got you now, you rascal," she snarled. "What's this red smudge on your shirt collar?"

How had I ever managed to overlook that smudge? My mind raced, feverishly searching for a plausible lie.

"It's probably just a lipstick smudge from one of the girls at the office," I tried.

"Ha!" Bun snapped. "I wasn't born yesterday, you know! This is salmon-egg juice! Here I think you're down at the office working, and actually you're sneaking off to go fishing. You've probably rented a secret apartment where you keep an extra set of fishing gear!"

"But there's this other woman . . ." That's as far as I got. If there's one thing I can't stand about Bun, it's the way she expresses her jealousy by laughing uncontrollably.

Actually, there *was* another woman. Her name was Jennifer, and she worked in the same advertising agency I did. There was something about her that made it almost impossible for me to keep my eyes off of her. As with most women, she made a great show of ignoring my existence. There was that time, for instance, when I was standing by the coat rack and she tried to hang her coat on me. Of course she had laughed in an embarrassed way, but not until she had made repeated efforts to keep her coat from slipping off my shoulders.

My job at the agency was to invent benevolent lies about a client's product. So distracted was I by Jennifer that one day I allowed a truth to slip into my copy and was nearly fired. Naturally, I was upset by the mishap, and as soon as the boss had gone down to the shop to resharpen his reamer, I whipped out my portable fly-tying outfit and began to tie a few Royal

Henchmen to soothe my nerves. Suddenly I felt a pair of eyes on me. At first I thought it was Charley Fife, playing another one of his grotesque practical jokes. Then I realized it was Jennifer watching me. She came over to my desk.

"Hello," she said, holding out a hand. "I'm Jennifer. You must be new here."

"Oh, I've been here awhile," I replied suavely.

"How long?"

"Four years."

"Strange that I've never noticed you before. Our desks are only twenty feet apart."

"Yes, well *I've* noticed you, Jennifer."

"You have? Anything in particular."

"Is there ever!" I breathed. "For one thing, there's the way you read *Field & Stream* so avidly at lunch while the other girls are gawking at *Glamour*. Then I saw the way you took that casting reel apart and put it back together when you were supposed to be typing the annual report."

"Oh dear!" she cried, tittering. "You caught me in the act, did you? I was just cleaning my Protron Ninety Double-Widget Power-Glide Pro-Caster."

"You're telling me!" I said. "You have about the prettiest little Pro-Caster I've ever laid eyes on."

A flush of embarrassment filled Jennifer's cheeks, reminding me of the red-bellies I used to catch in the creek behind our house when I was a kid. As she bent over to whisper in my ear, I detected the faint, lingering fragrance of OFF! "Did you notice anything else?" Her voice was husky.

"You mean . . . the way you rewrapped the split bamboo rod during your coffee breaks last February? Of course I noticed! It nearly drove me wild!"

She smiled. "You're really a very attract . . . You're not that bad look . . . I like large ears a lot, I really do."

I chuckled. The poor girl was practically tongue-tied.

"What attracted me to you most, though," she continued, "was your little portable fly-tying outfit. It's lovely! Say, I've got an idea Why don't you stop by my place tonight and we'll . . . well, you know?"

"I know!" I said. "I know!"

After I had slipped into Jennifer's apartment that evening, she poured us each a glass of wine and turned on the stereo. Then we got right down to business. I was amazed, I must tell you, at what that woman knew. In fifteen minutes she taught me more about how to cure fresh steelhead eggs for bait than all the grizzled old anglers I've ever known. Such was our mad frenzy of curing steelhead eggs that some of the juice apparently splashed on my collar. That was the spot my wife detected.

"No one must ever find out about us," I told Jennifer as we shook hands at the door of her apartment as I was leaving.

"Oh, I know, I know," she said. "But next time, next time . . ."

"What?" I gasped. "Tell me what, Jennifer!"

"Next time . . . I'll show you how to filet perch!"

I was puzzled. "But, Jennifer, I know how to filet perch."

She gave me a lascivious smile. "Not the way *I* do it."

My imagination did a wild dance, raising goose bumps on my flesh the size of bongo drums. "When can we do it?" I asked. "When can we filet perch together?"

"Maybe next Tuesday night. Call me after eight. But if a man's voice answers, hang up."

"A man's voice?"

"Yes, my husband's. He is very big, with a short temper. And he hates fishing and fish. It would be most unfortunate for you if he caught us — you know — fileting together."

I shuddered at the image conjured up by her warning.

It was a long week. Every time I looked up, I saw Jennifer typing reports a few yards away. I could scarcely tear my eyes away from her flying fingers, those very fingers which, but a few days before, I had watched . . . had watched knead alum into a sinewy mess of steelhead eggs. Once a man, an angler, has experienced that with a woman, there is no turning back. And she had this lovely way of tossing her head. It reminded me of the way a fly fisher, hands filled with rod and line, will toss his head in order to shake a deer fly off his nose. It was beautiful.

At home during supper, I found myself staring absently at my plate. All I could think about was fileting with Jennifer.

"What's wrong with Pop?" one of the kids asked one evening. "How come he doesn't tell us those stupid stories about his childhood any more?"

"Don't complain," their mother said. "Your father has important things on his mind."

"We ain't complaining!" the kids said in unison. "We ain't complaining!"

"Have some respect!" I shouted at them. "I never once talked to one of my parents like that! Why, one time when I was only eight years old and had just walked the fifteen miles home from school in knee-deep snow . . ."

"Forget I mentioned it," the first kid said.

After supper Bun followed me into my den, also jestingly referred to as "the hole under the stairs." She put her hands on my shoulders and said, "Something's wrong. I know something's wrong. You get upset over the smallest things. I saw the way your eyes became all teary when you couldn't stab that last pea with your fork at supper. You can tell me! What's wrong?"

"Nothing's wrong," I said. What made me feel so bad about my affair with Jennifer is that Bun's a great wife. Sure, she has her faults. There was that time she screamed as if she had found Jack the Ripper in our refrigerator instead of merely a mayonnaise jar containing live hellgrammites. Heck, Jennifer would never have screamed at the sight of a few crummy live hellgrammites.

The truth was that Jennifer didn't really stand a chance of coming between my wife and me. Ol 'Bun and I had just been through too many things together. She had stuck with me through thin and thin. The only thing to do, I told myself, was to try to forget Jennifer. But I couldn't.

When Tuesday night rolled around, I slipped out to a pay phone and called Jennifer's number. Jennifer answered.

"Is it all right?" I asked.

"Yes," she said, breathlessly. "Hammer is flying out of town on a business trip tonight and won't be back until tomorrow."

"Great!" I said. "I'll sneak right over."

I told Bun I was going to spend the evening with the boys down at Kelly's Bar & Grill and not to expect me home too early. She said fine, that she would leave the key under the cushion on the porch swing. I was halfway over to Jennifer's before it occurred to me that there isn't a cushion on the porch swing. We don't even have a porch swing. We scarcely have a porch. I wondered if Bun suspected anything.

A sudden thought jolted me: *Hammer? Her husband's name is Hammer?*

When Jennifer met me at the door, I was disappointed to find her dressed in a low-cut, filmy negligee.

"You're early," she said. "Mix yourself a drink while I slip into something a little more comfortable." Presently she returned from the bedroom dressed in baggy, patched fishing pants and a plaid wool shirt sprinkled with fish scales.

"Hey hey hey!" I said. "Now that's more like it!" I thrust a package into her hands. "By the way, here's a little something for you."

Her hands tore eagerly at the wrappings. Nervously, I wondered if maybe I had made a mistake, giving her such a personal gift so soon in our relationship.

"Oh!" she cried, clapping her hands together in delight. "They're beautiful! You shouldn't have! They must have cost you a small fortune!"

"Nope," I said, smiling modestly. "I caught them myself. Off the old Grand Street fishing pier. Do you really like them?"

Jennifer wiped her joy-streaked cheeks on her shirt sleeve. "Oh, I love them! They are absolutely gorgeous perch! All Hammer ever gives me are long-stemmed red roses and dumb furs."

It was obvious her husband was either a thoughtless clod or totally insensitive. Some men just don't know how to treat a woman!

Overcome by the excitement of the moment, Jennifer and I rushed into the kitchen and began to filet madly. Never have I known a woman who could filet like Jennifer! Perch after perch fell under her flashing knife. I became mesmerized by her very motions, the way she whacked off the heads, stripped away the skins, and sliced off the filets. Time ceased to exist for me, and all space seemed confined to Jennifer's laminated maple chopping block.

Then the earth moved.

"Did the earth move for you, Jennifer?" I asked.

"Yes yes yes yes yes!" she cried. "And do you know what made it move?"

"What?"

"Hammer! He always trips on the last step at the top of the stairs!"

"HAMMER?" I yelled. "I thought you said he was away on business!"

"Maybe he missed his flight! Maybe he suspects something! But that is Hammer coming down the hall!"

Now I could feel the earth move with every step Hammer took down the hallway. The steps sounded angry.

"What'll we do?" I hissed at Jennifer.

"What do you mean 'we,' you burglar you!" she snapped.

Somehow I felt that Jennifer had chosen that moment to break off our relationship. Very soon I expected her husband to break off more than that.

"Look at the evidence!" I hissed, as Hammer rattled his key in the lock. "He'll know we've been fileting together. No matter what you tell him, he'll know a burglar didn't break into the apartment and force you to filet!"

Jennifer scooped up all the evidence and flung it into the freezing compartment of the refrigerator.

"Jen?" called out Hammer, his voice rumbling into the kitchen like a slow freight.

A second before Hammer's shadow fell upon us, Jennifer lunged across the kitchen, threw her arms around me, and planted a big, wet, utterly disgusting kiss on my mustache. And then Hammer filled the doorway.

"Who dis?" he demanded, pointing at me with a finger the size of a zucchini.

"Oh," said Jennifer, "this is just one of my professors from night school who heard you were going to be out of town tonight and thought he'd sneak by."

"You 'spect me to buy a cock'n'bull story like dat? It smells fishy in here! You two been up to somethin' wid fish, ain'tcha? Filetin'! I'll bet the two of you have been filetin' behind my back. Or maybe even, even — I can't stand the thought of it — curin' steelhead eggs for bait! As soon as I leave town to do a little job for the Godfather . . . ."

"No, no, Hammy, it wasn't anything like

530

that," Jennifer cried. "Please don't kill him!"

"Repeat that last part, would you, Jennifer?" I whispered to her. "I don't think Hammy heard it."

At that moment Hammer blinked, giving me the opportunity to leap out the kitchen window and sprint to safety down the alley. When I finally stopped to catch my breath, I made up my mind right then and there that never again was I going to filet with another man's wife, particularly one whose apartment was higher than the ground floor. For one thing, it's so darn hard to sprint to safety with your legs protruding from your armpits.

I had learned my lesson about other women and decided that the thing to do was to give my own wife more instruction in the art of fileting. That way she might even learn to enjoy the sport. And the very next weekend I started her lessons.

"All right, Bun," I instructed, "just remember that balance is everything. There, you've nearly got it. Raise your right arm a bit more. Good. Now you've got the idea! Heck, you could carry the canoe all day like that if you had to. Get started toward the lake now, and I'll grab my fly rod and be right along behind."

Bun still isn't too enthusiastic about fishing yet. As a matter of fact, just the other day when we were out on the river she said if I would forget about the idea of making her my fishing pal, she wouldn't complain about another woman or two.

Not a chance! "Listen, Bun," I said, "you're the only woman for me, and I'm going to make you love fishing if it's the last thing you do."

I could have sworn that she was so touched by this remark that a single tear trickled down her cheek. It was hard to tell for sure, though, because of the cloud of mosquitoes around her.

The Kugelmass Episode

Woody Allen

Kugelmass, a professor of humanities at City College, was unhappily married for the second time. Daphne Kugelmass was an oaf. He also had two dull sons by his first wife, Flo, and was up to his neck in alimony and child support.

"Did I know it would turn out so badly?" Kugelmass whined to his analyst one day. "Daphne had promise. Who suspected she'd let herself go and swell up like a beach ball? Plus she had a few bucks, which is not in itself a healthy reason to marry a person, but it doesn't hurt, with the kind of operating nut I have. You see my point?"

Kugelmass was bald and as hairy as a bear, but he had soul.

"I need to meet a new woman," he went on. "I need to have an affair. I may not look the part, but I'm a man who needs romance. I need softness, I need flirtation. I'm not getting younger, so before it's too late I want to make love in Venice, trade quips at '21,' and exchange coy glances over red wine and candlelight. You see what I'm saying?"

Dr. Mandel shifted in his chair and said, "An affair will solve nothing. You're so unrealistic. Your problems run much deeper."

"And also this affair must be discreet," Kugelmass continued. "I can't afford a second divorce. Daphne would really sock it to me."

"Mr. Kugelmass —"

"But it can't be anyone at City College, because Daphne also works there. Not that anyone on the faculty at C.C.N.Y. is any great shakes, but some of those coeds . . ."

"Mr. Kugelmass —"

"Help me. I had a dream last night. I was skipping through a meadow holding a picnic basket and the basket was marked 'Options.' And then I saw there was a hole in the basket."

"Mr. Kugelmass, the worst thing you could do is act out. You must simply express your feelings here, and together we'll analyze them. You have been in treatment long enough to know there is no overnight cure. After all, I'm an analyst, not a magician."

"Then perhaps what I need is a magician," Kugelmass said, rising from his chair. And with that he terminated his therapy.

A couple of weeks later, while Kugelmass and Daphne were moping around in their apartment one night like two pieces of old furniture, the phone rang.

"I'll get it," Kugelmass said. "Hello."

"Kugelmass?" a voice said. "Kugelmass, this is Persky."

"Who?"

"Persky. Or should I say The Great Persky?"

"Pardon me?"

"I hear you're looking all over town for a magician to bring a little exotica into your life? Yes or no?"

"Sh-h-h," Kugelmass whispered. "Don't hang up. Where are you calling from, Persky?"

Early the following afternoon, Kugelmass climbed three flights of stairs in a broken-down apartment house in the Bushwick section of Brooklyn. Peering through the darkness of the hall, he found the door he was looking for and pressed the bell. I'm going to regret this, he thought to himself.

Seconds later, he was greeted by a short, thin, waxy-looking man.

"*You're* Persky the Great?" Kugelmass said.

"The Great Persky. You want a tea?"

"No, I want romance. I want music. I want love and beauty."

"But not tea, eh? Amazing. O.K., sit down."

Persky went to the back room, and Kugelmass heard the sounds of boxes and furniture being moved around. Persky reappeared, pushing before him a large object on squeaky roller-skate wheels. He removed some old silk handkerchiefs that were lying on its top and blew away a bit of dust. It was a cheap-looking Chinese cabinet, badly lacquered.

"Persky," Kugelmass said, "what's your scam?"

"Pay attention," Persky said. "This is some beautiful effect. I developed it for a Knights of Pythias date last year, but the booking fell through. Get into the cabinet."

"Why, so you can stick it full of swords or something?"

"You see any swords?"

Kugelmass made a face and, grunting, climbed into the cabinet. He couldn't help noticing a couple of ugly rhinestones glued onto the raw plywood just in front of his face. "If this is a joke," he said.

"Some joke. Now, here's the point. If I throw any novel into this cabinet with you, shut the doors, and tap it three times, you will find yourself projected into that book."

Kugelmass made a grimace of disbelief.

"It's the emess," Persky said. "My hand to God. Not just a novel, either. A short story, a play, a poem. You can meet any of the women created by the world's best writers. Whoever you dreamed of. You could carry on all you like with a real winner. Then when you've had enough you give a yell, and I'll see you're back here in a split second."

"Persky, are you some kind of outpatient?"

"I'm telling you it's on the level," Persky said.

Kugelmass remained skeptical. "What are you telling me — that this cheesy homemade

536

box can take me on a ride like you're describing?"

"For a double sawbuck."

Kugelmass reached for his wallet. "I'll believe this when I see it," he said.

Persky tucked the bills in his pants pocket and turned toward his bookcase. "So who do you want to meet? Sister Carrie? Hester Prynne? Ophelia? Maybe someone by Saul Bellow? Hey, what about Temple Drake? Although for a man your age she'd be a workout."

"French. I want to have an affair with a French lover."

"Nana?"

"I don't want to have to pay for it."

"What about Natasha in *War and Peace?*"

"I said French. I know! What about Emma Bovary? That sounds to me perfect."

"You got it, Kugelmass. Give me a holler when you've had enough." Persky tossed in a paperback copy of Flaubert's novel.

"You sure this is safe?" Kugelmass asked as Persky began shutting the cabinet doors.

"Safe. Is anything safe in this crazy world?" Persky rapped three times on the cabinet and then flung open the doors.

Kugelmass was gone. At the same moment, he appeared in the bedroom of Charles and Emma Bovary's house at Yonville. Before him was a beautiful woman, standing alone with her back turned to him as she folded some linen. I can't believe this, thought Kugelmass, staring at the doctor's ravishing wife. This is uncanny. I'm here. It's her.

Emma turned in surprise. "Goodness, you startled me," she said. "Who are you?" She spoke in the same fine English translation as the paperback.

It's simply devastating, he thought. Then, realizing that it was he whom she had addressed, he said, "Excuse me. I'm Sidney Kugelmass. I'm from City College. A professor of humanities. C.C.N.Y.? Uptown. I — oh, boy!"

Emma Bovary smiled flirtatiously and said, "Would you like a drink? A glass of wine, perhaps?"

She is beautiful, Kugelmass thought. What a contrast with the troglodyte who shared his bed! He felt a sudden impulse to take this vision into his arms and tell her she was the kind of woman he had dreamed of all his life.

"Yes, some wine," he said hoarsely. "White. No, red. No, white. Make it white."

"Charles is out for the day," Emma said, her voice full of playful implication.

After the wine, they went for a stroll in the lovely French countryside. "I've always dreamed that some mysterious stranger would appear and rescue me from the monotony of this crass rural existence," Emma said, clasping his hand. They passed a small church. "I love what you have on," she murmured. "I've never seen anything like it around here. It's so . . . so modern."

"It's called a leisure suit," he said romantically. "It was marked down." Suddenly he kissed her. For the next hour they reclined under a tree and whispered together and told each other deeply meaningful things with their eyes. Then Kugelmass sat up. He had just remembered he had to meet Daphne at Bloomingdale's. "I must go," he told her. "But don't worry, I'll be back."

"I hope so," Emma said.

He embraced her passionately, and the two walked back to the house. He held Emma's face cupped in his palms, kissed her again, and yelled, "O.K., Persky! I got to be at Bloomingdale's by three-thirty."

There was an audible pop, and Kugelmass was back in Brooklyn.

"So? Did I lie?" Persky asked triumphantly.

"Look, Persky, I'm right now late to meet the ball and chain at Lexington Avenue, but when can I go again? Tomorrow?"

"My pleasure. Just bring a twenty. And don't mention this to anybody."

"Yeah. I'm going to call Rupert Murdoch."

Kugelmass hailed a cab and sped off to the city. His heart danced on point. I am in love, he thought, I am the possessor of a wonderful secret. What he didn't realize was that at this very moment students in various classrooms across the country were saying to their teachers, "Who is this character on page 100? A bald Jew is kissing Madame Bovary?" A teacher in

Sioux Falls, South Dakota, sighed and thought, Jesus, these kids, with their pot and acid. What goes through their minds!

Daphne Kugelmass was in the bathroom-accessories department at Bloomingdale's when Kugelmass arrived breathlessly. "Where've you been?" she snapped. "It's four-thirty."

"I got held up in traffic," Kugelmass said.

Kugelmass visited Persky the next day, and in a few minutes was again passed magically to Yonville. Emma couldn't hide her excitement at seeing him. The two spent hours together, laughing and talking about their different backgrounds. Before Kugelmass left, they made love. "My God, I'm doing it with Madame Bovary!" Kugelmass whispered to himself. "Me, who failed freshman English."

As the months passed, Kugelmass saw Persky many times and developed a close and passionate relationship with Emma Bovary. "Make sure and always get me into the book before page 120," Kugelmass said to the magician one day. "I always have to meet her before she hooks up with this Rodolphe character."

"Why?" Persky said. "You can't beat his time?"

"Beat his time. He's landed gentry. Those guys have nothing better to do than flirt and ride horses. To me, he's one of those faces you see in the pages of *Women's Wear Daily*. With the Helmut Berger hairdo. But to her he's

540

hot stuff."

"And her husband suspects nothing?"

"He's out of his depth. He's a lacklustre little paramedic who's thrown in his lot with a jitterbug. He's ready to go to sleep by ten, and she's putting on her dancing shoes. Oh, well . . . See you later."

And once again Kugelmass entered the cabinet and passed instantly to the Bovary estate at Yonville. "How you doing, cupcake?" he said to Emma.

"Oh, Kugelmass," Emma sighed. "What I have to put up with. Last night at dinner, Mr. Personality dropped off to sleep in the middle of the dessert course. I'm pouring my heart out about Maxim's and the ballet, and out of the blue I hear snoring."

"It's O.K., darling. I'm here now," Kugelmass said, embracing her. I've earned this, he thought, smelling Emma's French perfume and burying his nose in her hair. I've suffered enough. I've paid enough analysts. I've searched till I'm weary. She's young and nubile, and I'm here a few pages after Leon and just before Rodolphe. By showing up during the correct chapters, I've got the situation knocked.

Emma, to be sure, was just as happy as Kugelmass. She had been starved for excitement, and his tales of Broadway night life, of fast cars and Hollywood and TV stars, enthralled the young French beauty.

"Tell me again about O. J. Simpson," she

541

implored that evening, as she and Kugelmass strolled past Abbé Bournisien's church.

"What can I say? The man is great. He sets all kinds of rushing records. Such moves. They can't touch him."

"And the Academy Awards?" Emma said wistfully. "I'd give anything to win one."

"First you've got to be nominated."

"I know. You explained it. But I'm convinced I can act. Of course, I'd want to take a class or two. With Strasberg maybe. Then, if I had the right agent —"

"We'll see, we'll see. I'll speak to Persky."

That night, safely returned to Persky's flat, Kugelmass brought up the idea of having Emma visit him in the big city.

"Let me think about it," Persky said. "Maybe I could work it. Stranger things have happened." Of course, neither of them could think of one.

"Where the hell do you go all the time?" Daphne Kugelmass barked at her husband as he returned home late that evening. "You got a chippie stashed somewhere?"

"Yeah, sure, I'm just the type," Kugelmass said wearily. "I was with Leonard Popkin. We were discussing Socialist agriculture in Poland. You know Popkin. He's a freak on the subject."

"Well, you've just been very odd lately," Daphne said. "Distant. Just don't forget about my father's birthday. On Saturday?"

"Oh, sure, sure," Kugelmass said, heading for the bathroom.

"My whole family will be there. We can see the twins. And Cousin Hamish. You should be more polite to Cousin Hamish — he likes you."

"Right, the twins," Kugelmass said, closing the bathroom door and shutting out the sound of his wife's voice. He leaned against it and took a deep breath. In a few hours, he told himself, he would be back in Yonville again, back with his beloved. And this time, if all went well, he would bring Emma back with him.

At three-fifteen the following afternoon, Persky worked his wizardry again. Kugelmass appeared before Emma, smiling and eager. The two spent a few hours at Yonville with Binet and then remounted the Bovary carriage. Following Persky's instructions, they held each other tightly, closed their eyes, and counted to ten. When they opened them, the carriage was just drawing up at the side door of the Plaza Hotel, where Kugelmass had optimistically reserved a suite earlier in the day.

"I love it! It's everything I dreamed it would be," Emma said as she swirled joyously around the bedroom, surveying the city from their window. "There's F. A. O. Schwarz. And there's Central Park, and the Sherry is which one? Oh, there — I see. It's too divine."

On the bed there were boxes from Halston and Saint Laurent. Emma unwrapped a package and held up a pair of black velvet pants against her perfect body.

"The slacks suit is by Ralph Lauren," Kugelmass said. "You'll look like a million bucks in it. Come on, sugar, give us a kiss."

"I've never been so happy!" Emma squealed as she stood before the mirror. "Let's go out on the town. I want to see *Chorus Line* and the Guggenheim and this Jack Nicholson character you always talk about. Are any of his flicks showing?"

"I cannot get my mind around this," a Stanford professor said. "First a strange character named Kugelmass, and now she's gone from the book. Well, I guess the mark of a classic is that you can reread it a thousand times and always find something new."

The lovers passed a blissful weekend. Kugelmass had told Daphne he would be away at a symposium in Boston and would return Monday. Savoring each moment, he and Emma went to the movies, had dinner in Chinatown, passed two hours at a discothèque, and went to bed with a TV movie. They slept till noon on Sunday, visited SoHo, and ogled celebrities at Elaine's. They had caviar and champagne in their suite on Sunday night and talked until dawn. That morning, in the cab taking them to Persky's apartment, Kugelmass thought, It was hectic, but worth it. I can't bring her here too often, but now and then it will be a charming contrast with Yonville.

At Persky's, Emma climbed into the cabinet, arranged her new boxes of clothes neatly around her, and kissed Kugelmass fondly. "My place next time," she said with a wink. Persky rapped three times on the cabinet. Nothing happened.

"Hmm," Persky said, scratching his head. He rapped again, but still no magic. "Something must be wrong," he mumbled.

"Persky, you're joking!" Kugelmass cried. "How can it not work?"

"Relax, relax. Are you still in the box, Emma?"

"Yes."

Persky rapped again — harder this time.

"I'm still here, Persky."

"I know, darling. Sit tight."

"Persky, we *have* to get her back," Kugelmass whispered. "I'm a married man, and I have a class in three hours. I'm not prepared for anything more than a cautious affair at this point."

"I can't understand it," Persky muttered. "It's such a reliable little trick."

But he could do nothing. "It's going to take a little while," he said to Kugelmass. "I'm going to have to strip it down. I'll call you later."

Kugelmass bundled Emma into a cab and took her back to the Plaza. He barely made it to his class on time. He was on the phone all day, to Persky and to his mistress. The magician told him it might be several days before he got to the bottom of the trouble.

"How was the symposium?" Daphne asked him that night.

"Fine, fine," he said, lighting the filter end of a cigarette.

"What's wrong? You're as tense as a cat."

"Me? Ha, that's a laugh. I'm as calm as a summer night. I'm just going to take a walk." He eased out the door, hailed a cab, and flew to the Plaza.

"This is no good," Emma said. "Charles will miss me."

"Bear with me, sugar," Kugelmass said. He was pale and sweaty. He kissed her again, raced to the elevators, yelled at Persky over a pay phone in the Plaza lobby, and just made it home before midnight.

"According to Popkin, barley prices in Kraków have not been this stable since 1971," he said to Daphne, and smiled wanly as he climbed into bed.

The whole week went by like that.

On Friday night, Kugelmass told Daphne there was another symposium he had to catch, this one in Syracuse. He hurried back to the Plaza, but the second weekend there was nothing like the first. "Get me back into the novel or marry me," Emma told Kugelmass. "Meanwhile, I want to get a job or go to class, because watching TV all day is the pits."

"Fine. We can use the money," Kugelmass said. "You consume twice your weight in room service."

"I met an Off Broadway producer in Central Park yesterday, and he said I might be right for a project he's doing," Emma said.

"Who is this clown?" Kugelmass asked.

"He's not a clown. He's sensitive and kind and cute. His name's Jeff Something-or-Other, and he's up for a Tony."

Later that afternoon, Kugelmass showed up at Persky's drunk.

"Relax," Persky told him. "You'll get a coronary."

"Relax. The man says relax. I've got a fictional character stashed in a hotel room, and I think my wife is having me tailed by a private shamus."

"O.K., O.K. We know there's a problem." Persky crawled under the cabinet and started banging on something with a large wrench.

"I'm like a wild animal," Kugelmass went on. "I'm sneaking around town, and Emma and I have had it up to here with each other. Not to mention a hotel tab that reads like the defense budget."

"So what should I do? This is the world of magic," Persky said. "It's all nuance."

"Nuance, my foot. I'm pouring Dom Pérignon and black eggs into this little mouse, plus her wardrobe, plus she's enrolled at the Neighborhood Playhouse and suddenly needs professional photos. Also, Persky, Professor Fivish Kopkind, who teaches Comp Lit and who has always been jealous of me, has identified me as the sporadically appearing character in the Flaubert book. He's threatened to go to Daphne. I see ruin and alimony; jail. For adultery with Madame Bovary, my wife will reduce me to beggary."

"What do you want me to say? I'm working on it night and day. As far as your personal anxiety goes, that I can't help you with. I'm a magician, not an analyst."

By Sunday afternoon, Emma had locked herself in the bathroom and refused to respond to Kugelmass's entreaties. Kugelmass stared out the window at the Wollman Rink and contemplated suicide. Too bad this is a low floor, he thought, or I'd do it right now. Maybe if I ran away to Europe and started life over . . . Maybe I could sell the *International Herald Tribune*, like those young girls used to.

The phone rang. Kugelmass lifted it to his ear mechanically.

"Bring her over," Persky said. "I think I got the bugs out of it."

Kugelmass's heart leaped. "You're serious?" he said. "You got it licked?"

"It was something in the transmission. Go figure."

"Persky, you're a genius. We'll be there in a minute. Less than a minute."

Again the lovers hurried to the magician's

apartment, and again Emma Bovary climbed into the cabinet with her boxes. This time there was no kiss. Persky shut the doors, took a deep breath, and tapped the box three times. There was the reassuring popping noise, and when Persky peered inside, the box was empty. Madame Bovary was back in her novel. Kugelmass heaved a great sigh of relief and pumped the magician's hand.

"It's over," he said. "I learned my lesson. I'll never cheat again, I swear it." He pumped Persky's hand again and made a mental note to send him a necktie.

Three weeks later, at the end of a beautiful spring afternoon, Persky answered his doorbell. It was Kugelmass, with a sheepish expression on his face.

"O.K., Kugelmass," the magician said. "Where to this time?"

"It's just this once," Kugelmass said. "The weather is so lovely, and I'm not getting any younger. Listen, you've read *Portnoy's Complaint?* Remember The Monkey?"

"The price is now twenty-five dollars, because the cost of living is up but I'll start you off with one freebie, due to all the trouble I caused you."

"You're good people," Kugelmass said, combing his few remaining hairs as he climbed into the cabinet again. "This'll work all right?"

"I hope. But I haven't tried it much since all

the unpleasantness."

"Sex and romance," Kugelmass said from inside the box. "What we go through for a pretty face."

Persky tossed in a copy of *Portnoy's Complaint* and rapped three times on the box. This time, instead of a popping noise there was a dull explosion, followed by a series of crackling noises and a shower of sparks. Persky leaped back, was seized by a heart attack, and dropped dead. The cabinet burst into flames, and eventually the entire house burned down.

Kugelmass, unaware of this catastrophe, had his own problems. He had not been thrust into *Portnoy's Complaint*, or into any other novel, for that matter. He had been projected into an old textbook, *Remedial Spanish*, and was running for his life over a barren, rocky terrain as the word *tener* ("to have") — a large and hairy irregular verb — raced after him on its spindly legs.

The Socks Problem

Roy Blount, Jr.

I wish to broach a matter close to every man's, and most modern women's, feet: "Whatever happened to socks?"

Everybody I know agrees: It doesn't matter whether you are living alone in a tepee, or married to two different people in two different bungalows, or just floating around with no fixed address, or pursuing a career as a recluse in the family manse, or lying chained to the floor in a tiny basement room off the initiation chamber in a sorority house. The one result you can depend on is attrition of your socks. A person could stay in the same room with all of his or her socks for a month, never (except to sleep) taking his or her eyes off the drawer in which his or her socks are kept, and at the end of that period he or she would have three to seven fewer socks than he or she began with.

In my case, I believe I have considered all of the natural outlets:

- A member of my household, who is being

blackmailed and can't make the payments out of the change on the dresser, sells them. I doubt this, because no member of my household can keep a secret. If they were involved in something that would worry me if I knew about it, they would tell me.

• The washing machine, or the dryer, digests them. This may be. The dryer produces, I know for a fact, something that is very suggestive of socks. This is probably why so many of my washables are translucent — and if any member of my household were handier, a good many socks could no doubt be re-created annually from this lint, or fluff, three or four washloads' worth of which would cover a sheep. But this ongoing leaching of fiber from the nation's clothing, while it is something that the Federal Trade Commission might well look into, appears to be a gradual process, which cannot account for the sudden disappearance of whole socks.

• The modern sock is made of a material designed to disintegrate, of its own accord, after a period of time. I would not put this past American industry, but in this case a sock would occasionally go poof while I was wearing it, or while I was holding it up to the morning light trying to decide what color it was.

• Dust is dead socks. If it isn't dead socks, what is it? Certainly if you let the dust of two or three rooms accumulate for a while, you can shuffle your feet around the baseboards and have bedroom slippers that will serve in mild climates. But I have in my drawer, where hope springs eternal (and where, in fact, a sock has been known to resurface, magically, after up to eighteen months' absence), single socks whose ages range from three months to four years. Some of the older ones have been with me at seven different addresses. If the socks that match have gone to dust, why haven't they? Often, heartrendingly, it is almost-new socks that are missing. The poets have not written adequately of the near-erotic pleasure of easing your foot into a new, lissome, gladly yielding sock. And then one day it is gone, and you are left with shrunken, cankered old socks that may require lubrication.

Of course, one thing about socks is that they don't mate for life. You can buy fourteen identical black ones, and at the end of three weeks, even if they were all still extant in sock form, no two of them would quite match. It may be that people across the country should get together on socks. I have a newspaper clipping that tells of two one-legged ladies who, although one lives in Wisconsin and one in Ohio, have been sharing pairs of shoes for more than two years. (Incidentally, the report notes, both ladies "agreed they wouldn't want an artificial leg even if it could be easily fitted. The extended reach of a crutch is great for disciplining recalcitrant children, Mrs. Gruenbaum said, and Mrs. Harma sticks a cloth on the end of hers and washes ceilings.'') People could advertise single socks in a newsletter and trade off by mail.

I don't know. Maybe one of my loved ones is saving all my missing socks to present to me, sewn together into an effigy of someone I admire, on the occasion of my retirement from active life. Maybe if the cat could only talk she could explain quite simply how it is that socks are transmuted into kittens. But I think it more likely that socks get off in some supernatural or wholly illegal way. I will not presume to trace the process by which they do it. But I think I know what becomes of them.

Every so often, usually at the change of seasons, when I dig into my closet for my summer or winter wardrobe, I find things I have never seen before in my entire life: a pair of pants, perhaps, that resembles a pair of pants only as a raisin resembles a grape; a sweater that a Red Guard might have denounced as too tacky; a knit tie with a horse painted on it.

Let us assume, then, in the absence of any compelling evidence to the contrary, that socks die and are reincarnated, perhaps in groups, as a variety of garments.

It is the work of the Devil — maybe — or maybe a sock-manufacturing-and-rummage-sale cabal, about which the media are so strangely silent.

The Outfit

Garrison Keillor

Years ago the Old Wilderness Outfitter started sending me his catalog of surplus outdoor gear: slightly battered canoes, scruffy rucksacks, dulled trail axes, tarnished cook kits, saggy tents, limp snowshoes, and the like. I spent many a fine winter hour thumbing through his catalog. Indeed, such was my enjoyment that occasionally I would lose control of my faculties and actually order some of the stuff. One surplus wilderness tent arrived with authentic wilderness dirt still on the floor, not to mention a few pine needles, a fir cone, a sprinkling of fish scales, and a really nice selection of squashed insects. The Old Wilderness Outfitter never charged for any of these extras, and in numerous other ways revealed himself to be a man of generosity and all-round good character. He put out a fine catalog, too.

The catalog arrived each winter with the same regularity as the snow, and at about the same time. Then it stopped coming. I thought maybe the Old Wilderness Outfitter had died, or was peeved at me because I had sent a letter telling him I would just as soon furnish my own fish scales and squashed insects, and there was no need to include them with my orders. I hadn't intended to offend him though, and if sending the extras meant that much to him it was all right with me.

A few days ago, I was surprised to find in the mail a new catalog from the Old Wilderness Outfitter. Happily, I licked my thumb and started flipping through the pages. I was flabbergasted. There wasn't a single scruffy rucksack in the thing, let alone a slightly battered canoe. The Old Wilderness Outfitter had filled up his catalog with glossy, color pictures of beautiful people.

Glancing at the prices, I thought at first the beautiful people themselves must be for sale. There was one blonde lady who looked well worth the seventy-five dollars asked, and I would have been interested, too, if I didn't already have one of my own worth almost twice that amount.

Then I determined the prices were for the clothes the beautiful people were wearing! The seventy-five dollars wasn't the price of the blonde lady but what she had on, something described as "a shooting outfit." (I can tell you with absolute certainty that if that lady ever shot anything in her life it was a sultry look across a crowded room.) The men were almost as beautiful as the women, and dressed in a month's wages plus overtime. Their haircuts alone probably cost more than my shooting outfit, if you don't count my lucky sweatshirt with the faded Snoopy on it.

Most of the clothes were trimmed in leather made from the hides of Spanish cows, which was appropriate, I thought, because most of the catalog copy was American bull.

After about ten minutes of studying the catalog, I could see what had happened. Some unemployed high-fashion clothes designers had got to the Old Wilderness Outfitter and persuaded him to chuck his rucksacks and the like and replace them with fancy clothes. The old codger should have known better. If American outdoorspersons were interested in fancy clothes, outdoor magazines would be written like this:

Doc stood up in the blind and squinted his eyes at the jagged rip of first light beyond the marsh. His closely woven virgin-wool shirt with the full sleeves and deep cape was beaded with rain.

"Hey, Mac," he said, "it's starting to rain. Better hand me my sage-green parka of water-repellent, super-tough eight-ounce cotton canvas duck with the handstitched leather flaps."

"Right," I said. "But first I'm going to drop that lone honker, which you'll notice is attractively attired in 100 percent goose down."

The truth is we outdoorspersons just aren't that interested in high fashion. Our preference runs more to low fashion. I myself have turned out a number of outstanding low-fashion designs. There was, for example, my free-form stain made by dropping an open bottle of dry-fly dressing in a shirt pocket. This design should not be confused with the one originating from a leaky peanut butter sandwich. My own favorite is the ripped pant leg laced shut with twenty-pound monofilament line, split-shot sinkers still attached.

Striking as these designs may be, I am just too old to design really first-rate low fashions. I no longer have the time, patience, nerves, or stomach for it. As a matter of fact, low-fashion designers usually reach their peak about age fourteen. From then on they undergo a gradual decline until their last shred of self-respect is gone and they will think nothing of going out wearing, say (shudder) a brand-spanking-new red felt hat.

You'd never catch a fourteen-year-old wearing such a monstrosity as a new red felt hat. No sir. The first thing a fourteen-year-old does with a new hunting or fishing hat is to redesign it. Immediately upon returning home from the store, he turns the hat over to his dog. After the dog has exhausted his imagination and ingenuity on the hat, it is retrieved by the kid and pounded full of holes with a large spike and hammer. The edges of the holes are burnt with a match. This simulates the effect of the kid's having been fired upon at close range with an elephant gun. (Nobody knows why this is important to a kid, but it is.) A band of squirrel, skunk, or muskrat hide, more or less tanned by the kid himself, is fastened to the crown. Next the brim is folded up on three sides and pinned with the thigh bones of a fried chicken or other equally attractive fasteners. And finally, several tail feathers from a pheasant are artfully arranged about the crown. The hat now resembles the year-old remains of a high-speed collision between a large bird and a small mammal.

Not all youngsters, by the way, are born with this talent for low fashion. Some have to learn it. I recall an incident back in my junior high school days when my friends Retch and Peewee and I gave Hair Forsyth his first lesson in low fashion. (The nickname "Hair," by the way, derived from an observation by Retch, one of the more scholarly of my companions, that rich kids who stand to inherit the family fortune are known as "hairs.") Hair had taken to hanging out with us at school, and when it came time for the annual early spring camping trip, we thought we should invite him along. Several bare patches of earth had been reported to us, and we decided this was sufficient evidence that winter was over and camping weather had begun. There was still a bit of a chill in the air, not to mention several inches of snow on the ground, and we thought it likely that Hair would find these sufficient reasons for refusing our invitation. But he said he thought it was a great idea.

Since I lived out in the country at the edge of the Wilderness (sometimes referred to locally as Fergussen's woodlot and north pasture), our farm was selected as the jumping-off place for the weekend expedition. When Hair climbed out of his father's car that day, we regular low-fashion campers nearly burst trying to keep from laughing. Ol' Hair was dressed up just like a dude. He had on these insulated leather boots, special safari pants, a heavy wool shirt, a down jacket, a hat with fur earflaps, and so on. Naturally, we didn't want to hurt his feelings by pointing out how ridiculous he looked. Nevertheless, we thought we should instruct him on the proper attire for a spring camping trip.

"I hate to say this," Retch told Hair, "but you're absolutely gonna roast in all those clothes."

"Yeah," Peewee put in, "and those boots are gonna be awfully heavy for walking. Too bad you don't have tennis shoes like we're wearing."

"Right," I said. "Next time, Hair, why don't you see if you can get some tennis shoes like these, with holes in the canvas so the sweat can drain out."

Hair thanked us for straightening him out

and said the next time he would have a better idea how to put together a suitable outfit.

After getting Hair squared away, we loaded up and headed out into the Wilderness. The snow out in the Wilderness was much deeper than any of us had expected. Bit by bit the depth of the snow increased until it was about halfway up to our knees. From time to time we would have to stop and chip the compacted snow off our tennis shoes and try to unplug the drain holes. These stops were occasion for much clowning around by us regulars for the benefit of Hair. Retch and Peewee would pound their feet against trees and make moaning and howling sounds, while I would tear off my tennis shoes and socks and blow on my blue feet in a comical manner. Hair laughed until tears streamed down his cheeks. Indeed, we all had tears streaming down our cheeks.

The wind came up shortly after it started to snow, and pretty soon we were slogging along through what we would have called a blizzard except that this was spring and the first of the good camping weather. Retch came up with the idea that maybe we should try to make it to an old abandoned trapper's cabin a couple of miles away and spend the night there.

"Otherwise, we might freeze to death," Retch joked.

"Heh," Peewee and I laughed.

"Freeze!" Hair cried. "You must be joking.

I'm burning up inside of this darn coat. Dang, I hate to ask but, Peewee, could I get you to trade me your shirt for this coat? What do you call that kind of shirt anyway?"

"A t-t-t-t-t-t-tee shirt," Peewee said, thrusting it into Hair's hand.

"Well, I guess I'll just have to leave this wool shirt of mine behind unless I can get one of you fellas to wear it for me," Hair said, taking it off and putting on Peewee's T-shirt over his thick, creamy wool underwear.

I said, "Dang I'll wear it rather than have you leave it behind."

"That underwear's not too hot for you, is it?" asked Retch.

Hair said it wasn't, but that he sure wouldn't mind slipping his boiling feet into a nice cool pair of tennis shoes. So Retch says he has about the coolest pair of tennis shoes a person is likely to find, and he swaps shoes with Hair.

By dark we had made it to the trapper's cabin and had a roaring fire going in the barrel stove and were sitting around roasting ourselves a few marshmallows and listening to the wind howl outside. From then on, Hair was one of the regulars and, as far as I know, nobody ever again mentioned the ridiculous outfit he wore on that first camping trip with us. It was obvious to everyone that he had learned his lesson, and there was no point in hurting his feelings any more than was necessary.

The ultimate in low fashion, at least that I ever saw, was created spontaneously on one of our camping trips by Harold Munster, a tall, gangling, wild-haired youth whose chief claim to fame was an uncanny ability for taking a bad situation and making it worse. Sometimes you would be absolutely certain that a situation couldn't be any worse and then Munster would show up and make it nine times as bad as before.

Back in those days, our camping clothes were referred to by our mothers as "your OLD clothes." A mother would stick her head out the back door and yell at her kids, "Wear your OLD clothes, you hear!" Since all our clothes were old — most of them had been in our families longer than we had — OLD designated the oldest grade. OLD clothes were never discarded, they just faded away. Sometimes they faded away while you were wearing them, and that is what led to Harold Munster's creation of the ultimate in low fashion.

Retch, Peewee, Munster, and I had been backpacking for nearly a week and now were attempting to extricate ourselves from the mountains as expeditiously as possible. In part, this consisted in wild, free-for-all gallops down steep trails, with packs, axes, and iron skillets flailing about on all sides. It was during one of these maniacal charges downhill that Munster, hurtling a windfall, caught his OLD pants on a limb. The pants exploded in midair. Munster

563

landed half naked in a shower of tiny bits of cloth, old patches, buttons, belt loops, and a broken zipper still held shut with a safety pin.

Well, we were all startled, a little embarrassed, and, of course, worried, because here was a bad situation. Nobody knew in what manner Munster would strive to make it worse and which of us might be swept into the vortex of whatever catastrophe he came up with.

The mosquitoes in that area were about the size of piranhas and twice as voracious. As Hemingway might have put it, Munster had been turned into a moveable feast. His expanse of bare skin drew the mosquitoes off the rest of us like a magnet, and, though appreciative of the respite, we became concerned that our unfortunate companion might be eaten alive or, even more likely, slap himself to death.

A small spring issued from the edge of the trail at that point, creating a large muddy bog on the downhill side of the trail. Before we knew what was happening, Munster had leaped into this bog and begun smearing his lower half with great globs of mud.

"Hey," he yelled up at us. "This really feels great!" We stared down at him with a mounting sense of foreboding, knowing from past experience that this was the beginning of something that would lead to dire consequences.

Not satisfied with coating his lower half with mud, Munster peeled off his OLD shirt and coated his upper half as well. Then he took handfuls of goop and rubbed it in his hair and on his face, all the while oohing and ahhing with relief and saying, "This will take care of those blinkety-blank mosquitoes for a while."

The rest of us divided Munster's load up among ourselves so that his mud coating would not be rubbed off by his pack. Thus unburdened, he took the lead and strolled along light of heart and mosquito-free, occasionally whistling a few bars or counting cadence for the rest of us. As we plodded along and the day grew hotter, we noticed that Munster's mud coating was beginning to bake into a hard, whitish shell, with webs of tiny cracks spreading out from his joints and seams. Grass, moss, sticks, and small stones protruded from the shell in a rather ghastly manner. Munster began complaining about what he described as a blinkety-blank unbearable itch, and occasionally would stop wild-eyed and claw furiously at his mud cast. His claw marks served only to make his overall appearance even more grisly.

Our plan was to intersect a logging road and then try to catch a ride out of the mountains with some gyppo loggers who were working in the area. We encountered the loggers much sooner than expected. Three of them had hiked back in from the end of the road to eat their lunch by the edge of a small stream. They were now sprawled out resting, smoking, and digging the dirt out from among the calks on their

565

boots. The trail we were on wound around the mountain about a hundred feet above them.

Retch, Peewee, and I had fallen some distance behind Munster, partly because of fatigue and partly because we could no longer endure the sight of him. As we rounded a bend in the trail, we caught sight of the three unsuspecting loggers, languid pools of tobacco smoke hanging in the still air about them. Poised like a silent gargoyle on the lip of the trail directly above this peaceful scene, was Munster, staring down at the loggers. We tried to shout but our tongues were momentarily paralyzed from the sheer horror of the scene before us. And then Peewee found his voice.

"MUNSTER!" he shrieked.

The startled loggers looked up. I could see the lips of one of them, puzzled, silently form the word "monster?"

Then Munster bounded down the hill toward the loggers, waving his arms ecstatically and croaking out his relief at being saved from having to walk the last ten miles home.

Walking the last ten miles home, we attempted to reconstruct the events of the ten seconds following Munster's lunge over the brink of the trail. It was agreed that we had all witnessed superb performances by three of the world's fastest gyppo loggers. Of particular interest was the fact that calked boots traveling at a high rate of speed throw up a fine spray of earth not unlike the plumes of water behind hydroplanes.

Harold Munster and his family moved away from town shortly after the last of his outfit wore off and I haven't seen him since, nor have I seen anything to match his masterpiece of low-fashion design. But if the Old Wilderness Outfitter had a lick of sense left, he would leave no stone unturned in his search for him.

My North Dakota Railroad Days

Garrison Keillor

*O Engineer, I cannot hear her mighty whistle
   blow —
Have you seen the Prairie Queen, where did
   she go?*

At present, our Brotherhood of North Dakota
State Railroad Employees is broke, flat busted,
beat down, and a *sorrier* mess than can be
imagined even by a Railroad Man such as
myself. It would take a crew of trained
Politicians two weeks working split shifts to
explain (1) Why was our Pension Fund played
with and wiped out in 1948 in a burst of
enthusiasm for sunflower futures (birdseed!) by
a State Appointed Guardian who had been
drunk for twenty years? (2) Why was our Free
Pass Right stolen by Amtrak in broad daylight
in June 1970 and nobody told us until we were
on board for the Annual Excursion to Minot?
(3) Why is our Brotherhood Office and Club-
room here in Devils Lake, that the State

568

solemnly promised to keep up, cold in winter, along with that the toilet leaks, plaster is cracked and falling daily in big chunks, the lock broken, the stove smokes, and all but three chairs bunged up and useless, so now we must move in with the Elks? And two or three other curious matters. But why should the Politicians bother? They know we had to be good and dumb to go on the Road in the first place and they are right. An old shack and a gold watch fob our total "Thank you" for years of service, plus an annuity hardly big enough to plug your nose, and yet we all stand up and sing like Children on a Picnic, and me as loud as the rest: "You may talk about your Santa Fee or the Wabash Cannonball, but the North Dakota Prairie Queen was the finest of them all!" Yes, she was Quite The Deal.

When I first heard the Call of the Road I guess was 1912 when I was twelve and the campaign train of President Theodore Roosevelt passed through my home town of Lakota N.D. one warm September morning at 3:30 A.M. Lakota was strong for the Rough Rider and turned out *en force* at the Town Hall for a bean supper followed by musical presentations and speeches by everyone and his cousin. We had all night, it was only 8:30. There were contests of all sorts — foot-races and sheep judging and a sledge-pull of fifty yards between Lakota Grange and Volunteer Fire teams, each harnessed to a two-ton load — followed by a dance and the grand procession to the Depot and more speeches by all those left out in the first round. Finally it was almost time. The children were awakened, torches lit, and all of Lakota assembled on the platform. Far away, Roosevelt's train could be heard coming down the main line of the old Grand Forks & Minot.

It had been agreed we would shout in unison as the train passed and that this salute should be something quite brief and to the point but at the last minute it was decided that as a courtesy to the sleeping President we would delay the shout until the train had gone through. With a burst of steam and a shower of sparks and a mighty roar that shook the earth President Roosevelt's train came into town highballing west. I grabbed on to my Dad's leg and watched the swinging red lanterns on the last car disappear into the dark. Then up went the shout, "Welcome to Lakota! All Aboard with Roosevelt!" and they fired a shotgun and we went home to bed. Oh, I thought, if only I could be on that train it would be *something*. It was the Greatest Day in my life at that age and is still fresh in my memory.

Four years later I took over Mark Jonson's spot as newsboy on the Dakota Mail. Then worked for Mr. Jack Roy, the Lakota agent, and finally I became a Trainman in 1923 and Assistant Conductor in 1928. The Mail was a good old train and the Flyer too — the Best in the West — so when the GF & M became the

North Dakota State Railroad (1930), of course they kept the old crews, and on March 10 I drew my Conductor's cap and braid from Mr. R. G. Houtek, President and General Manager, in person, and boarded the Prairie Queen in Fargo for her first run — the beginning of twelve great years for the most part, certainly for those of us who loved her.

She was new then and oh, what a Beauty. Blue the color of a clear summer sky, with dazzling white running stripes and a red-crown insignia of the N.D.S.R. or "Andy Yes Sir" as we called it, "Yes Sir" for short. Rosewood and spruce and mahogany trim, and crystal lamps, red and blue plush seats, brass fittings, the ceilings of molded copper with tiny electric stars, and underfoot a deep carpet of green and brown in all fourteen cars, each car named for a county — and me and Mr. Houtek giving the Highball as she steamed from Fargo station for Grand Forks, Minot, and Williston, full of Politicians, Railroad Bosses, and Canadian whisky.

It was the Queen I loved and not the Yes Sir, so a full account of that bunch of crooks I will leave to someone with a strong stomach except to say that the North Dakota people had long been gouged and stripped by the Rail Monopolies to the point of agitation for state ownership, which was the battle cry of the Popular League when it made quite a dent in the 1928 election and scared the Railroads up

571

a tree. One year and six months later, the spring of 1930, the Yes Sir was brought forth with great benedictions and anointing of feet, the Railroad Trust donating to the State the GF & M, plus the Queen, to be operated as the State Railroad by a Board of Directors to be appointed by the Governor and purchased by the Trust, which would make it the Greatest Train in the World, and operated all for the People's profit and welfare, minus a modest return on capital investment, etc., etc., and subject to other conditions, stipulations, understandings, etc. . . . Yes, that N.D.S.R. Charter was a wonder. Three volumes plus and not light reading even for the Lawyers, it was a by-God Tabernacle in the Desert, built just so and the parts joined tight, and great was the wealth thereof and all was pleasing in the eyes of the Law, including much that the human eye could not see: long strings and little traps and sieves and siphons built in by Houtek and his crack attorneys, besides which the Railroads' tax would be fixed low, and all to be in effect until three months before the Second Coming. But the State of North Dakota was helpless as an old maid asked to dance, and bought the deal on sight alone and overlooked the smell. It was hard times in a poor country, and the N.D.S.R. would give jobs to thousands, and the Queen would be a Great Draw and Natural Asset in a land with no mountains, forests, or ocean. Our people were then migrating in droves to the San Joaquin Valley, and this would help keep some home by showing that North Dakota could do great things.

I took this at one-half face value at first, my faith going down from there, but when you were on the Queen, boy, she took your mind away. She was the fastest thing on wheels — could hit 130 some places, and rode as smooth as if standing still. You see, North Dakota is a flat state, and then too Houtek spared no expense on tracks, so they were the best. We were proud of the fact she was the only train to ever carry a billiard table, and one could enjoy a good game anywhere on the route except one curve north of the Forks named the "Debs Transit" for its tendency to redistribute the balls. Many rode the Queen for the restfulness alone — in fact, we carried a special sleeper Friday nights out of Fargo and dropped it in Grand Forks for the eastbound to take back, arriving at Fargo at breakfast time. Many others were bound, summer and winter, for the Dakota Hot Springs resort and baths near Devils Lake, to take the health cure, but believe me, the real attraction was the Queen herself.

To the older person especially, who knew the privations of homesteading in the "little old sod shanty on the plains," a ride on the Queen was Heaven at Home, and we spared no effort to please the people. We were ever prepared to stop at pleasure's call, knowing the time could be made up quickly later. Not a day passed but what we would pull up four or five times so the people might stroll by the track to gather wild flowers or photograph scenic spots, the "Poplar Grove at the Geographical Center of North America," near Rugby, being a favorite. In season, we paused to hunt pheasant and duck, and west of the Forks slowed to a crawl, permitting passengers to troll in the adjacent Trans-Dakota Canal from the observation-car porch. Many towns along the line threw gala dinners and receptions for the Queen. A station agent would put out the message on a forked stick "Knox invites you to dance Saturday," and we'd pick it up and go, of course, and bring one of our bands — the Kolachy Brothers, the Big Pisek Hot Band, Cecil Pootz and His Grafton Spuds, the Wonderbar Orchestra, and yes, the great Bill Baroon and His Paloreenies. We had the best playing nightly in the dance car, The Club Dakota, and were happy to share.

Yes, the trip was considered *quite* the deal then and fun for one and all, and of course the fun didn't stop when the train was in motion. In addition to billiards and poker, there were regular meetings of the Camera, Norwegian, Kiwanis, Writers, Old Settlers, and Fargo clubs. Liquor flowed at the bars, and we had the Queen's own brand of spirits brewed in a "baggage car" ahead. In the dining cars, one found culinary delights beyond compare: Prairie

Queen ribs with candied yams, sauerbraten and hot potato salad, blueberry pancakes rolled in sugar, sweet rhubarb pie, Polish peppers, and fresh canal fish. And then there was Houtek, quite a fellow and a show in himself.

Houtek was a Railroad Baron and acted the part, but he liked to make others feel important too, I will say that for him. He kept his office back in the last Pullman, never missed a run, and as the Board of Directors seldom caught him for a meeting, ruled with a free hand. He walked through twice daily with his black spaniel, General Sheridan, tasting the pie and rubbing the nap and analyzing the liquor, and woe befall the man who slipped from *his* standards, but to the faithful servant he extended an arm of Brotherhood and Trust. Seemed like his arm was *always* around somebody, and always there was the smell of his rich wool suit, the flash of a pinkie ring, a cloud of Havana, and Houtek's barony voice saying you and him were friends, understood each other, and knew what Railroading was all about. No matter what your name, you were either Bill or Jim to Houtek — I guess he liked those names — and you stayed Bill or Jim and answered to it. I was a Jim.

Houtek had a grand manner. He wrote the souvenir booklet that we gave free to passengers. "Men travel far and wide to see and ride upon this Train," it said. "They marvel at its Speed, its Comfort, its luxurious Appointments. Racing

through the Heartland of America, it strikes
Confidence and Determination into the heart
of every Native Son. Truly, it may be called

THE TRAIN OF THE CENTURY
AND
THE JEWEL OF THE PLAINS."

There were also two pages on the Hot Springs
baths — how they cured arthritis and other
ailments brought on by cold weather, and
promoted restful nerves and invigorated the
marital relationship — and a big spread on
Houtek, pictured at the throttle: "North Dakota's Efficient Public Servant."

(Did we have any idea Houtek *owned* 36 per
cent interest in one of the biggest Hot Springs
spas and held partnership in the Springs itself?
No, but when this came out, about 1946, it
was like we had always known it. In a way, it
fitted him.)

Well, I will say this. Houtek was King, and
when you rode his train, why, you felt like a
Prince of the Realm, and all of us enjoyed it to
the hilt and none would say a word against him
on *that* account. When you rode the Prairie
Queen, employee or paying customer, why, the
state of North Dakota rolled along beneath
your feet. You sipped Houtek's prize bourbon
and looked out across at the farms dried up
and the farmers still poking the dust — a little
white house out in the middle of nowhere, and

not a stick of shade, and a lady's pale face in the window, her raggedy kids lined up by the track where they'd put pennies, all of them wishing they could be on the great train — well, you did feel like a Prince with a noseful of diamonds or a Potentate on Tour, and I guess that's how we looked to them too. They probably thought we were *all* Houtek. As I say, I don't claim not to have enjoyed this as much as the next one. Or to understand it any better or think, Oh, it was Houtek, Houtek did it — we had no idea.

On account of her irregular schedule and high speed at night, the Prairie Queen killed more people in her twelve years than floods and blizzards put together. She must have wiped out half a county. Crossing-lights were rare items then and people just never got used to expecting her. A little bump was all we felt. We'd pull up slow in the night and back her up, me and a trainman walking alongside with flares, a mile or so back to the crossing. Most often, we'd find a little coupe, with a young couple in it, or an old farmer in a pickup, and most of the time they were busted up bad and beyond help. But now and then we'd find a breather and haul him up into a Pullman and go on to the next town, and it was amazing how he'd seem sort of awestruck, *proud* even, to have been hit by the Queen. Houtek would come to his bedside as we started up again, and lean down and shake the hand of the victim and shout, "You are aboard the Prairie Queen! You are going to be all right!" And the poor bleeding soul would look up with whatever sense he had left and sort of *thank* him. Oh, it was strange business and would tear at your heart to see it, but there it was. There it was.

And now this brings me to certain events of 1940 to '42.

One fine summer night in 1940, we attended an Indian Corn Dance near Minnewaukan. Houtek and I rounded up the stragglers near midnight and hiked back to the Queen through a horse pasture. We came up over a hill, climbed through some barbed wire, and there, far off, were the lights of the waiting Queen and the faint low hiss as the big ten-wheeler fired up. She lay out there in the dark looking like a whole city, and I felt like I just wanted to spend the rest of my life on our beautiful Prairie Queen.

Houtek saw this — he had been advising me on investments, telling me to put my extra dollars into chemicals because the war was coming and we would be in it soon — and he added, "By all means, don't invest in that," meaning the Queen.

"There is no chance of that, I'm afraid," I replied. "The Queen is owned by the State of North Dakota."

"Well, there is more to it than that," he said. "Just don't you get involved in it in any way. I have made a couple mistakes in that department — and they are going to cost me in the end."

That was about it, but even that little remark gave me a stir. Houtek was not one to gab about business. He always kept his hands in his pockets and had a pair of adder eyes for anyone whose mind should wander into the executive domain. For example, the Queen carried an extra "mail car" (which was not a mail car), which was kept locked and to which Houtek alone had a key. Now, every man on the Yes Sir roll knew that that car was full of Railroad files and papers. Many times we saw Houtek and his assistants take stuff out and put it in, but once, when a brave engineer asked him if indeed those were Railroad papers in there, Houtek gave him both eyes full-face and dead poison. "You keep your hand on the throttle, Jim, and I'll take care of the line," he said.

So we made it a habit not to see or hear too much. Oh, we thought the contracts were funny — some of us had to sign for loads of groceries and various other train supplies, and the prices were ridiculous — and we noticed all the Lawyers on board and the agents for companies nobody'd ever heard of. They were perfectly obvious. These were men who'd warm up their voices in the morning — those rolling Episcopalian tones — and then gather round and lie in wait for Houtek, spreading out their papers on a table in one of the dining cars and listening, heads down and tails up, waiting for his "Morning, gentlemen!" Then it was every man for himself.

They'd walk right up each other's backs to get close to Houtek's ear. They fussed over General Sheridan — what a fine dog he was, if he ever sired pups to let them know, and so forth and so on — and now and again Houtek would take one of these grifters and make a pet of *him*, let him eat at the Houtek table, give him some choice concession, or so we guessed.

And then, too, there was the thirty-five miles of track east of Williston that got heaved up in the 1941 thaw something awful and never did get fixed. The dining cars had to shut down on that stretch and the band took a break, for though the Queen slowed to yard speed, she rode as if in a cyclone. It was a nightmare, screeching and scraping and clattering along like an old milk train and everybody hanging on to the seats and it was shameful and just made you *sick* to see her suffer that way. And then there was a stretch east of Stanley, and later the whole Hillsboro section went bad. Now some thought the whole mess was due to the steel shortage — maybe some old rails hadn't been replaced. But in actual fact the rail was practically new, laid the previous summer and obviously not up to grade — inferior light-gauge rail you'd use for siding at a pillow factory, maybe. Why? We didn't ask why, nobody asked. We knew. Deep down in the marrow of his bones where it is dry and cold and he keeps a little hard common sense the size of buckshot, the Railroad Man knew. Houtek was a crook — how else could you figure it? A plain out-and-out thief and egg-sucker like every other Railroad Boss or Lawyer, though you still hear a few fellows speak fondly of "Old Hooty," and many North Dakotans today will solemnly swear the Queen would be running yet if Houtek had not been hog-tied by the Labor Unions! Yes, this was the line put out by the Republican newspapers — in an editorial paid for by the Trust and issued annually like a Valentine. Come spring and time for the Directors' meeting to set rates and see the books, those papers would say the Queen was losing money due to Political Interference. Time to give Free Enterprise room to do the Job, they'd say — the government knows nothing about running a Railroad, but here we have Politicians dictating from Bismarck decisions that are not sound Business Practice, such as featherbed work rules and lavish pension benefits for the B.N.D.S.R.E. freeloaders.

I am never surprised by anything I read in newspapers, nor do I blame them any more than I would hold a grudge against a goat. But just to set the record straight, the Yes Sir Board of Directors was strictly on the tit and regarded the Trust with humble piety and obedience and

581

never sat but what it knelt, and as for the Brotherhood, why, it was about as powerful as the United Orphans & Widows. A Republican court had found us to be state employees and thus made it illegal for us to have collective bargaining or to strike. We were Houtek's Boy Scouts and that's gospel truth, but just you try telling truth to someone born and raised on a bed of lies. You can lay it at their feet, draw pictures, say it in Swedish, spread it with jelly, or put it in a knuckle sandwich — they will always think it was us in the Brotherhood that ran the Prairie Queen out of business.

Well, it wasn't. It was that bone-cracking rail east of Williston, to begin with, that busted the eggs in Houtek's basket. At the time, in the summer of 1942, I was absent — off fishing on the beautiful Lake Lakota with my good friend Ramon Kilgore — but as I understand it a loose coupling was spotted on a coach a few minutes before the Queen's scheduled departure from Williston. The yard crew took a long while deciding they couldn't fix it, and by the time the coach was pulled and the Queen remade, the Trainmaster hadn't time to make a final inspection. If he had, he surely would've seen the bolt was not dropped in the lock on the "mail car" door.

When the Queen hit bad track and went into her regular convulsions, the "mail car" bounced around, shaking loose the catch, and the door slid open. When she came to good track and the engineer put the coals to her — well, they say it was Houtek saw it first: what looked like a funnel cloud of paper boiling out that car and up over the prairie, where a strong wind took hold and carried it off southeast. They say Houtek saw it and stood up and fell against the window and his knees buckled and he caught the emergency cord on the way down. They thought he was dead of a stroke. His face was blood-purple, and four men hauled him to his bed.

The Queen stopped there three hours on a little rise looking east, and every man, woman, and child aboard went out and combed the grass for loose paper. Oh, it was a sight, they say, how boxes jumped from the speeding train, fell to the ground, and burst like bombs, and the written history of the N.D.S.R., its coin, its harvest, its every bill of theft, the index of its lies, the worthless bonds, in short The Goods, all was released and flew away and scattered itself over thousands of square miles of North Dakota to be plowed under as compost, and so poisonous was the ink that crops were thin for years thereafter. Oh, I wish I had been there to see it, it was *something!*

Meanwhile, Houtek came to and went out of control. They had to lock him in his office with a bottle of whisky and hope for the best. He was hollering and kicking the walls and firing people through the door, but then finally he calmed down and began to brood. Of course, it's only a guess, but I tend to think he got to missing all that paper something fierce now it was gone. Maybe he feared it was lost, maybe he feared it would be found, maybe he saw blackbirds swooping at his head and other voracious creatures come to meet him now that he had nothing to beat them back with, but mostly I think he just grieved. I believe he went some kind of loony in there, though among powerful men it is not so noticeable. He was silent, unlike himself, and wouldn't be roused.

"Mr. Houtek, shall we move?" the conductor called again and again through the door. No answer. Up ahead, the engineer, "Captain Jim" Hinkley, hauled on the whistle, wanting to be off. Finally, orders or no, the Queen started up. Houtek stayed hid through Minot and was not seen until Devils Lake. It was dark and the yard lights were blacked out, but they say it was him who snuck from the Queen to the station office and stayed locked in there for twenty-five minutes, until a car came for him — a black Chrysler.

The scheduled stop was ten minutes and the Queen was set to leave when smoke was noticed coming from the "mail car." It was a smoldering fire. They had it almost put out, but it flamed up again, and all passengers were taken off as a precaution. Just then a Yes Sir detective appeared from the station — a short man with a big cigar — and took charge, said all crew was to report to the desk immediately, Houtek's orders. This was contrary to rules, to order the crew off a standing train, and Captain Jim demanded to have it in writing, so the detective wrote it on the back of a freight bill: "Crew relieved, Queen/11:24P by RGH." She was burning, the mail and the first baggage, and Jim was cursing and crying, but the old veteran took his orders and, with his fireman, Steve, stood off across the platform from his cab, and Houtek's man climbed in and he was shutting her down, loosing steam, they *thought*, and then she began to roll. They dashed for the engine, and Steve had one hand on the ladder when the dick stepped on his hand and jumped clear and fell on him, and 11:30 P.M. on June 14 the Prairie Queen slipped out the station on her final journey.

The word went down the line that she was coming, and coming fast. In several towns, straw bales were piled on the tracks to slow her down, and in Lakota the Volunteer Fire Brigade stationed themselves with a pumper by the depot to cool off her firebox, but she came by going 60, her whistle moaning, and fire glowed in every window, and we knew, and some wept, that we would never see the Prairie Queen again.

The call went down to the Forks to open switches all the way to Fargo, but the great crowd that had gathered at the Debs Transit curve was not to be disappointed. They say she hit the curve at 80 — some say 100 — and her wheels screamed as she jumped the track. She dug a double furrow three feet deep in the ground, and flew from the high bank of the Red River. They say she was airborne for only four seconds but it seemed like a week. They say a million birds rose from the valley and all was suddenly silent but for the rush of wings and the cry of a child in the crowd, and then she hit water. Hit so hard, they say, she sent a three-foot wave two miles upstream and four down, and the steam was so thick the eastern shore could not be seen until noon of the next day. There, they say, rests the Prairie Queen today, and they say on a quiet day if you put your head underwater you can still hear the slow tolling of her bell rocked by the current and the groaning of her joints as she sinks ever deeper in the mud.

I have not done so myself, nor have I seen the wreck, though maybe I have looked in the wrong place. Nor did I see Houtek again, though I heard he died some years back in Minneapolis, where he had become rich again and a pillar of the community. Anyway, after a few years and the general excitement of the war, he was forgotten by the people of North Dakota — all except us. We sit in our shack, we old Railroad Boys, and now and then remember him to the extent of wishing him safely in Hell. May his soul be forever tormented by fire and his bones be dug up by dogs and dragged through the streets of Minneapolis, and God damn his name and wipe it from every account and take all his money and that of his heirs and put it in a Certified Check made out to the Brotherhood of North Dakota State Railroad Employees (B.N.D.S.R.E.).

The Last Laugh

Fran Lebowitz

Coming from a family where literary tradition runs largely toward the picture postcard, it is not surprising that I have never really succeeded in explaining to my grandmother exactly what it is that I do. It is not that my grandmother is unintelligent; quite the contrary. It is simply that so firmly implanted are her roots in retail furniture that she cannot help but view all other occupations from this rather limited vantage point. Therefore, every time I see my grandmother I am fully prepared for the following exchange:

"So, how are you?"

"Fine, Grandma. How are you?"

"Fine. So how's business, good?"

"Very good, Grandma."

"You busy this time of year? Is this a good season for you?"

"Very good, Grandma."

"Good. It's good to be busy."

"Yes, Grandma."

Satisfied with my responses, my grandmother will then turn to my father and ask the very same questions, a dialogue a bit more firmly grounded in reality, since he has not deviated from the Lebowitz custom of fine upholstered furniture.

The lack of understanding between my grandmother and myself has long troubled me, and in honor of her recently celebrated ninety-fifth birthday I have prepared the following business history in order that she might have a clearer vision of my life and work.

My beginnings were humble, of course, but I am not ashamed of them. I started with a humor pushcart on Delancey Street — comic essays, forty cents apiece, four for a dollar. It was tough out there on the street; competition was cutthroat, but it was the best education in the world because on Delancey "mildly amusing" was not enough — you had to be *funny*. I worked ten-hour days, six days a week, and soon I had a nice little following. Not exactly a cult, maybe, but I was doing okay. It was a living. I was able to put aside some money, and things looked pretty good for a store of my own in the not too distant future. Oh sure, I had my troubles, who doesn't? The housewives browsing through every essay on the cart, trying to contain their glee in the hope that I'd come down a little in price. The kids snitching a couple of paragraphs when my back was turned.

And Mike the cop with his hand out all the time looking for a free laugh. But I persevered, never losing sight of my objective, and after years of struggle I was ready to take the plunge.

I went down to Canal Street to look for a store, a store of my own. Not being one to do things halfway, I was thorough and finally found a good location. Lots of foot traffic, surgical supplies on one side, maternity clothes on the other — these were people who could use a good laugh. I worked like a dog getting ready for that opening. I put in a very reasonable ready-to-hear line, an amusing notions counter, a full stock of epigrams, aphorisms and the latest in wit and irony. At last I was ready; Fran's Humor Heaven: Home of the Devastating Double Entendre was open for business. It was tough going at first, but my overhead was low. I wrote all my own stock. And eventually I began to show a nice healthy gross and a net I could live with.

I don't know when it all began to go sour — who can tell about these things, I'm a humorist, not a fortuneteller — but business began to slip. First I took a bath with some barbed comments I was trying out, and then I got stuck with a lot of entertaining anecdotes. I hoped it was just an off season, but it didn't let up, and before I knew it I was in really big trouble. I tried everything, believe you me. I ran big sales — "Buy one epigram, get one free," "Twenty percent off all phrases." I even instituted a "Buy now, say later" plan. But nothing worked. I was at my wits' end; I owed everybody and was in hock up to my ears. So one day, pen in hand, I went to Morris "The Thesaurus" Pincus — a shy on East Houston who lent money to humorists in a jam. The interest rates were exorbitant but I signed my life away. What else could I do?

But it wasn't enough, and I was forced to take in a collaborator. At first he seemed to be working out. He specialized in parodies and they were moving pretty good, but before too long I began to get suspicious of him. I mean, I could barely put food on my table, and there he was, riding around in a Cadillac a block long. One night after dinner I went back to the store and went over the books with a fine-tooth comb. Just as I thought, there it was in black and white: the guy was a thief. He'd been stealing my lines all along. I confronted him with the evidence and what could he do? He promised to pay me back a few pages a week, but I knew that was one joker I'd never see again.

I kicked him out and worked even harder. Eighty-hour weeks, open every night until ten, but it was a losing battle. With the big humor chains moving in, what chance did an independent like me have? Then the day came when I knew all was lost. Sol's Discount Satire opened up right across the street. He wrote in bulk; I couldn't meet his prices. I, of course, was wittier, but nobody cared about quality anymore. Their attitude was "So it's a little broad, but at forty percent below list we'll forsake a little subtlety." I went in the back of the store and sat down, trying desperately to figure something out. There was a sharp rap at the door, and in walked Morris, a goon on either side, ready to collect. I told him I didn't have it. I begged for more time. I was pleading for my life. Morris stared at me coolly, a hard glint in his eye as he cleaned his nails with a lethal-looking fountain pen.

"Look, Fran," he said, "you're breaking my heart. Either you pay up by next Monday, or I'm gonna spread it around that you're mixing your metaphors."

With that he turned on his heel and walked out the door followed by the two gorillas. I was sweating bullets. If Morris spread that around, I'd never get another laugh as long as I lived. My head swam with crazy plans, and when I realized what I had to do, my heart thumped like a jackhammer.

Late that night I went back to the store. I let myself in through the side door and set to work. I poured a lot of gasoline around, took a last look, threw in a match and beat it the hell out of there. I was twenty blocks away when the full realization of what I'd done hit me. Overcome by remorse, I ran all the way back, but it was too late. The deed was done; I'd burned my comic essays for the insurance money.

The next day I met with the adjuster from That's Life, and thank God he bought the fire and paid me off. It was just enough to settle with Morris, and then I was broke again.

I started to free-lance for other stores, writing under a pseudonym, of course. My heart wasn't in it, but I needed the cash. I was grinding it out like hamburger meat, trying to build up some capital. The stuff was too facile, I knew that, but there was a market for it, so I made the best of it.

The years went by and I was just getting to the point where I could take it a little easy, when I was struck by an idea that was to change not only my own life but that of everyone in the entire humor business. The idea? Fast humor. After all, the pace had picked up a lot since my days on Delancey Street. The world was a different place; humor habits had changed. Everyone was in a hurry. Who had time anymore for a long comic essay, a slow build, a good long laugh? Everything was rush, rush, rush. Fast humor was an idea whose time had come.

Once again I started small, just a little place out on Queens Boulevard. I called it Rapid Repartee and used every modern design technique available. All chrome and glass, everything sleek and clean. Known in the business for my cunning and waggish ways, I couldn't resist a little joke and so used as my trademark a golden arch. No one got it. So I added another one, and got a great reaction. You really have to hit people over the head, don't you? Be that as it may, the place caught on like wildfire. I couldn't keep Quick Comebacks in stock, and the Big Crack was the hit of the century. I began to franchise, but refused to relinquish quality control. Business boomed and today I can tell you I'm sitting pretty. I've got it all: a penthouse on Park, a yacht the size of the *Queen Mary* and a Rolls you could live in. But still, every once in a while I get that old creative itch. When this happens I slip on an apron and cap, step behind one of my thousands of counters, smile pleasantly at the customer and say, "Good morning. Something nice in a Stinging Barb?" If I'm recognized, it's always good for a laugh, because, believe you me, in this business unless you have a sense of humor you're dead.

Index of Titles and Authors

597

The publishers hope that this
Large Print Book has brought
you pleasurable reading.
Each title is designed to make
the text as easy to see as possible.
G. K. Hall Large Print Books are
available from your library and
your local bookstore. Or you can
receive information on upcoming
and current Large Print Books by
mail and order directly from the
publisher. Just send your name
and address to:

G. K. Hall & Co.
70 Lincoln Street
Boston, Mass. 02111

or call, toll-free:

1–800–343–2806

A note on the text
Large print edition designed by
Bernadette Montalvo
Composed in 16 pt Plantin
on a Mergenthaler Linotron 202
by Modern Graphics, Inc.